Advanced Graphics with the BBC Model B Microcomputer

**Macmillan Microcomputer Books**

*General Editor*: Ian Birnbaum

Advanced Graphics with the BBC Model B Microcomputer
Ian O. Angell and Brian J. Jones
Assembly Language Programming for the BBC Microcomputer
Ian Birnbaum

**Also from Macmillan**

Advanced Graphics with the Sinclair ZX Spectrum
Ian O. Angell and Brian J. Jones
Advanced Programming for the 16K ZX81 Mike Costello
Beginning BASIC Peter Gosling
Continuing BASIC Peter Gosling
Practical BASIC Programming Peter Gosling
Program Your Microcomputer in BASIC Peter Gosling
Codes for Computers and Microprocessors P. Gosling and Q. Laarhoven
Microprocessors and Microcomputers – their use and programming
Eric Huggins
The Sinclair ZX81 – Programming for Real Applications
Randle Hurley
More Real Applications for the ZX81 and ZX Spectrum Randle Hurley
Z80 Assembly Language Programming for Students Roger Hutty
Digital Techniques Noel Morris
Microprocessor and Microcomputer Technology Noel Morris
The Alien, Numbereater, and Other Programs for Personal Computers – with notes on how they were written John Race
Understanding Microprocessors B. S. Walker
Assembly Language Assembled – for the Sinclair ZX81 Anthony Woods

# Advanced Graphics with the BBC Model B Microcomputer


Ian O. Angell and Brian J. Jones

*Department of Statistics and Computer Science*
*Royal Holloway College*
*University of London*
*Egham, Surrey*

*First published 1983 by*
THE MACMILLAN PRESS LTD
*London and Basingstoke*
*Companies and representatives*
*throughout the world*
*Reprinted 1984*

*Typeset by RDL Artset Ltd, Sutton, Surrey*

*Printed in Great Britain at*
*The Camelot Press Ltd, Southampton*

ISBN 0 333 35052 9 (book)
0 333 35053 7 (cassette 1)
0 333 36141 5 (cassette 2)

# *Contents*

# *Preface*

With the rapid advance of computer technology has come a substantial reduction in the price of computer hardware. In the coming years the price of peripheral devices will also tumble. This means that users with a limited budget, who previously had access only to the most elementary computing devices, will soon be able to afford the most sophisticated computers. They will also be able to escape from the limitation of tabular numerical output and buy microprocessor attachments for television monitors or inexpensive special-purpose colour graphics devices. Software, however, does not appear to be getting cheaper.

Because of the enormous capital expenditure that was required to set up graphical output in the past, both for machines and for software, the subject of computer graphics has so far been the preserve of large research groups. This inaccessibility has led to a mystique growing up around the subject and it has thus achieved a false reputation for difficulty. This book is an attempt to lay the ghost of complexity; it will also show that complicated (and hence expensive) software packages, which are naturally of great value in research organisations, need not frighten away the average computer user. For most purposes these packages are unnecessary. This book, as well as being an introduction to computer graphics, may be considered a (very inexpensive) software package: it is a lot cheaper than commercially available packages! Naturally, because of this fundamental approach, users have to achieve a reasonable understanding of their graphics device before pictures, other than those provided, can be drawn. This need not be a disadvantage; the amount of groundwork required will be seen to be very limited and, as a direct result, the user's knowledge grows along with the package and he is far less likely to misinterpret any of the graphical procedures. References are given and relevant further reading material is also recommended in order to expand the reader's horizons in the subject.

It is assumed that the reader has an elementary knowledge of Cartesian coordinate geometry (the authors recommend books detailed in Cohn, 1961, Coxeter, 1974 and McCrae, 1953 – see the references) and also the BASIC programming language (see the BBC User Guide – page numbers are not given because this excellent handbook is constantly being updated as the BBC micro is being extended). Many interesting programming exercises are proposed, and these should raise the standard of the reader's BASIC expertise. BASIC is a universally popular language that is available (in various guises) on all types of microcomputer, so the programs can be easily adjusted to run on micros other than the Model B: it is also a good medium for transmitting the algorithms that are used in computer graphics, so enabling readers to translate these ideas readily into any other computer language of their choice.

The concepts necessary for the study of computer graphics are organised as a combination of theory and worked examples; these are introduced as and when they are needed in the natural progression of the subject. Program listings that form part of the examples may be considered not only as algorithms that describe solutions to fundamental graphical problems, but also as a computer graphics software package in BASIC, or just as programs to draw patterns. Alongside the examples is a series of exercises that expand on these ideas. The practical problems that are implicit in programming the various concepts of computer graphics are often more a source of difficulty to the student than the concepts themselves. Therefore it is essential that readers implement many of the program listings given in the book in order to understand the algorithms, as well as attempt a large number of the exercises. As an extra learning aid, two companion audio-cassette tapes are being made available; these contain most of the larger program listings that are given in this book. If readers are frightened by the mathematics they should run the programs first before studying the theory.

This approach to the subject has been used with great success in teaching computer graphics to undergraduates and postgraduates at Royal Holloway College. Quickly producing apparently complex pictures results in the positive feedback of enthusiastic interest. The ability to construct pictures on line-drawing and colour interactive graphics VDUs makes a long-lasting impression on the student; and the step by step approach brings him very quickly to the level of very sophisticated computer graphics. That level is outside the scope of this book, but where necessary the reader will find relevant references to guide him into the more advanced topics.

This book is aimed at those who are competent BASIC programmers but who are complete beginners in graphics. It contains the elementary ideas and basic information about pixel and two-dimensional graphics which must be mastered before attempting the more involved ideas of character and three-dimensional graphics. This is followed by a section relating to character graphics and the display of data (in line drawings and colour) – probably the most important non-specialised, commercial use of computer graphics. Later chapters introduce the reader to the geometry of three-dimensional space, and to a variety of projections of this space on to the two-dimensional space of graphics devices. The related problems of hidden lines and hidden surfaces, as well as the construction of complex three-dimensional objects, are dealt with in detail. Finally we return to advanced ideas in BASIC programming and give a large worked example of a video game (to be found on cassette 2).

Graphics is one of the most rapidly expanding areas of computer science. It is being used more and more in the fields of Computer Aided Design (C.A.D.), Computer Assisted Management (C.A.M.) and Computer Assisted Learning

(C.A.L.). At one time it was only the big corporations such as aircraft and automobile manufacturers who used these techniques, but now most companies are realising the potential and financial savings of these ideas. What is more, not only is computer graphics profitable, it is fun! The BBC microcomputer is an ideal machine on which to learn the basics of computer graphics, and an excellent springboard up to the most sophisticated (and expensive) graphics devices.

We hope this book will display some of the excitement and enthusiasm for computer graphics experienced by us, our colleagues and students. To demonstrate just how useful computer drawings are for illustrating books and pamphlets, all the pictures in the following chapters were drawn by computer specifically for this book.

Ian O. Angell
Brian J. Jones

# *Introduction*

This book may be read at a number of different levels. Firstly, it can be considered as a recipe book of graphics programs for those who simply want to draw complex pictures with their BBC microcomputer. We naturally hope that the reader, having drawn these figures, will be inspired to delve more deeply into the book in order to understand how and why the programs were constructed. Secondly, some of the programs can be used as a package to produce and to label data diagrams (pie-charts, histograms and graphs) for business and laboratory applications. Finally, and the main objective in writing the book, it is an introductory text to computer graphics that leads the reader from the elementary notions of the subject to such advanced topics as character graphics, construction of three-dimensional objects and hidden surface (and line) algorithms.

The complex programs given later in the book are much too involved to be compiled as single listings; furthermore, there is a great deal of repetition in the use of elementary algorithms. Therefore the *top down* or *modular* approach is used in writing and in explaining programs. The solution to each major graphics problem is conceived as a series of solutions to subproblems. These subproblems can be further broken down into a set of problems to be solved (*modules*). Such modules are programmed in the form of BASIC procedures. Each is given an identifier (in lower case characters) and will solve a particular subtask. Submodules are then combined to solve the major graphics problem. The program listings present the algorithms that are needed for the solution of subtasks, and the naming of the procedures makes an understanding of the algorithms easier. We use lower case characters for procedure identifiers (and groupings of procedures in the text) only: all other program variables are in upper case characters to avoid confusion.

Two cassette tapes are available to accompany the text; they contain all the larger listings in the book, as well as the data for diagrams and character sets used in later programs (which would otherwise have to be constructed by the readers themselves – a rather time-consuming process). The first cassette consists of the two- and three-dimensional geometrical programs, and the second contains the character graphic manipulation, diagram construction and video games etc.

A list of complete programs is given at the end of each chapter, together with suitable data values, for those who want nothing more than to run these programs. In fact it is a good idea for everyone, including the more serious readers, to LOAD the relevant programs from the tape and run them before reading any particular chapter.

There are many REMarks in the program listings, however, and hence some of the programs approach the storage limits of the BBC micro. In these cases you should delete the REMarks before saving the programs. To make the listings easy to read we advise readers to LISTO1 the programs in MODE 7. We have placed a REMark in red before each procedure (on lines with numbers that end in 0) so that they stand out: all other REMarks are in green (on lines with numbers that end in 9). You may find that the latter REMarks take up too much store in which case you should strip them away by typing AUTO9, 10 and by holding the RETURN key down. Even then some of the programs are too big to fit into the store, in which case you must LOAD them after setting PAGE = &1100.

As an example of what to expect we give the program that is required to draw figure I.1, a drawing of a body of revolution in which all the hidden surfaces have been suppressed.

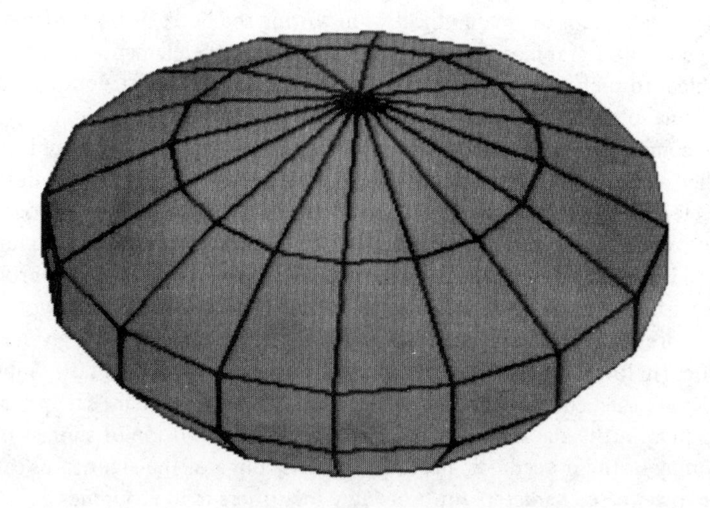

*Figure I.1*

The program requires the listings 2.1 ('start'), 2.2 (two functions FN X and FN Y), 2.3 ('setorigin'), 2.4 ('moveto'), 2.5 ('lineto') and 2.7 ('triangle'). This combination of procedures will be called 'lib1', and it was designed for drawing line figures on the television screen.

To 'lib1' must be added listings 3.3 ('angle'), 8.1 ('mult3' and 'idR3'), 8.2 ('tran3'), 8.3 ('scale3'), 8.4 ('rot3'), 9.1 ('look3') and 9.2 ('main program'). Procedures, which when combined we call 'lib3', are used for transforming and for observing objects in three-dimensional space.

Listing 10.5 ('revbod') is also needed, together with the 'scene3' procedure given in listing I.1.

*Listing I.1*

```
6000 REM scene3 / flying saucer
6010 DEF PROCscene3
6020 LOCAL I%
6030 DIM X(12),Y(12),XD(6),YD(6)
6040 DIM A(4,4),B(4,4),R(4,4)
6050 DATA 0,3, 3,2, 5,1, 5,0, 4,-1, 0,-3
6060 RESTORE
6069 REM INPUT horizontal data
6070 NUMV=5
6080 INPUT"NUMBER OF HORIZONTAL LINES",NUMH
6090 INPUT"INITIAL ROTATION",PHI
6099 REM READ definition set
6100 FOR I%=1 TO NUMV+1
6110 READ XD(I%),YD(I%)
6120 NEXT I%
6130 PROCidR3 : PROClook3
6140 PROCrevbod
6150 ENDPROC
```

Figure I.1 requires the data HORIZ = 12, VERT = 9, EX = 1, EY = 2, EZ = 3, DX = 0, DY = 0, DZ = 0, number of horizontal lines NUMH = 16 and initial rotation PHI = 0. Each value has to be typed in individually, when requested by the machine. Run the program with different data values. What happens if HORIZ = 6 and VERT = 4 and the other values stay the same? Set HORIZ = 16, VERT = 12, EX = 1, EY = –2, EZ = 3, DX = 1, DY = 0 and DZ = 0. Try NUMH = 20, PHI = 0.1. You will have to read up to and including chapter 10 to understand the details of what is happening.

This example illustrates the reasoning behind the layout of this book. Assuming that you are a fast typist, or that you have bought the accompanying cassettes, then a relatively complex three-dimensional picture can be constructed very quickly with a minimum of effort. Even one-finger typists (like the authors) will have little difficulty in implementing this and the other programs, before they go on to study the book in detail.

We hope that this example will inspire you to implement *all* the programs in this book, to try most of the examples, and then to go on and draw your very own computer graphics pictures.

Now read the rest of our book and we wish you many happy hours with your BBC microcomputer.

# *1 Graphics Operations of the BBC Model B Microcomputer*

Throughout the course of this book it will be assumed that the BASIC programming language of the BBC micro is reasonably familiar to the reader. In this first chapter, therefore, we shall be looking at some of the BASIC commands – those concerned wholly or partly with graphics. The display capabilities of the micro will be explored by means of a series of example programs and simple exercises. In the chapters that follow we shall use this knowledge to develop a sound understanding, both practical and mathematical, of computer graphics.

Initially we shall consider the hardware and software facilities that are available for producing pictures. On the BBC computer there is a choice of eight different display MODEs numbered 0 to 7 (the last of which is the special TELETEXT mode which is discussed separately in chapter 13). All the modes produce television pictures by using *raster scan* technology; this is also true of most of the newer commercial mini and main-frame computers. An area of memory at least 1 K(ilo)byte long (1 Kbyte = $2^8$ bytes = 1K for short), known as the *screen memory*, is reserved out of the available RAM (Random Access Memory – the area available for programming use) to hold the display information for the screen. This memory is examined, bit by bit, as the electron beam sweeps across the raster screen. The display is composed of dots or *pixels* (from picture-cells) each of which, in the simplest case of modes 0, 3, 4 and 6, is represented by a single bit (a binary on/off switch) in the memory. Whenever a binary-on is detected during the raster scan, the beam is switched on for a short period, so producing a dot of light on the screen. In the other modes more than one bit corresponds to each pixel (see later). The screen can be considered in two ways; either as a grid of individual points that are addressed by *graphics* commands or as a grid of blocks in which characters can be placed by *text* commands.

### The MODE Command

On the BBC micro there is a palette of sixteen different *actual* colours/effects (numbered 0 to 15) and the MODE command is used to decide how many different colours from this palette will be available and what type of display is used.

MODE N switches to display mode N and decides how much memory must be set aside for the screen memory. The number of pixels (known as the resolution) and TEXT characters available, as well as their physical size, alter with each MODE. The various modes are detailed in table 1.1.

Table 1.1

| MODE | TEXT characters (column × row) | Graphics pixels (horizontal × vertical) | Number of colours | Memory used | Pixel |
|---|---|---|---|---|---|
| 0 | 80 × 32 | 640 × 256 | 2 | 20K | 2 × 4 |
| 1 | 40 × 32 | 320 × 256 | 4 | 20K | 4 × 4 |
| 2 | 20 × 32 | 160 × 256 | 16 | 20K | 8 × 4 |
| 3 | 80 × 25 | – | 2 | 16K | – |
| 4 | 40 × 32 | 320 × 256 | 2 | 10K | 2 × 4 |
| 5 | 20 × 32 | 160 × 256 | 4 | 10K | 8 × 4 |
| 6 | 40 × 25 | – | 2 | 8K | – |
| 7 TELETEXT | 40 × 25 | 80 × 75 | 16 | 1K | – |

In the two-colour modes (0 and 4) each pixel is represented by one bit in the ately in chapter 13, nor the two text-only MODEs (3 and 6) will be considered. In the two-colour modes (0 and 4) each pixel is represented by one bit in the memory. This bit defines which *logical* colour is used for that pixel and initially it is set to display a white pixel for a logical 1 and a black pixel for a logical 0. It is possible to change these default assignments (see listing 1.9) so that any actual colour may be displayed for either logical colour. In the four-colour modes (1 and 5) two bits of memory are used to represent each pixel. These two bits represent, in binary notation, a number between 0 and 3 which is the numerical code of the logical colour displayed for that pixel. This allows us to distinguish between four types of pixel and to use a different colour for each type. In the sixteen-colour mode (2) four bits are used per pixel to make up a logical colour between 0 and 15. For all the standard graphics modes the number of pixels vertically is 256; however, since more memory is required to represent a sixteen-colour pixel compared with a four-colour pixel, the number of points available horizontally varies inversely with the number of colours used.

**Screen Memory**

This type of screen picture is referred to as a *memory mapped* display since it corresponds directly to the contents of an area of memory. On the BBC micro the memory used for the display, called the screen memory, starts at location

HIMEM (which is reset by the MODE command) and ends at location 32767 (the end of RAM). A simple exploration of how the screen is affected by changing the contents of the memory can be made with a program such as listing 1.1.

*Listing 1.1*

```
10 REPEAT
20 INPUT'" Which mode ",M
30 MODE M
40 ?HIMEM=137
50 UNTIL FALSE
```

This program uses the indirection operator '?' (see the user guide) to indicate the intention of placing a number (VALUE) in the memory location with address HIMEM. This is the first location of the display file and it holds the information for the top left-hand corner of the screen. Run the program and select mode 4 (or 0). Since each location, or *byte*, contains eight binary *bits*, the first eight pixels on the display are affected in such two-colour modes. These change to show a pattern of dots that is equivalent to the binary representation of the VALUE, in this case 10001001. Run the program again but now choose a four-colour mode (1 or 5). This time only four pixels will be affected since two bits are used per pixel. Try the same program with the sixteen-colour mode (2) and you will see that only two pixels are now affected since four bits per pixel are used. Table 1.2 shows how the eight bits in one byte are split up by different modes to represent the logical colours of the different number of pixels that use the specific value 10001001.

From the above we see that it is possible to construct a complete picture by storing various values in the locations of the display file. This is tedious for two-colour pictures, and extremely complicated for pictures with a greater number of colours. Obviously we need a simpler method for altering the contents of the screen memory. BASIC provides the graphics commands that deal precisely with this problem. The first command to be considered is PLOT, a very complicated command that offers many options, as we shall see later. For the time being, however, we shall limit ourselves to using just three options, PLOT 69, PLOT 4 and PLOT 5. Two of these are considered so important that they are given alternative names: PLOT 4 is MOVE and PLOT 5 is DRAW.

Because the number of pixels and their relative positions are MODE-dependent, a new object is defined for the BBC micro, the *addressable point* (or *point* for short). All the graphics commands treat the display as a grid of 1280 addressable points horizontally by 1024 addressable points vertically (1 310 720 in total). Each point is uniquely defined by a pair of integers such that point (X, Y) is X addressable points to the left and Y points above the screen origin (point (0, 0) at the bottom left-hand corner of the screen). We have already seen that the number of available pixels is mode-dependent; in fact each pixel is composed

Table 1.2

Two-colour MODES

| | 1 | 0 | 0 | 0 | 1 | 0 | 0 | 1 | |
|---|---|---|---|---|---|---|---|---|---|
| pixel 1 = | $B_7$ | | | | | | | | = 1 = logical colour 1 |
| pixel 2 = | | $B_6$ | | | | | | | = 0 = logical colour 0 |
| pixel 3 = | | | $B_5$ | | | | | | = 0 = logical colour 0 |
| pixel 4 = | | | | $B_4$ | | | | | = 0 = logical colour 0 |
| pixel 5 = | | | | | $B_3$ | | | | = 1 = logical colour 1 |
| pixel 6 = | | | | | | $B_2$ | | | = 0 = logical colour 0 |
| pixel 7 = | | | | | | | $B_1$ | | = 0 = logical colour 0 |
| pixel 8 = | | | | | | | | $B_0$ | = 1 = logical colour 1 |

Four-colour MODES

| | 1 | 0 | 0 | 0 | 1 | 0 | 0 | 1 | |
|---|---|---|---|---|---|---|---|---|---|
| pixel 1 = | $B_7$ | | | | $B_3$ | | | | = 11 = logical colour 3 |
| pixel 2 = | | $B_6$ | | | | $B_2$ | | | = 00 = logical colour 0 |
| pixel 3 = | | | $B_5$ | | | | $B_1$ | | = 00 = logical colour 0 |
| pixel 4 = | | | | $B_4$ | | | | $B_0$ | = 01 = logical colour 1 |

Sixteen-colour MODE

| | 1 | 0 | 0 | 0 | 1 | 0 | 0 | 1 | |
|---|---|---|---|---|---|---|---|---|---|
| pixel 1 = | $B_7$ | | $B_5$ | | $B_3$ | | $B_1$ | | = 1010 = logical colour 10 |
| pixel 2 = | | $B_6$ | | $B_4$ | | $B_2$ | | $B_0$ | = 0001 = logical colour 1 |

of a small block of addressable points (see the last column of table 1.1). This correspondence between points and pixels is all worked out by the computer and means that, since we are working with addressable points, we can switch between MODEs without having to change the programs. Any command that affects one point will actually affect the whole pixel that contains this point. The use of points is a great help when changing between MODEs since point (640, 512) always represents the middle of the screen, whereas if we counted in pixels then pixel (80, 128) is close to the left side of the screen in mode 0, one-quarter of the way across the screen in mode 1 and the middle of the screen for mode 2 only. The graphics commands help in constructing pictures by allowing us to control a *graphics pen*, which is initially positioned over point (0, 0).

PLOT 4, X, Y or MOVE X, Y moves the pen from its current position and places it above the pixel that contains the point (X, Y).

PLOT 69, X, Y moves the pen to the point (X, Y) and plots a pixel there.
PLOT 5, X, Y or DRAW X, Y draws a line from the pen's current position to the point (X, Y).

After the execution of these commands the pen remains over the last point that was visited, while awaiting the next command. Before examining the other more advanced graphics commands, a simple example and some exercises will serve to demonstrate what can be achieved with only the few commands that have been dealt with so far.

*Example 1.1*
PLOT 69 can be used to scatter pixel dots over the screen. The program in listing 1.2 illustrates the flexibility of addressing the pixels via the overlying grid of addressable points.

*Listing 1.2*

```
10 INPUT"Which mode",M : MODE M
20 REPEAT
30 PLOT 69,RND(1280),RND(1024)
40 UNTIL FALSE
```

*Exercise 1.1*
Alter listing 1.2 to DRAW lines, either between the random points as they are generated or from the middle (point (640, 512)) to each point.

*Exercise 1.2*
Write a program to calculate the position of lines that form a grid on the screen. DRAW them by using two FOR. . .NEXT loops (one for horizontal lines, the other for vertical lines).

*Exercise 1.3*
Write a program that accepts the INPUT of N pairs of addressable point co-ordinates from the keyboard, and then DRAWs an irregular polygon of N sides by joining the points in order. (Remember to join the last point to the first.)

**PRINT, LIST and VDU**

So far we have not discussed the most obvious method of changing the display, namely the text commands PRINT (PRINT TAB), LIST and VDU (consult the user manual for a full description of these commands). This is because these use character-size text blocks and are designed primarily for use with low-resolution graphics. This will be dealt with in chapter 5, but since the BBC micro allows high-resolution and low-resolution graphics to be freely intermixed we shall give a minor example here. Suppose we alter the program from exercise 1.2 to draw a grid of the appropriate size for character blocks. If we run the program, select a MODE and press control E (mix text and graphics) followed by LIST, followed by control D (separate text and graphics), we get a display similar to figure 1.1, which shows the size and position of the character blocks.

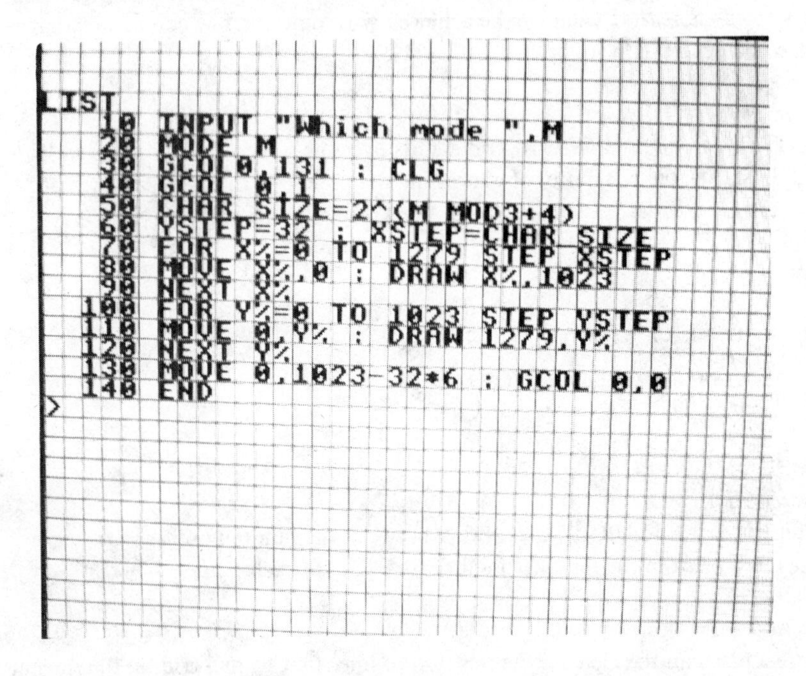


*Figure 1.1*

*Example 1.2*

We can use the PLOT command to demonstrate the high-resolution capabilities of the BBC micro by drawing *fractals* (see Mandelbrot, 1977).

To draw a simple fractal we proceed as follows. Imagine a square with sides of length $4^n$. This may be divided into 16 smaller squares, each with sides of length $4^{n-1}$; the smaller squares are numbered 1 to 16 in accordance with the pattern of figure 1.2. Four of these smaller squares, numbers 2, 8, 9 and 15, are rearranged to produce figure 1.3.

Each of the squares in the pattern is now split up into 16 even smaller squares in the same way and these are similarly rearranged. This process is repeated until we have squares with sides of length 1. The resulting fractal pattern consists entirely of unit squares which we can PLOT 69 as single pixels (since we know how many pixels are available in each mode we can work out the area covered by one pixel in terms of addressable points). The program in listing 1.3 starts from a square with sides of length 64, which is $4^3$; thus in the program there must be three FOR. . .NEXT loops nested inside each other. The final picture produced is shown in figure 1.4.

*Listing 1.3*

```
 10 MODE 1
 20 DIM X(16),Y(16)
 29 REM assign an X and Y coordinate to each square
 30 FOR I%=1 TO 4
 40 FOR J%=1 TO 4
 50 K%=4*I%+J%-4
 60 X(K%)=J%-3 : Y(K%)=I%-3
 70 NEXT J% : NEXTI%
 79 REM move squares 2,8,9 and 15
 80 X(2)=0    : Y(2)=-3
 90 X(8)=2    : Y(8)=0
100 X(9)=-3   : Y(9)=-1
110 X(15)=-1 : Y(15)=2
119 REM plot each square inside a square inside a square as
        a single pixel
120 FOR I%=1 TO 16
130 FOR J%=1 TO 16
140 FOR K%=1 TO 16
150 XX=16*X(I%)+4*X(J%)+X(K%)
160 YY=16*Y(I%)+4*Y(J%)+Y(K%)
170 PLOT 69,640+XX*4,512+YY*4
180 NEXT K% : NEXT J% : NEXT I%
190 END
```

We shall now consider the options that affect the colour of the lines and the points that are placed on the screen. There are two commands that allow us to select a new logical colour (one affects text and the other affects graphics).

COLOUR COL is the command used to change text colours. COL is an integer between 0 and the number of colours available in the present mode, and represents the new foreground colour for text. If we use COLOUR 128 + COL we can change the background colour of the text. All subsequent printing of characters will be affected by this command.

| 13 | 14 | 15 | 16 |
|---|---|---|---|
| 9 | 10 | 11 | 12 |
| 5 | 6 | 7 | 8 |
| 1 | 2 | 3 | 4 |

*Figure 1.2*

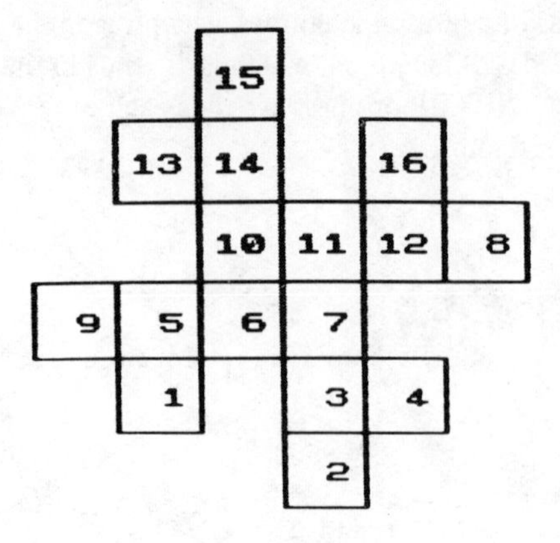


*Figure 1.3*

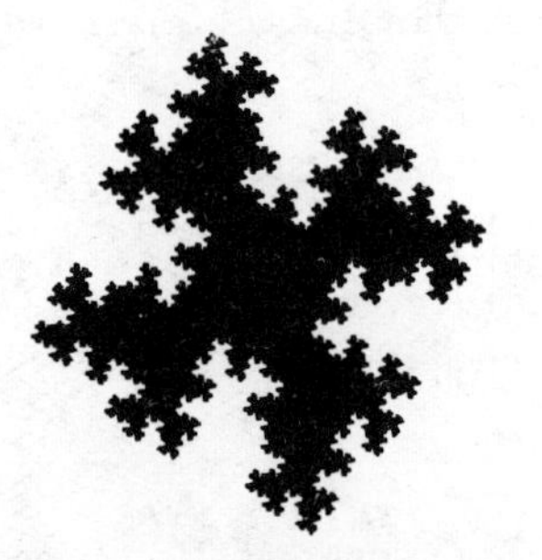

*Figure 1.4*

GCOL G, COL ($0 \leqslant G \leqslant 4$) is the command that affects the colour produced by further PLOT (and DRAW) commands. As with COLOUR above, COL can select a foreground colour and the colour for the lines and points plotted, or with GCOL G, 128 + COL a background colour. Graphics background colours will be seen only when a CLG (clear graphics) command is executed, so filling the whole of the graphics area with the background colour.

Before we go on to explain the other part of the GCOL command (the G option), try the program in listing 1.4 which uses the simplest form of GCOL (GCOL 0), . . . to change the colour that is used for drawing lines. This sort of pattern, joining equivalent points on two curves, is known as a Lissajous figure.

The G-parameter in the GCOL command affects the way in which the colours are added to the screen. The effect produced by various values of G are explained opposite. (For further explanation of the operators AND, EOR and OR see the user guide.)

*Listing 1.4*

```
  9 REM Lissajous figures
 1Ø MODE 2
 2Ø MOVE 114Ø,512
 3Ø FOR I=Ø TO 2*PI STEP PI/1ØØ
 39 REM calculate the 2 points on 2 curves and join with
        a line drawn in a random colour
 4Ø S=SIN(I) : C=COS(I)
 5Ø S2=SIN(2*I) : C2=COS(2*I)
 6Ø X1=64Ø+C^3*5ØØ : Y1=512+S^3*5ØØ
 7Ø R=(C2^3+S2^3)*5ØØ
 8Ø X2=64Ø+R*C : Y2=512+R*S
 9Ø GCOL Ø,RND(7)
1ØØ MOVE X1,Y1 : DRAW X2,Y2
11Ø NEXT I
```

| G *Operator* | *Effect* |
|---|---|
| 0 REPLACE | All pixels affected are changed to the colour that is specified by COL |
| 1 OR | Pixels affected become the colour that is given by their present (logical) colour OR COL. For example, in mode 1 a pixel that was colour 1 (binary 01) replotted in colour 2 (binary 10) would become colour 3 (binary 11 = 01 OR 10) |
| 2 AND | Pixels affected become the colour that is given by their present (logical) colour AND COL. Thus, in mode 2 a pixel that was colour 5 (binary 0101) replotted in colour 6 (binary 0110) would become colour 4 (binary 0100 = 0101 AND 0110) |
| 3 EOR | Pixels affected become the colour that is given by their present (logical) colour EOR COL. For example, in mode 2 a pixel that was colour 5 (binary 0101) replotted in colour 7 (binary 0111) would become colour 2 (binary 0010 = 0101 EOR 0111). It is worth noting that two identical EOR operations have the effect of cancelling each other out. If we were to PLOT the same pixel again with colour 7 it would be returned to colour 5 |
| 4 INVERT | Pixels affected become the colour that is given by inverting all the binary digits in their present (logical) colour. Note that this is exactly the same as EOR with 15 (binary 1111). Thus, in mode 2 a pixel that was colour 5 (binary 0101) replotted in any colour would become colour 10 (binary 1010 = 0101 EOR 1111) |

*Exercise 1.4*
Experiment with the program in listing 1.4 by using different GCOL options and perhaps by making the colours change in a non-random way. Try different equations for calculating the radius at each angle of the Lissajous figures.

*Example 1.3*
Using these options for the GCOL command we can produce simple programs that generate seemingly complex patterns. Listing 1.5 gives a program that uses option 3 (EOR) for GCOL combined with a method of creating complicated patterns.

On a display that is composed of discrete points (pixels), angled lines will be drawn as a series of short, horizontal or vertical steps. Many of the steps on the lines will overlap when two such lines are drawn close together at slightly different angles. Consider figure 1.5, which is drawn by listing 1.5. The lines that form the central area overlap each other many times and so this area would have been solid white if EOR had not been used. However those pixels that lie on an even number of lines are not affected (as noted above) and only those that are PLOTted an odd number of times are lit up. This produces the striking pattern at the middle of the figure. On the other hand the outer area of the pattern is produced by holes (of pixels not lying on any line) that are left by the line steps.

*Listing 1.5*

```
 9 REM joins points around a square to form a Moiré pattern
10 MODE1
20 GCOL 3,3
30 FOR I%=0 TO 1023 STEP 12
40 MOVE I%+128,0
50 DRAW (1023-I%)+128,1023
60 MOVE 128,I%
70 DRAW 1023+128,1023-I%
80 NEXT I%
```

*Exercise 1.5*
Alter listing 1.5 to INPUT the value of the STEP-size used and also INPUT the variable that indicates which GCOL option is to be used.

*Example 1.4: Simple Animation*
We note from listing 1.5 that the EOR option ensured that the display changed with each new command, even if the previous command was repeated by DRAWing the same point, or line. This property may be used to display an object briefly by drawing it twice – the first to put it on the screen and the second to take it off. Listing 1.6 moves a dot around the screen by PLOTting it at its new position and immediately PLOTting its last position again to remove the old point.

*Figure 1.5*

*Listing 1.6*

```
 1Ø MODE 2 : VDU 19,Ø,6,Ø,Ø,Ø
 2Ø GCOL 3,1
 3Ø SPEED=8 : X=Ø : Y=Ø
 4Ø XADD=SPEED : YADD=SPEED
 5Ø PLOT69,X,Y
 6Ø REPEAT : OLDX=X : OLDY=Y
 7Ø X=X+XADD : IF X > 1279-SPEED OR X < SPEED THEN XADD=-XADD :
    SOUND 1,-15,2ØØ,1
 8Ø Y=Y+YADD : IF Y > 1Ø23-SPEED OR Y < SPEED THEN YADD=-YADD :
    SOUND 2,-15,1ØØ,1
 9Ø PLOT 69,X,Y
1ØØ PLOT 69,OLDX,OLDY
11Ø UNTIL FALSE
```

***Example 1.5***

We may extend this program to allow keyboard control of the moving point (listing 1.7). The cursor control keys (either singly or in combination) enable the point to move in eight separate directions under our control. If a 'P' is typed then the point leaves a trailing line that indicates its past movements: if a 'Q' is typed then the point ceases to leave this trail.

This type of animation is an important and commonly used technique. We shall use it extensively both in programs such as the game in chapter 15, and in programs such as the 'cursor' routine in chapter 6.

*Listing 1.7*

```
 10 MODE 1
 20 GCOL 3,1
 30 X=0 : Y=0
 40 PLOT69,X,Y
 50 REPEAT
 60 XADD=0 : YADD=0
 70 OLDX=X : OLDY=Y
 79 REM check cursor keys for direction of movement
 80 IF INKEY(-58) AND Y < 1019 THEN YADD=4
 90 IF INKEY(-42) AND Y > 0 THEN YADD=-4
100 IF INKEY(-26) AND X > 0 THEN XADD=-4
110 IF INKEY(-122) AND X < 1275 THEN XADD=4
119 REM check 'p' to leave a trail
120 IF INKEY(-56) THEN GCOL 0,1
130 IF INKEY(-17) THEN GCOL 3,1
140 IF XADD=0 AND YADD=0 THEN 80
150 X=X+XADD : Y=Y+YADD
160 PLOT 69,X,Y
170 PLOT 69,OLDX,OLDY
180 UNTIL FALSE
```

***Example 1.6: Relative Plotting***
All the PLOT commands that have been given so far have used the absolute co-ordinates of the points that we were drawing; however, there are equivalent relative commands for PLOTting. These commands move the pen to the position that is X points to the left of and Y points above the original point. Listing 1.8 uses the relative version of the DRAW option to produce an animated effect over a large area simply by changing the lines around the edge of the area.

*Listing 1.8*

```
 10 MODE 2 : UP=255 : ACROSS=159
 20 X=0 : Y=0 : DIF=1 : I%=1
 30 REPEAT
 39 REM draw the ever decreasing or ever increasing rectangles
 40 GCOL 0,I%
 50 MOVE X,Y
 60 PLOT 1,0,UP*4 : PLOT 1,ACROSS*8,0
 70 MOVE X,Y
 80 PLOT 1,ACROSS*8,0 : PLOT 1,0,UP*4
 90 X=X+DIF*8 : Y=Y+DIF*4
100 UP=UP-2*DIF : ACROSS=ACROSS-2*DIF
109 REM if rectangle is a trivial line then start drawing outwards,
        if it is the outer rectangle then draw inwards
110 IF ACROSS<0 OR ACROSS=159 THEN DIF=-DIF : I%=(I% MOD 7)+1
120 UNTIL FALSE
```

**Logical and Actual Colours (VDU 19 and VDU 20)**

On the BBC microcomputer there is a palette of sixteen different colours/effects known as *actual* colours, any of which can be assigned to an available *logical* colour. We can redefine the relationship between logical and actual colours with the VDU 19 command. The format of this command is the characters VDU 19 followed by a list of five integers, these numbers being the code for the logical colour, the code for the actual colour and three zeros (to allow for future expansion of the number of colours in the palette). The program in listing 1.9 allows us to see all the colours available in each mode, and to redefine them. VDU 20 will restore all logical colours to their original (default) settings.

We can make a simplified interpretation of the pixels on a colour television screen by imagining them as groups of three dots of light that are packed closely together at the vertices of an equilateral triangle. For each pixel there is one red,

*Listing 1.9*

```
  9 REM N(I) is the number of colours in mode I.
       C(I,J) is the actual colour of logical colour J in mode I
 1Ø DIM N(6),C(6,15)
 2Ø FOR M=Ø TO 6: READ N(M) : NEXT
 3Ø FOR M=Ø TO 6 : FOR C=Ø TO N(M)-1
 4Ø READ C(M,C)
 5Ø NEXT C : NEXT M
 6Ø REPEAT : CLS : INPUT "Which mode ",M
 7Ø MODE M
 8Ø PRINT TAB(Ø,1);"MODE ";M;" : ";N(M);" COLOURS"
 9Ø PRINT TAB(Ø,3);"LOGICAL     ACTUAL"
 99 REM for given mode draw a table of logical/actual relationships
1ØØ FOR I=Ø TO N(M)-1
11Ø COLOUR 128+Ø : COLOUR (N(M)-1) MOD 8
12Ø PRINT TAB(2,I+4);I
13Ø PRINT TAB(7,I+4);"= ";
14Ø COLOUR 128+I : PRINT"    ";
15Ø COLOUR 128+Ø : PRINT"  ";C(M,I)
16Ø NEXT I
17Ø COLOUR 128+Ø : COLOUR (N(M)-1) MOD 8
179 REM change array C for a new logical/actual relation
18Ø PRINT TAB(Ø,21); :
    INPUT "Do you want to alter colour settings ",A$
19Ø IF A$<>"Y" THEN 26Ø
2ØØ PRINT"Alter LOGICAL colour    "; : VDU 8,8,8 : INPUT A
21Ø PRINT"to be ACTUAL  colour    "; : VDU 8,8,8 : INPUT B
22Ø A=A MOD N(M) : B=B MOD 16
229 REM change the display table
23Ø VDU 19,A,B,Ø,Ø,Ø : C(M,A)=B
24Ø PRINT TAB(14,A+4);C(M,A);" "
25Ø GOTO 18Ø
26Ø UNTIL FALSE
27Ø MODE 7
28Ø END
289 REM DATA about mode/colour
29Ø DATA 2,4,16,2,2,4,2
3ØØ DATA Ø,7
31Ø DATA Ø,1,3,7
32Ø DATA Ø,1,2,3,4,5,6,7,8,9,1Ø,11,12,12,14,15
33Ø DATA Ø,7
34Ø DATA Ø,7
35Ø DATA Ø,1,3,7
36Ø DATA Ø,7
```

one green and one blue dot, and the binary value of the actual colour is used to control the illumination of the three different dots. A location in the screen memory holds the information that indicates the logical colour of a particular pixel, and the equivalent actual colour to be displayed is looked up by the computer. The lowest three bits (bits 0 to 2) of the actual colour are used to decide whether the red, green and blue dots of that pixel are on or off. Our eyes contain only three types of colour sensor (red, green and blue). Our brains take the signals from the three dots and combine them into a single pixel of composite colour. So if the last three bits of the actual colour are 111, equivalent to colour 7, we get red plus green plus blue, which corresponds to white light. The other colour codes, when written in binary form, can be translated in this way: see table 1.3.

Table 1.3

| Colour | Number | Binary | Illuminated dots |
|---|---|---|---|
| Black | 0 | 000 | |
| Red | 1 | 001 | Red |
| Green | 2 | 010 | Green |
| Yellow | 3 | 011 | Green + Red |
| Blue | 4 | 100 | Blue |
| Purple | 5 | 101 | Blue + Red |
| Cyan | 6 | 110 | Blue + Green |
| White | 7 | 111 | Blue + Green + Red |

If the actual colour has the fourth bit set (bit 3), then the colour will flash between the colour that corresponds to the lower three bits and the inverse of this colour, that is colour EOR 7 (binary 111). The speed of flashing depends on a counter in the computer, and the setting can be changed by the *FX9 and *FX10 calls to the computer. This counter is at location &251; it is loaded first with the value stored at &252 which is then decremented every 1/100th of a second until zero is reached. Then the second colour is displayed while the counter goes from the value at &253 to zero, and the process is repeated. Listing 1.10 shows this process in action in mode 2. Change the values at &252 and &253 and rerun the program to see their effect.

*Exercise 1.6*
Experiment with different colours by using the programs from this chapter. Certain colour combinations can be too complicated for an ordinary television screen to handle. Unless you are using an expensive monitor rather than a television screen, the combination of clashing colours for the program in

*Listing 1.10*

```
10 MODE 2
20 VDU 23,1,0;0;0;0;
30 COLOUR 9
40 *FX10,99
50 *FX9,99
60 PRINT "THIS SHOWS THE FLASH COUNTER"
70 COLOUR 13
80 REPEAT PRINT TAB(0,1) : PRINT ?(&251) DIV 10 : UNTIL FALSE
```

listing 1.5 should produce a rather interesting effect of waves washing across the screen.

***Example 1.7: Colour Animation***

We can produce more animated effects by using flashing and non-flashing colours. Listing 1.11 shows some interesting techniques of colour animation. The first part of the program (which produces the boundary) is particularly useful because the display, once set up, needs no maintenance. The boundary is a sequence of blocks that is made up of alternate blocks of flashing blue/yellow and flashing yellow/blue foreground colours. On seeing this our brains are tricked into believing that the yellow and blue colours are moving around the boundary sequence. The second part of the program simply scrolls the words 'HELLO THIS IS YOUR BBC COMPUTER SPEAKING' in different colours up the screen.

*Listing 1.11*

```
 10 MODE 2
 19 REM print boundary
 20 FOR I%=0 TO 1
 30 COLOUR 128+11+I%
 40 FOR X%=0 TO 9
 50 PRINT TAB(X%*2+I%,0);" " : PRINT TAB(X%*2+1-I%,29);" "
 60 NEXT X%
 70 FOR Y%=0 TO 14
 80 PRINT TAB(0,2*Y%+I%);" " : PRINT TAB(19,2*Y%+1-I%);" "
 90 NEXT Y%
100 NEXT I%
109 REM read message
110 DIM A$(7)
120 FOR I%=1 TO 7 : READ A$(I%) : NEXT I%
130 DATA " HELLO  ","  THIS  ","   IS   ","  YOUR  ",
         " B.B.C. ","COMPUTER","SPEAKING"
140 C%=1
150 REPEAT
159 REM scroll message
160 FOR I%=1 TO 28
170 COLOUR 128+C% : COLOUR (C% EOR 7)
180 PRINT TAB(1,I%);SPC(5);A$(C%);SPC(5)
190 C%=(C% MOD 7)+1
200 NEXT I%
210 C%=(C% MOD 7)+1
220 UNTIL FALSE
```

*Exercise 1.7*
Write text and colour versions of the bouncing point program and the other animation programs. In your programs move characters instead of pixels around the screen.

**Filling in Areas**

The BBC micro has still more PLOT options, some of which deal with drawing dotted lines where only every other pixel in their path is illuminated. Try filling the MODE 0 screen with dotted white horizontal lines on a black background by using the dotted equivalent of DRAW, that is PLOT 21. It is possible that some areas appear pale purple while others are pale green. This is because the size of the points plotted is almost as small as the three-coloured dots that make up the colours and in some areas the points lie more towards the green side of the triangle while in others they are more to the red or the blue sides. Try redefining the background and foreground colours of the display to see what other effects can be produced.

Now we will look at the group of PLOT commands that fill in triangles. The most important of these is PLOT 85, the absolute, foreground colour version (see the user guide). This command constructs a triangle between the point currently being plotted and the last two points visited, and the area enclosed is filled with the current graphics colour. As a simple example, try typing the following commands, which will produce a large red triangle.

```
MODE 2 : GCOL 0, 1 : MOVE 100, 100 : DRAW 500, 900 : PLOT 85,
1000, 100
```

*Example 1.8*
The program in listing 1.12 produces a pattern by PLOTting a series of equilateral triangles in varying orientations and in different colours. It then uses the VDU 19 command to redefine each colour in turn, so producing the illusion of rotational movement. It requires the INPUT of two integers N and ST; N controls the rotation of consecutive triangles and ST gives the difference in radius between the triangles.

*Example 1.9: A Simple Game*
We now include a small game program (listing 1.13) to demonstrate the use of the techniques discussed in this chapter. A worm can move in character-size steps about the screen, horizontally or vertically, under control of the keyboard. The aim of the game is for the worm to eat the money (or target). The worm gets longer whenever it eats the target. If at any time the head of the worm runs headlong into the boundary or into its own body, then the worm dies. After ten successful meals the worm returns to its original size, with a fanfare; the game then continues.

*Listing 1.12*

```
 10 MODE 2
 20 VDU23,1,0;0;0;0;
 30 DIM X(96),Y(96)
 39 REM setup 96 points on a circle
 40 THETA=0 : TD=PI/48
 50 FOR I%=1 TO 96
 60 X(I%)=COS(THETA) : Y(I%)=SIN(THETA)
 70 THETA=THETA+TD
 80 NEXT I%
 90 COLOUR128
100 REPEAT
109 REM every new triangle is rotated through N points,
        its radius changes by ST
110 INPUT "N " N
120 IF N=0 THEN STOP ELSE INPUT "ST " ST : CLS
130 N3=N/3-1
140 I1=1 : COL=1
150 FOR R=500 TO 5 STEP -ST
159 REM draw triangle in colour COL
160 GCOL 0,COL
170 I2=I1+32 : I3=I2+32
180 MOVE 640+R*X(I1),500+R*Y(I1)
190 MOVE 640+R*X(I2),500+R*Y(I2)
200 PLOT 85,640+R*X(I3),500+R*Y(I3)
210 COL=(COL MOD 7 )+1
220 I1=((I1+N3) MOD 32 ) +1
230 NEXT
239 REM wait 5 seconds
240 T=TIME+500 : REPEAT UNTIL TIME>T
249 REM rotate picture by colour swap for 8 seconds
250 T=TIME+800 : REPEAT
260 FOR J%=1 TO 7
270 FOR I%=1 TO 7
280 VDU 19,I%,((I%+J%) MOD 7)+1,0,0,0
290 NEXT I%
300 ST=TIME+10 : REPEAT UNTIL TIME>ST
310 NEXT J%
320 UNTIL TIME>T
330 VDU 20
340 UNTIL FALSE
```

This game was developed using the modular, structured methods that are preferred by programmers. These methods help quickly to produce a working and understandable program. Put simply, we must approach the program as a series of small tasks that build up block by block into the completed program. For the game below these tasks were tentatively defined as

(1) Initialise variables
(2) Set up board
(3) Control game
(4) Update and print score

From this overview of the program we can set about solving each problem or if necessary splitting it into yet smaller, more manageable, problems. For example, task (3) above could be split into

(A) Generate target
(B) Use keyboard to change direction of worm
(C) Move worm

Task (C) could be further split into

(a) Draw worm
(b) Make worm die if it hits boundary or itself
(c) Make worm grow if it eats money
(d) Generate fanfare

No specific order is implied in this breakdown; for example, you may find that you want to regenerate the target from inside the fanfare section of the program. These headings are simply lists of tasks that reflect the problems that come to mind when attempting the solution of a larger problem.

Examine the game below and try to identify which tasks are carried out, where, in what order, and which have been further subdivided. (Throughout this book the names of procedures are in lower case characters and are preceded by a red REMark when listed in MODE 7. This helps to make the program more readable and gives a clear picture of the algorithm; hence it is good general practice.)

Note the use of logical expressions (for example, UNTIL DEAD OR WON) – see the user guide. Also note the use of the OSBYTE call with A% = &87 to detect collisions by examining the contents of character blocks. Figure 1.6 shows a typical state of the game.

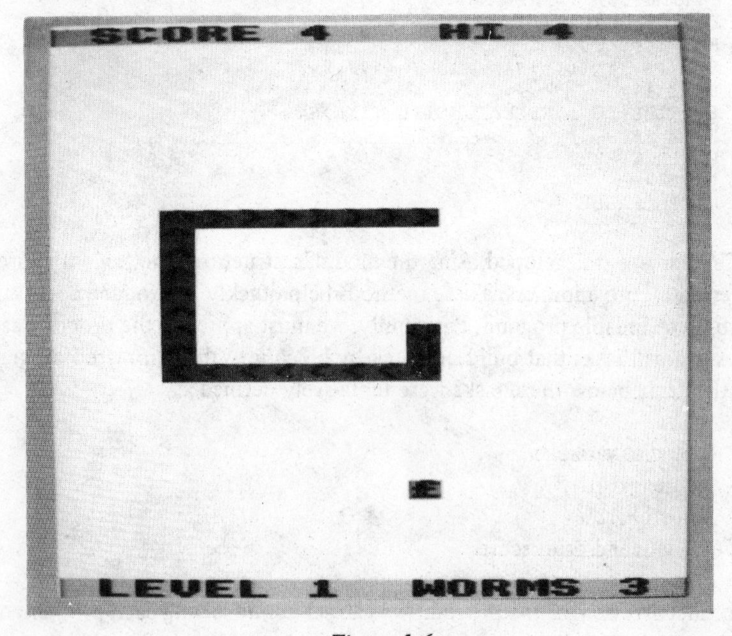


*Figure 1.6*

*Listing 1.13*

```
1000 REM WORM GAME
1010 DIM R(55),C(55) : HSC=0
1019 REM prepare screen
1020 REPEAT : MODE 2 : SCORE=0 : WORMS=3 : LEVEL=1
1030 VDU 23,1,0;0;0;0; : GCOL 0,128+4 : CLG
1040 GCOL 0,7 : MOVE 64,32 : MOVE 64,992
1050 PLOT 85,1215,32 : PLOT 85,1215,992
1059 REM initialise worm
1060 S=5 : P=1 : R=1 : C=RND(18)
1070 RMOVE=1 : CMOVE=0 : H$="V"
1080 FOR I%=0 TO 55 : R(I%)=-1 : NEXT I%
1090 WON=FALSE : DEAD=FALSE : *FX15,1
1100 COLOUR 128+3 : PRINT TAB(1,1);SPC(18) :
     PRINT TAB(1,30);SPC(18)
1109 REM display score and set target
1110 PROCstatus : PROCtarget
1119 REM main loop
1120 REPEAT
1130 PROCkey : PROCworm : PROCdelay(5-LEVEL)
1140 UNTIL DEAD OR WON
1150 IF WON THEN PROCfanfare : GOTO 1030
1159 REM wipe out dead worm and make crashing noise
1160 FOR I%=-15 TO 1 : SOUND 0,I%,4,1 : NEXT I%
1170 COLOUR 128+7
1180 PRINT TAB(X,Y);" "
1190 FOR I%=1 TO S
1200 IF R(P)<>-1 THEN PRINT TAB(C(P),R(P));" "
1210 P=(P MOD S)+1 : SOUND1,-15,10,1
1220 NEXT I%
1230 WORMS=WORMS-1 : IF WORMS<>0 THEN 1060
1239 REM if no worms left then wait for return to start again
1240 COLOUR 128+12 : COLOUR 11 : PRINT TAB(0,31); : *FX15,1
1250 INPUT "HIT RETURN FOR GAME" A$
1260 UNTIL FALSE

2000 REM fanfare
2010 DEF PROCfanfare
2019 REM congratulatory jingle
2020 DATA 2,69,117,165, 2,73,121,169, 2,81,129,177,
          5,102,150,198, 2,81,129,177, 7,102,150,198
2030 RESTORE : FOR N%=1 TO 6 : READ D
2040 FOR C%=&201 TO &203
2050 READ P : SOUND C%,-15,P,D
2060 NEXT C%
2070 NEXT N%
2080 ENDPROC

3000 REM worm
3010 DEF PROCworm
3019 REM move worm by adding new head segment and deleting tail
3020 COLOUR 128+7 : IF R(P)<>-1 THEN PRINT TAB(C(P),R(P));" "
3030 R=R+RMOVE : C=C+CMOVE
3040 IF R<2 OR R>29 OR C<1 OR C>18 THEN DEAD=TRUE : ENDPROC
3050 PRINT TAB(C,R); : A%=135 : I%=USR(&FFF4)
3060 A$=CHR$((I% AND &FF00)/&100) : IF A$=" " THEN 3100
3070 COLOUR 128+2 : COLOUR 0 : A%=135 : I%=USR(&FFF4)
3080 A$=CHR$((I% AND &FF00)/&100)
3089 REM if not space it was either a wall or edible money.
3090 IF A$="`" THEN PROCgobble ELSE DEAD=TRUE : ENDPROC
3100 R(P)=R : C(P)=C : COLOUR 128+1 : PRINT TAB(C,R);H$
3110 P=(P MOD S)+1
3120 ENDPROC
```

```
4000 REM key input
4010 DEF PROCkey
4020 A$=CHR$(ASC(INKEY$(0)) AND &4F)
4030 IF A$="I" AND CMOVE THEN RMOVE=-1 : CMOVE=0 : H$="^"
4040 IF A$="M" AND CMOVE THEN RMOVE=1 : CMOVE=0 : H$="V"
4050 IF A$="J" AND RMOVE THEN RMOVE=0 : CMOVE=-1 : H$="<"
4060 IF A$="K" AND RMOVE THEN RMOVE=0 : CMOVE=1 : H$=">"
4070 ENDPROC

5000 REM gobble
5010 DEF PROCgobble
5019 REM make noise while chewing and add to score.
5020 FOR I%=1 TO 6 : SOUND1,I%-15,20+I%*6,1: NEXT I%
5030 SCORE=SCORE+1 : PROCstatus
5039 REM if worm is 55 segments long you have eaten `10, you win
5040 S=S+5 : IF S=55 THEN WON=TRUE : ENDPROC
5050 PROCtarget
5060 ENDPROC

6000 REM status
6009 REM show score and no. of worms
6010 DEF PROCstatus
6020 COLOUR 128+3 : COLOUR 0
6030 IF SCORE>HSC THEN HSC=SCORE
6040 PRINT TAB(1,1);" SCORE ";SCORE," HI ";HSC
6050 PRINT TAB(1,30);" LEVEL ";LEVEL,"WORMS ";WORMS
6060 ENDPROC

7000 REM target
7010 DEF PROCtarget
7019 REM produce randoml@positioned target, not inside worm.
7020 X=RND(18) : Y=RND(28)+1 : COLOUR128+7
7030 PRINT TAB(X,Y); : A%=135 : I%=USR(&FFF4)
7040 A$=CHR$((I% AND &FF00)/&100) : IF A$<>" " THEN 7020
7050 IF X=C AND Y=R THEN 7020
7060 COLOUR 128+2 : COLOUR 0
7070 PRINT "`"
7080 ENDPROC

8000 REM delay
8010 DEF PROCdelay(T)
8020 IF T>0 THEN TT=TIME+T : REPEAT UNTIL TIME>TT
8030 ENDPROC
```

*Exercise 1.8*

As a final miniproject for this chapter, write a squash game or ping-pong video game (or both!) using low-resolution colour graphics. The ball can be a pixel or character block, and the bat(s) should be controlled from the keyboard like the worm in listing 1.13. You may find it useful to turn some of the program sections from this chapter into procedures, which is readily done if you approach program writing in a prepared modular manner.

In this chapter we have restricted ourselves to using the screen as a fixed area for patterns and games. To step up from pixel graphics to drawing pictures of real objects we need commands that will relate the real world to our screen. We shall now explore and develop the techniques that are needed to draw real graphics pictures. Before we go on to this you should experiment with the three programs given in listings 1.14, 1.15 and 1.16 and ensure that you understand the graphics commands, since these are fundamental to understanding the rest of this book.

*Listing 1.14*

```
 10 MODE 1 : VDU23,1,0;0;0;0;
 20 VDU 19,0,4,0,0,0
 30 PROCcircle(640,750,1000,0,1)
 40 PROCcircle(640,750,150,2,2)
 50 PROCcircle(740,650,70,3,3)
 60 PROCcircle(865,680,100,3,3)
 70 PROCcircle(950,660,80,3,3)
 80 MOVE 740,580 : MOVE 740,720
 90 PLOT 85,950,580
100 END

110 REM circle
120 DEF PROCcircle(X,Y,R,C1,C2)
130 MOVE X,Y
140 F=TRUE : GCOL 0,C1
150 FOR I=0 TO 2*PI STEP PI/50
160 MOVE X,Y
165 PLOT 81,R*COS(I),R*SIN(I)
170 F=NOT F
180 IF F THEN GCOL0,C1 ELSE GCOL0,C2
190 NEXT I
200 ENDPROC
```

*Listing 1.15*

```
 10 MODE 1 : VDU 23,1,0;0;0;0;
 20 VDU 19,2,4,0,0,0 : VDU 19,3,2,0,0,0
 30 FOR S=48 TO 200 STEP 24
 40 FOR J=1 TO (250-S)/25
 50 PROCcube(RND(1280-3*S/2),RND(1024-3*S/2),S,RND(4)-1)
 60 NEXT J
 70 NEXT S
 80 END

100 REM fake cube
110 DEF PROCcube(X,Y,S,C1)
120 IF C1<2 THEN C2=3 ELSE C2=0
130 T=S*.5
140 PROCquad(X,Y,X,Y+S,X+S,Y+S,X+S,Y)
150 PROCquad(X+S+T,Y+S+T,X+S+T,Y+T,X+S,Y,X+S,Y+S)
160 PROCquad(X+S+T,Y+S+T,X+T,Y+S+T,X,Y+S,X+S,Y+S)
170 ENDPROC

200 REM quad_rilateral
210 DEF PROCquad(XA,YA,XB,YB,XC,YC,XD,YD)
220 GCOL 0,C1 : MOVE XA,YA : MOVE XB,YB :
    PLOT 85,XD,YD : PLOT 85,XC,YC
230 GCOL 0,C2 : DRAW XD,YD : DRAW XA,YA :
    DRAW XB,YB : DRAW XC,YC
240 ENDPROC
```

*Listing 1.16*

```
 1Ø DIM X%(81),X(1ØØ),Y(1ØØ)
 2Ø A=4ØØ : B=1ØØ : I%=Ø
 29 REM calculate data for ellipse
 3Ø FOR I=Ø TO 2*PI STEP PI/5Ø
 4Ø X(I%)=A*COS(I) : Y(I%)=B*SIN(I) : I%=I%+1
 5Ø NEXT I
 6Ø MODE 1 : GCOL Ø,1 : VDU 19,1,6,Ø,Ø,Ø
 69 REM put on sky
 7Ø MOVE Ø,5Ø4 : MOVE 128Ø,5Ø4
 8Ø PLOT 85,Ø,1Ø24 : PLOT 85,128Ø,1Ø24
 9Ø GCOL Ø,2 : VDU 19,2,4,Ø,Ø,Ø : DRAW 128Ø,5ØØ
 99 REM calculate data for planks
1ØØ FOR I%=Ø TO 81
11Ø X%(I%)=64*(4Ø-I%-(I% MOD 2)*Ø.66)
12Ø NEXT I%
129 REM draw planks
13Ø FOR I%=Ø TO 8Ø STEP 2
14Ø MOVE I%*16,5ØØ : MOVE I%*16+16,5ØØ
15Ø PLOT 85,64Ø-X%(I%),Ø : PLOT 85,64Ø-X%(I%+1),Ø
16Ø NEXT I%
169 REM draw pyramid with outline
17Ø GCOL Ø,3 : VDU 19,3,5,Ø,Ø,Ø
18Ø MOVE 1136,4ØØ : MOVE 96Ø,35Ø
19Ø PLOT 85,975,6ØØ : PLOT 85,864,424
2ØØ GCOL Ø,Ø : DRAW 96Ø,35Ø : DRAW 1136,4ØØ
21Ø DRAW 975,6ØØ : DRAW 96Ø,35Ø : MOVE 975,6ØØ : DRAW 864,424
219 REM draw cuboid with outline
22Ø GCOL Ø,3 : MOVE 125,29Ø : MOVE 48Ø,34Ø
23Ø PLOT 85,125,49Ø : PLOT 85,48Ø,51Ø
24Ø PLOT 85,8,51Ø : PLOT 85,38Ø,522
25Ø MOVE 125,29Ø : MOVE125,49Ø
26Ø PLOT 85,8,314 : PLOT 85,8,51Ø
27Ø GCOL Ø,Ø : MOVE 125,29Ø : DRAW 48Ø,34Ø : DRAW 48Ø,51Ø
28Ø DRAW 125,49Ø : DRAW 8,51Ø : DRAW 8,314
29Ø DRAW 125,29Ø : DRAW 125,49Ø
3ØØ MOVE 8,51Ø : DRAW 38Ø,522 : DRAW 48Ø,51Ø
3Ø9 REM draw ellipse
31Ø X=6ØØ : Y=2ØØ
32Ø GCOL Ø,3 : MOVE X,Y
33Ø FOR I%=Ø TO 1ØØ
34Ø MOVE X,Y : PLOT 81,X(I%),Y(I%)
35Ø NEXT I%
359 REM join lower side of ellipse to bottom of screen
36Ø FOR I%=5Ø TO 1ØØ : J%=(I%+1) MOD 1Ø1
37Ø MOVE X+X(I%),Y+Y(I%) : MOVEX+X(J%),Y+Y(J%)
38Ø PLOT 85,X+X(I%),Ø : PLOT 85,X+X(J%),Ø
39Ø NEXT I%
399 REM draw outline around top of cylinder
4ØØ GCOL Ø,Ø : MOVE X+X(1ØØ),Y+Y(1ØØ)
41Ø FOR I%=Ø TO 1ØØ
42Ø DRAW X+X(I%),Y+Y(I%)
43Ø NEXT I%
439 REM draw lines down to bottom of screen from
        lower edge of ellipse
44Ø FOR I%=5Ø TO 1ØØ
45Ø MOVE X+X(I%),Y+Y(I%) : DRAW X+X(I%),Ø
46Ø NEXT I%
```

**Complete Programs**

I Listing 1.1. Data required: a mode value between 0 and 6.
II Listing 1.2. Data required: a mode value of 0, 1, 2, 4 or 5.
III Listing 1.3. No data required.
IV Listing 1.4. No data required.
V Listing 1.5. No data required.
VI Listing 1.6. No data required.
VII Listing 1.7. Use the cursor keys to move the red point about the screen. Type 'p' to leave a trail, and 'q' if no trail is wanted.
VIII Listing 1.8. No data required.
IX Listing 1.9. Data required:

Mode? Type the required value between 0 and 6.
Do you want to alter colour settings? Type Y(es) or N(o) as appropriate.
Alter LOGICAL colour? Type a mode-dependent integer that is defined to be an ACTUAL colour; that is, type an integer between 0 and 15.

X Listing 1.10. No data required.
XI Listing 1.11. No data required.
XII Listing 1.12. Data required: two integers N and ST; try N = 14 and ST = 5.
XIII Listing 1.13. Keys 'I', 'J', 'K' and 'M' move the worm.
XIV Listing 1.14. No data required.
XV Listing 1.15. No data required.
XVI Listing 1.16. No data required.

# 2 From Real Coordinates to Pixels

Throughout the two-dimensional and three-dimensional sections of this book we shall divide the television screen into a text window (of two lines at the top of the screen) and a graphics window (the rest of the screen). As already discussed, on the Model B the graphics window (or *graphics frame*) consists of a rectangular matrix of coloured pixels; the size and number of the pixels and the number of possible colours depend on the MODE setting of the computer (0 to 7). Unless otherwise stated, two-dimensional and three-dimensional geometrical programs will be run in MODE 1. This means that access to these pixels is MODE-dependent and hence we shall consider the graphics frame to be made up of the rectangular matrix of *addressable points* (*points* for short) that are stacked in NXPIX (= 1280) vertical columns and NYPIX (= 960) horizontal rows. Each pixel on the screen corresponds to a number of different points; although the exact correspondence is naturally MODE-dependent, this need not concern us since the operating system deals with this problem of relationship. Unfortunately the word 'pixel' has several different meanings (as do 'point' and 'dot'), so it must be remembered that in this book 'pixel' refers to a MODE-dependent group of addressable points on the television screen (see the last column of table 1.1).

Individual points from the set of NXPIX by NYPIX points can be uniquely identified by a bracketed pair of integers, sometimes called a point vector, (I, J), where $0 \leqslant I \leqslant NXPIX - 1$ and $0 \leqslant J \leqslant NYPIX - 1$; the vector specifies the position of the addressable point in the $I^{th}$ column and $J^{th}$ row, so that the vector (0, 0) identifies the bottom left-hand corner point of the frame. The Model B has its own set of BASIC instructions which enables users to operate on the matrix of addressable points (and hence pixels), so converting them to dots of light on the screen which can be switched off or on in various colours. This enables the operator to produce approximate points, lines, polygons or other special types of area, with a series of colour dots.

The reader will now be taken some way towards generating a two-dimensional and three-dimensional graphics package for the Model B: the programs are given in BASIC and rely (with a few exceptions) on the small number of *primitive* procedures that are given in this chapter.

## Primitives that Map Continuous Space on to the Graphics Frame

In general, computer graphics deals with points, lines, areas and volumes in continuous two-dimensional and three-dimensional Euclidean space. The use of addressable point coordinates by themselves for graphics is rather limiting. The definition of objects by means of only discrete pairs of integers is very rare in practical applications. We therefore need to consider ways of plotting views of objects on a graphics screen where positions are measured in real units such as inches, miles or even light-years(!). Therefore we must consider the relationship between two-dimensional real space and the screen pixels (via addressable points). Before we can even attempt this step, however, we must first discuss ways of representing two-dimensional space by means of Cartesian coordinate geometry.

We may imagine two-dimensional space as the plane of this page, but extending to infinity in all directions. Our description of the coordinate geometry starts by arbitrarily choosing a fixed point in this space, which is called the *coordinate origin*. Through the origin a line is drawn that extends to infinity in both directions – the *x-axis*. The normal convention is to place the $x$-axis from left to right on the page (the horizontal). Another two-way infinite line, the *y-axis*, is drawn through the origin perpendicular to the $x$-axis; hence conventionally this is placed from the top to the bottom of the page (the vertical). We now draw a scale along each axis; unit distances need not be the same on both axes, but this is normally the case (see figure 2.1). We assume that values on the $x$-axis are positive to the right of the origin and negative to the left: values on the $y$-axis are positive above the origin and negative below.

We can now uniquely fix the position of point $\boldsymbol{p}$ in space by specifying its *coordinates* (figure 2.1). The *x-coordinate*, X say, is that distance along the $x$-axis (positive to the right of the axis and negative to the left) at which a line perpendicular to the $x$-axis that passes through $\boldsymbol{p}$ cuts the $x$-axis. The *y-coordinate*, Y say, is correspondingly defined by using the $y$-axis. These two values, called a *coordinate pair* or *two-dimensional vector*, are normally written in brackets thus: (X, Y), the $x$-coordinate coming before the $y$-coordinate. We shall usually refer to the pair as a vector – the dimension (in this case dimension two) will be understood from the context in which we use the term. A vector, as well as defining a point (X, Y) in two-dimensional space, may also be used to specify a direction, namely the direction that is parallel to the line that joins the origin to the point (X, Y) – but more of this (and other objects such as lines, curves and polygonal areas) in chapter 3.

We are now in a position to devise means (the above-mentioned primitive procedures) for mapping such geometrical concepts on to the two-dimensional discrete rectangular matrix of pixels that forms the graphics frame.

For the present we shall concentrate on two-dimensional space: an extension into three-dimensional space is dealt with starting at chapter 7. In both cases we require a method of mapping a rectangular area of two-dimensional Cartesian

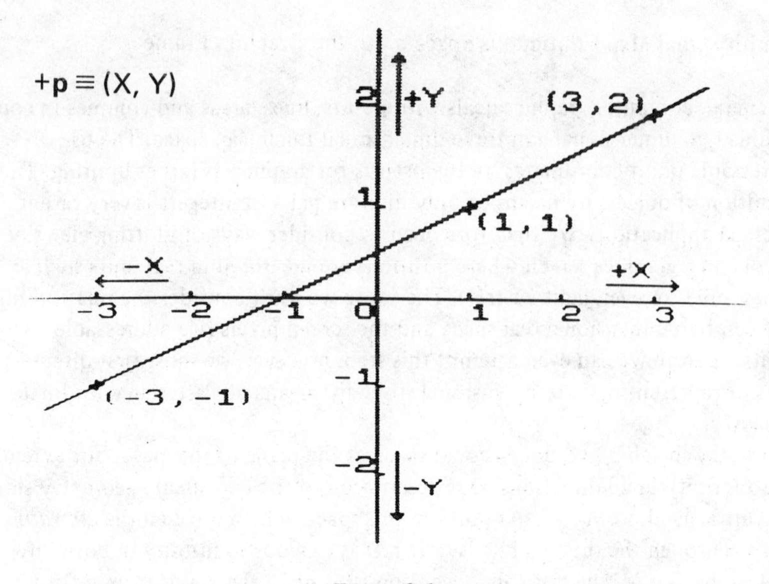


*Figure 2.1*

space on to the graphics frame. For simplicity we start by insisting that this area has its edges parallel to the *x*-axis and *y*-axis of Cartesian space. Initially we shall assume that this rectangular area of space has its *bottom left-hand corner* identified with the coordinate origin (0.0, 0.0), and that the lengths of the horizontal and vertical edges are HORIZ and VERT respectively. We first identify the origin with the pixel that contains the addressable point (0, 0), and then scale the rectangular area so that it fits into the frame; naturally the area exactly fits the frame only if the ratios HORIZ : VERT and NXPIX : NYPIX are equal (that is for 1280 : 960 = 4 : 3). This is rarely the case, so a scaling factor, XYSCALE, is chosen that maps the point (HORIZ, VERT) in two-dimensional space on to a pixel that is located either on the upper or the right-hand edge of the frame. We can consider this rectangle as a *window* on to Cartesian space; no longer anchored to the coordinate origin, it may wander about space and view rectangular areas that are the same size as the original, although the edges of such areas must be parallel to the original coordinate axes. As a general rule we make VERT roughly three-quarters of HORIZ. If you wish to select a differently shaped window, it is necessary simply to change the values of HORIZ and VERT.

At any time during the execution of the program we may move the coordinate origin from its original position at the bottom left-hand corner of the frame. Its position relative to the first origin will be stored as XORIG and YORIG; and *x*-component and *y*-component respectively. Initially (XORIG, YORIG) is identified with (0.0, 0.0). Hence any point in Cartesian space with coordinates (XPT, YPT), a pair of reals, maps into a pixel that contains an addressable point with a horizontal component INT((XORIG + XPT) * XYSCALE + 0.5) and a vertical component INT((YORIG + YPT) * XYSCALE + 0.5). Here INT is the BASIC function that truncates the fractional part of a decimal number and returns an integer. These two components are stored as functions FNX and FNY (see listing 2.2). During the construction of a picture we must consider a *plot pen*, a pair of integers that moves about the graphics frame; initially it is placed at the pixel that is equivalent to the coordinate origin. The constants NXPIX and NYPIX, and the variables XYSCALE, XORIG and YORIG, must be available at all times to the plotting procedures that follow, so these names must not be used for any other purpose. The procedures were written specifically for the Model B but the general principles of constructing similar procedures for other graphical devices will also be discussed. To start with, it would be necessary to change the values of NXPIX and NYPIX if a different machine was to be used.

Our first procedure 'start' defines the graphics and text windows, initialises the required variables and prepares the screen for plotting. Listing 2.1 is an example 'start' procedure for the Model B.

*Listing 2.1*

```
9700 REM start
9710 DEF PROCstart(B,F)
9720 XORIG=0 : YORIG=0
9730 NXPIX=1280 : NYPIX=960
9740 XYSCALE=NXPIX/HORIZ : YSCALE=NYPIX/VERT
9750 IF XYSCALE>YSCALE THEN XYSCALE=YSCALE
9760 VDU28,0,1,39,0 : VDU24,0;0;1279;959;
9770 GCOL 0,B+128 : CLG : GCOL 0,F
9780 ENDPROC
```

This procedure has two parameters B and F (integers) that represent the background and foreground logical colours respectively. The correct values of these variables for any choice of colours will depend on the MODE in use, so readers must refer to the user manual. For most purposes we shall use MODE 1 and default logical colours, with foreground black (F = 0) and background white (B = 3).

If we need to write this procedure for a different micro then all that is necessary is to replace the statements that contain the BASIC graphics instructions of the BBC micro by the equivalent commands for the new micro. Most of the other procedures in this book are independent of the structure of the Model B. If at any time during the execution of the program you wish to change the logical colour in which you are drawing, you must use the GCOL option and you can use the VDU 19 option to choose new colours from the list of actual colours.

In 'start' and in many other procedures that follow, it is necessary to transform the *x*/*y*-coordinates of a point into their pixel equivalents, so we introduce the two functions FNX and FNY in listing 2.2.

*Listing 2.2*

```
9800 REM real-to-pixel functions
9810 DEF FNX(Z)=INT((XORIG+Z)*XYSCALE+0.5)
9820 DEF FNY(Z)=INT((YORIG+Z)*XYSCALE+0.5)
```

The next primitive procedure (listing 2.3) is 'setorigin'; this enables us to move the coordinate origin by an amount XMOVE horizontally and YMOVE vertically (distances in the scale of the coordinate system), so adjusting the (XORIG, YORIG) values. After such a move the plot pen moves to the pixel that contains the addressable point that is equivalent to the new origin.

*Listing 2.3*

```
9600 REM setorigin
9610 DEF PROCsetorigin(XMOVE,YMOVE)
9620 XORIG=XORIG+XMOVE : YORIG=YORIG+YMOVE
9630 PROCmoveto(0,0)
9640 ENDPROC
```

We shall be in a position to draw straight lines after we have produced two further procedures: 'moveto' which moves the plot pen to a pixel equivalent of the point in coordinate space at one end of the line, and 'lineto' which draws the line by moving the plot pen from its present position (set by a previous call to 'setorigin', 'moveto' or 'lineto') to the pixel equivalent of the point on the other end of the line. Listings 2.4 and 2.5 show 'moveto' and 'lineto' procedures that are designed specifically for the Model B. The latter two procedures include statements that initiate the machine-dependent BASIC instructions that MOVE and DRAW between addressable points. Hence if you wish to implement these procedures on a different micro you must introduce the equivalent instructions.

*Listing 2.4*

```
9500 REM moveto
9510 DEF PROCmoveto(XPT,YPT)
9520 MOVE FNX(XPT),FNY(YPT)
9530 ENDPROC
```

*Listing 2.5*

```
9400 REM lineto
9410 DEF PROClineto(XPT,YPT)
9420 DRAW FNX(XPT),FNY(YPT)
9430 ENDPROC
```

In all but the most elementary machines, it is possible to set up these plotting procedures or their equivalents (and many others as our knowledge increases) in a library file or backing store. Then there is no need to explicitly retype them into each new program. On the Model B we can *SPOOL them as files on audio cassettes or disks, and merge them into other programs by using the *EXEC option. On the companion cassette to this section of the book you will find these procedures as part of the 'lib1' library.

*Example 2.1*
Identify a rectangle in Cartesian space, 40 units by 30 units, with the graphics frame of the Model B. Then draw a square (see listing 2.6) of side 20 units, centred in the rectangle (figure 2.2a). We centre the square on the screen by moving the origin to (20.0, 15.0) and thus define the corners of the square to be (± 10.0, ± 10.0).

*Listing 2.6*

```
100 REM drawing a square
110 MODE 1
120 HORIZ=40 : VERT=30
130 PROCstart(3,0)
140 PROCsetorigin(HORIZ/2,VERT/2)
150 PROCmoveto(10,10)
160 PROClineto(-10,10) : PROClineto(-10,-10)
170 PROClineto(10,-10) : PROClineto(10,10)
180 STOP
```

It is as well to note at this juncture that the order in which the points are joined is critical. For example, if the coordinates of the second and third corners of the square are interchanged then figure 2.2b will be drawn.

Next we write a primitive procedure 'triangle' (listing 2.7) which uses the MOVE and PLOT 85 instructions of the Model B for filling in a triangular area bounded by vertices (X1, Y1), (X2, Y2) and (X3, Y3) in logical colour FACECOL ($\geqslant 0$), and draws lines around the perimeter in logical colour EDGECOL ($>0$). If one of these values is negative then its corresponding section of the procedure is not entered. Extra lines have been added to cope with degenerate triangles: this is to stop a 'bug' in the early versions of the Model B operating system which produced spurious horizontal lines. If you have operating system OS 1.0 or later then you should simplify 'triangle'.

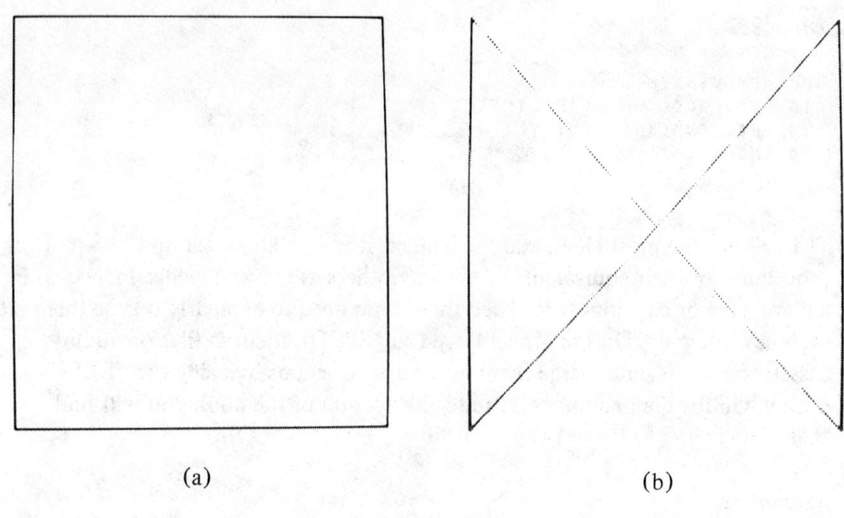

(a) (b)

*Figure 2.2*

*Listing 2.7*

```
10000 REM triangle
10010 DEF PROCtriangle(X1,Y1,X2,Y2,X3,Y3,FACECOL,EDGECOL)
10020 X1=FNX(X1) : X2=FNX(X2) : X3=FNX(X3)
10030 Y1=FNY(Y1) : Y2=FNY(Y2) : Y3=FNY(Y3)
10040 IF FACECOL<0 THEN 10090 ELSE GCOL 0,FACECOL
10050 IF Y1 DIV 4=Y2 DIV 4 AND Y2 DIV 4=Y3 DIV 4 THEN 10080
10060 MOVE X1,Y1 : MOVE X2,Y2 : PLOT 85,X3,Y3
10070 GOTO 10090
10080 MOVE X1,Y1 : DRAW X2,Y2 : DRAW X3,Y3
10090 IF EDGECOL>0 THEN GCOL 0,EDGECOL : MOVE X1,Y1
      : DRAW X2,Y2 : DRAW X3,Y3 : DRAW X1,Y1
10100 ENDPROC
```

*Exercise 2.1*
If we are using the Model B then it is possible to draw pictures in a variety of colours. We saw in 'triangle' that it is necessary to choose the logical colour by means of the GCOL command and we may even wish to define the actual colour by means of the VDU 19 command. Both tasks can be done explicitly in the program or you can write a procedure 'setcolour', which uses two integer parameters LOGCOL and ACTCOL to achieve this. Include this in a program that draws *solid* (as opposed to line) polygons from information read from the keyboard.

*Exercise 2.2*
In all the plotting procedures above, the scale of the mapping (XYSCALE) is fixed once and for all, and the horizontal and vertical scaling factors are identical.

There is no need to heed this convention: write a procedure 'factor' that alters the horizontal scale by FX and the vertical scale by FY. Naturally this implies that it is now necessary to define two separate scales (XSCALE and YSCALE say); and then of course the functions FNX and FNY must be altered (also see chapter 6).

*Exercise 2.3*

Furthermore, there is no reason for the $x$-axis and $y$-axis to be identified with the horizontal and vertical respectively. In fact they need not even be mutually perpendicular. Experiment with these ideas, which necessarily involves changing all the plotting procedures 'start', 'moveto' etc.

To demonstrate the use of these plotting procedures we shall draw some simple patterns. There are those who think that the construction of patterns is a frivolous waste of time. Nevertheless, we consider it to be a very useful first stage in understanding the techniques of computer graphics. Often patterns of an apparently sophisticated design are the result of very simple programs. Quickly to produce such graphical output is an immediate boost to morale, and gives a lot of confidence to the beginner. Furthermore new designs are always in demand: geometrical art is used for the covers of books and pamphlets and in advertising literature. It can do no harm at all to initiate artistic ideas that will be of great use later when we study the pictorial display of data. Patterns are also an ideal way of introducing some of the basic concepts of computer graphics in a very palatable way. Take the next two examples, which use our simple library of procedures, and look at the important role of trigonometric functions (sine and cosine) and of angular measurement in radians. Remember that $\pi$ radians is the same angular measure as 180 degrees.

*Example 2.2*

Figure 2.3, a very popular design, is constructed by joining each vertex of a regular N-sided polygon (an N-gon) to every other. N cannot be greater than 30.

We set the origin at the centre of the design, and all the vertices at a unit distance from the centre: the sizes of HORIZ and VERT (2.8, 2.1) are chosen so that the design fits neatly on to the screen. If one of these vertices lies on the positive $x$-axis (the horizontal), then the N vertices are all of the form (COS(ALPHA), SIN(ALPHA)), where ALPHA is an angle $2\pi I/N$ and I is chosen from 1, 2, . . . , or N. Here for the first time we see point coordinates being calculated by the program, not explicitly typed in, as in listing 2.6. Furthermore, since the program uses these values over and over again, it is sensible to store them in arrays and access them when required by specifying the correct array index. Note that in listing 2.8, if $1 \leqslant I < J \leqslant N$ then the $J^{th}$ point is not joined to the $I^{th}$ point as the line will have already been drawn in the opposite direction.

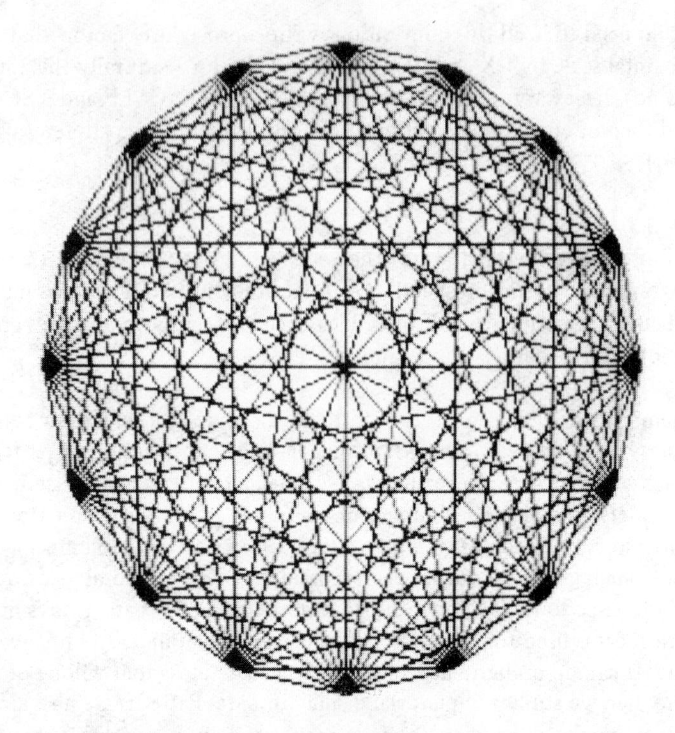

*Figure 2.3*

*Listing 2.8*

```
100 REM join points on regular N-gon
110 MODE 1
120 HORIZ=2.8 : VERT=2.1
130 PROCstart(3,0)
140 PROCsetorigin(HORIZ/2,VERT/2)
150 DIM X(30),Y(30)
160 INPUT"Type in N",N
169 REM calculate points in N-gon
170 ALPHA=0 : ADIF=2*PI/N
180 FOR I% = 1 TO N
190 X(I%)=COS(ALPHA) : Y(I%)=SIN(ALPHA)
200 ALPHA=ALPHA+ADIF
210 NEXT I%
219 REM join point I to POINT J , I<J
220 FOR I% = 1 TO N-1
230 FOR J% = I%+1 TO N
240 PROCmoveto(X(I%),Y(I%)) : PROClineto(X(J%),Y(J%))
250 NEXT J% : NEXT I%
260 STOP
```

*Figure 2.4*

***Example 2.3***
Figure 2.4 is constructed by listing 2.9 in a similar manner. M sets of N points on regular N-gons and one set of N coincident points are given by the following formula. The $I^{th}$ point in the $J^{th}$ set, $1 \leqslant I \leqslant N$ and $0 \leqslant J \leqslant M$, is $(R\cos\theta$, $R\sin\theta)$ where R and $\theta$ are given by

$$R = (M - J)/M$$

$$\theta = 2\pi I/N + \alpha$$

where $\alpha = 0$ if MOD (I,2) is zero, and $\pi/N$ otherwise.

Triangles are then formed by joining every pair of neighbouring points on all but the inner N-gon to the nearest point inside them.

There are two immediate observations to be made from these very simple examples. The first concerns *resolution*. Because the graphics frame is a discrete matrix then *straight lines* must be approximated by a sequence of pixels. Unfortunately the resolution of the Model B, like most microcomputer graphics systems, is low (that is, NXPIX and NYPIX are the order of hundreds) and the lines appear jagged.

The second observation is that, as N increases in listings 2.8 and 2.9, the outline of the figure (the N-gon) closely approximates to a circle. Therefore we can use this idea to write a procedure 'circle' (listing 2.10) which draws a solid

*Listing 2.9*

```
100 REM rose pattern
110 MODE 1
120 DIM X(30),Y(30),XD(30),YD(30)
130 HORIZ=2.8 : VERT=2.1
140 PROCstart(0,3)
150 PROCsetorigin(HORIZ/2,VERT/2)
160 INPUT"N,M",N%,M%
170 AD=PI/N% : AD2=2*AD : RD=1/M%
180 R=1 : AS=0 : A=AS
189 REM setup an outer regular N-gon of unit radius
190 FOR I%=1 TO N%
200 X(I%)=COS(A) : Y(I%)=SIN(A)
210 A=A+AD2 : NEXT I%
219 REM loop through M inner N-gons
220 FOR J%=1 TO M%
230 R=R-RD : AS=AS+AD : A=AS
239 REM setup inner N-gon of radius 1/M smaller than outer N-gon
240 FOR I%=1 TO N%
250 XD(I%)=R*COS(A) : YD(I%)=R*SIN(A)
260 A=A+AD2 : NEXT I%
269 REM form triangles with points from inner and outer N-gons
270 FOR I%=1 TO N%
280 NI%=(I% MOD N%)+1
290 PROCtriangle(X(I%),Y(I%),XD(I%),YD(I%),X(NI%),Y(NI%),1,2)
300 NEXT I%
309 REM reset outer to inner N-gon
310 FOR I%=1 TO N%
320 X(I%)=XD(I%) : Y(I%)=YD(I%)
330 NEXT I%
340 NEXT J%
350 STOP
```

circle with radius R about the centre (XCENT, YCENT) in logical colour FACECOL and circumference in EDGECOL to give a picture similar to figure 2.5. If either of these colour parameters is negative then the corresponding section of the procedure is not entered. Note that we are using angles that are measured in radians (that is we are incrementing by 10/(R*XYSCALE) each time through the loop), a value that depends on the size of the radius and produces a reasonable circle without waste of effort. Note that since the vertices of the N-gon are needed only once, we do not store their values but calculate them as required. Again the limitation in resolution of the screen is apparent on the perimeter of the circle. Also be wary of rounding errors as these could result in a slice being left out of the circle.

There is another way, other than PLOT 85, for filling in an area. PLOT 77, X, Y moves sideways left and right from the point (X, Y) changing the colour of the pixels until it meets pixels that are not in the background colour. As an example, see routine 'circle2' (listing 2.10). This method does however have obvious limitations when filling in non-convex areas.

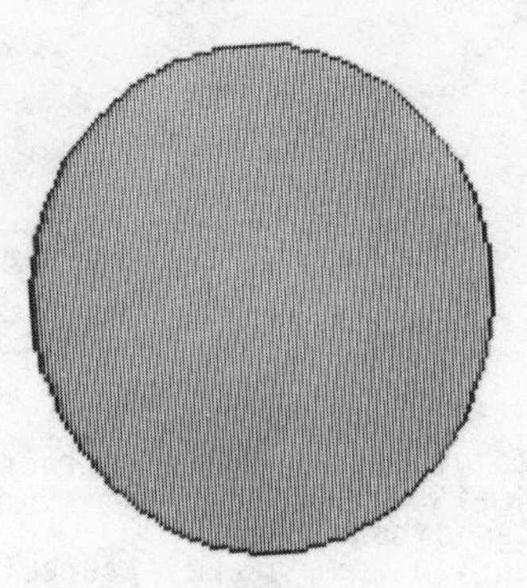

*Figure 2.5*

Whenever we use such procedures we must be aware of any *side effects* produced; for example, the origin or plot head might be moved by the procedure. Thus listing 2.10 changes the position of both the origin and the plot pen. It would therefore be sensible to add the following line to the 'circle' procedure:

```
480 PROCsetorigin(–XCENT, –YCENT) : ENDPROC
```

*Exercise 2.4*
Write a procedure to draw an ellipse of major axis A units (horizontal) and minor axis B units (vertical). Note that a typical point on this ellipse has coordinates (Acos $\alpha$, Bsin $\alpha$) where $0 \leqslant \alpha \leqslant 2\pi$. However it must be remembered that, unlike the circle, $\alpha$ is not the angle made by the radius through a point with the positive $x$-axis: it is simply a descriptive parameter.

Incorporate this procedure into a program that draws a diagram that is similar to figure 2.6. There are two things to note: (1) there is no need for A to be greater than B; (2) observe the optical illusion of the two apparent white diagonal lines. Another illusion can be seen in figure 2.3 – dark circles that radiate out from the centre of the pattern. The study of optical illusions is fascinating (see Tolansky, 1964) and it is a never-ending fount of ideas for patterns. This exercise was introduced because it leads the way into the general technique for drawing curves – see chapters 3 and 6.

*Example 2.4*
An extension of this idea, the natural next step, is the construction of a spiral. Again the general form of the curve about the origin is (Rcos $\alpha$, Rsin $\alpha$) but now $\alpha$ varies between angles $\beta$ and $\beta + 2N\pi$, where $\beta$ (the parameter BETA) is the initial angle that the normal to the spiral makes with the positive $x$-axis, and N is the number of turns in the spiral. The radius R is no longer a constant value

*Listing 2.10*

```
100 REM circle main program
110 MODE1
120 HORIZ=2.8 : VERT=2.1
130 PROCstart(3,0)
140 PROCsetorigin(HORIZ/2,VERT/2)
150 PROCcircle(0.1,-0.1,0.5,1,2)
160 STOP

300 REM circle
310 DEF PROCcircle(XCENT,YCENT,R,FACECOL,EDGECOL)
320 ADIF=10/(R*XYSCALE)
330 PROCsetorigin(XCENT,YCENT)
340 IF FACECOL<0 THEN 420 ELSE GCOL0,FACECOL
349 REM if required draw solid disc
350 MOVE FNX(R),FNY(0)
360 FOR A = ADIF TO 2*PI STEP ADIF
370 MOVE FNX(0),FNY(0)
380 PLOT85,FNX(R*COS(A)),FNY(R*SIN(A))
390 NEXT A
400 MOVE FNX(0),FNY(0)
410 PLOT85,FNX(R),FNY(0)
420 IF EDGECOL<0 THEN ENDPROC ELSE GCOL0,EDGECOL
429 REM if required draw outer circle
430 MOVE FNX(R),FNY(0)
440 FOR A = ADIF TO 2*PI STEP ADIF
450 DRAW FNX(R*COS(A)),FNY(R*SIN(A))
460 NEXT A
470 DRAW FNX(R),FNY(0)
480 ENDPROC

500 REM circle2
510 DEF PROCcircle2(XCENT,YCENT,R,FACECOL,EDGECOL)
520 ADIF=10/(R*XYSCALE)
530 PROCsetorigin(XCENT,YCENT)
540 GCOL0,EDGECOL
549 REM draw outer circle
550 MOVE FNX(R),FNY(0)
560 FOR A = ADIF TO 2*PI STEP ADIF
570 DRAW FNX(R*COS(A)),FNY(R*SIN(A))
580 NEXT A
590 DRAW FNX(R),FNY(0)
599 REM fill in circle
600 GCOL0,FACECOL
610 FOR Y%=FNY(-R) TO FNY(R)
620 PLOT 77,FNX(0),Y%
630 NEXT Y%
640 ENDPROC
```

but varies with the value of $\alpha$: if RMAX is the outer radius of the spiral then R is given by the formula

$$R = RMAX(\alpha - \beta)/2N\pi$$

Note that procedure 'spiral' (listing 2.11), which centres the spiral at (XCENT, YCENT), causes no side effects because we reset the origin back to its original position before leaving the procedure.

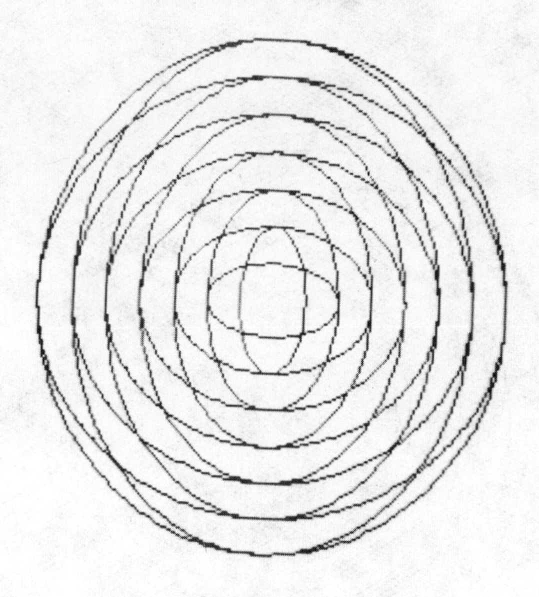

*Figure 2.6*

The complete program of listing 2.11 (run in MODE 2) shows another optical illusion. Fifteen spirals in logical colours 1 to 15 are drawn on the screen. Then all the logical colours are turned black and, one at a time, in order, they are turned to white and back to black. This has the effect of producing a rotating spiral: we have added a pause to reduce the speed of rotation. After 30 seconds the screen is cleared and a square is drawn. If you stare at the spirals for this short period and then look at the square, it will appear to expand!

***Exercise 2.5***
Procedure 'spiral' (with parameters XCENT = 0, YCENT = 0, N = 4, BETA = 1 and RMAX = 1) produces a diagram similar to figure 2.7a. What happens if you set RMAX to −1? Use the procedure in a program that generates figure 2.7b. Again note the optical illusion when the observer's head is moved in a circle in front of the diagram, keeping the horizontal (and hence also the vertical) direction parallel with the original. The spirals appear to rotate about the centre!

***Example 2.5***
Write a procedure (listing 2.12) that draws diagrams similar to figure 2.8. Here we introduce the concept of an *envelope*. Instead of drawing a curve by a sequence of small line segments (as in the circle of listing 2.9), we devise a sequence of lines that are tangential to the curve. For example, the figure shows four rectangular hyperbolae that are placed in the *quarters* of the plane.

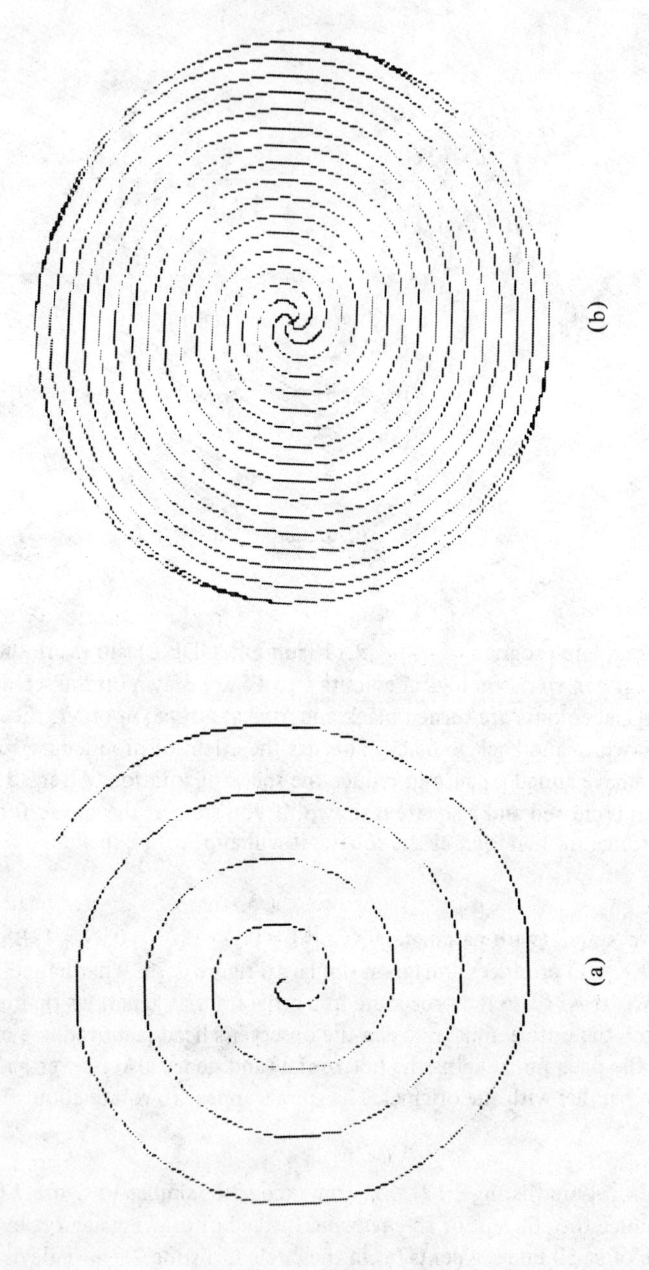

*Figure 2.7*

*Listing 2.11*

```
100 REM spiral example
110 MODE 2 : HORIZ=2.8 : VERT=2.1
120 PROCstart(0,3)
130 PROCsetorigin(HORIZ/2,VERT/2)
139 REM setup series of 15 spirals each of a different colour
140 FOR I%=1 TO 15
150 GCOL0,I%
160 PROCspiral(0,0,1.7,4,PI*I%/7.5)
170 NEXT I%
179 REM set each logical colour black
180 FOR I%=1 TO 15
190 VDU19,I%,0,0,0,0
200 NEXT I%
210 N%=1 : O%=15 : T=TIME+3000
220 REPEAT
229 REM set each logical colour to white in turn
        and black out previous 'logical white'
230 VDU19,N%,7,0,0,0,19,O%,0,0,0,0
240 O%=N% : N%= N% MOD 15 +1
249 REM pause
250 FOR I%=1 TO 30 : NEXT I%
260 UNTIL TIME > T
269 REM after 30 seconds draw square and watch the illusion of
        it apparently expanding
270 CLG : VDU20 : GCOL0,1
280 PROCmoveto(.7,.7)
290 PROClineto(.7,-.7) : PROClineto(-.7,-.7)
300 PROClineto(-.7,.7) : PROClineto(.7,.7)
310 STOP

500 REM spiral
510 DEF PROCspiral(XCENT,YCENT,RMAX,N%,BETA)
520 PROCsetorigin(XCENT,YCENT)
530 ADIF=PI/50 : A=BETA
540 RDIF=RMAX/(N%*100)
550 FOR R=RDIF TO RMAX STEP RDIF
560 PROClineto(R*COS(A),R*SIN(A))
570 A=A+ADIF
580 NEXT R
590 PROClineto(RMAX*COS(BETA),RMAX*SIN(BETA))
600 PROCsetorigin(-XCENT,-YCENT)
610 ENDPROC
```

N points are placed on each of the four arms (of unit length) which divide the plane into the four quarters. The 4N points are therefore $(\pm I/N, 0.0)$ and $(0.0, \pm I/N)$ where $I = 1, 2, \ldots, N$.

*Exercise 2.6*
Generalise this procedure so that there are a variable number of arms, M, that stretch out from the origin and divide the plane into equal segments.

*Exercise 2.7*
Draw a diagram similar to figure 2.9. The procedure will have an integer parameter N and should calculate 4N points $\{P(I): I = 1, 2, \ldots, 4N\}$ around the edges of

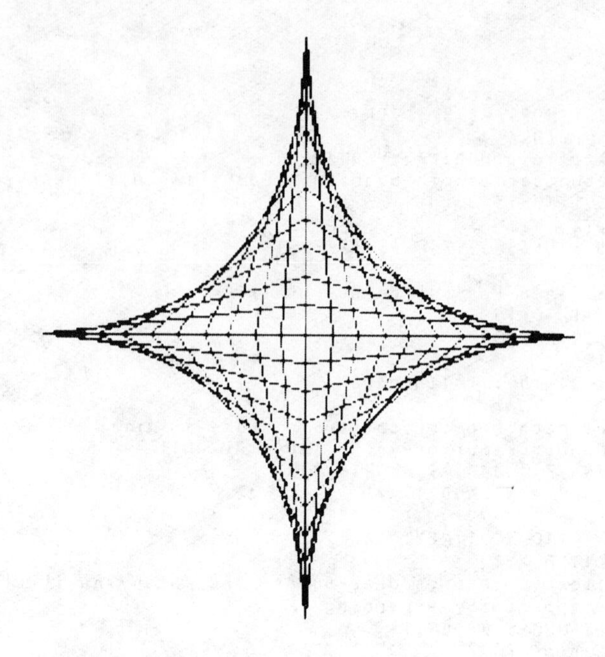

*Figure 2.8*

*Listing 2.12*

```
100 REM envelope example
110 MODE 1
120 HORIZ=2.8 : VERT=2.1
130 PROCstart(3,0)
140 PROCsetorigin(HORIZ/2,VERT/2)
150 INPUT"Type N",N%
160 PROCmoveto(1,0) : PROClineto(-1,0)
170 PROCmoveto(0,1) : PROClineto(0,-1)
180 FOR I%=1 TO N%
190 X=I%/N% : Y=(N%+1-I%)/N%
200 PROCmoveto(X,0)
210 PROClineto(0,Y) : PROClineto(-X,0)
220 PROClineto(0,-Y) : PROClineto(X,0)
230 NEXT I%
240 STOP
```

a square of unit side, starting at a corner. There is one point at each corner and the points are placed so that the distance between consecutive points is 1/N. Then pairs of points are joined according to the following rule: P(I) is joined to P(J) for all positive values of I and J less than or equal to 4N, such that J – I (subtraction modulo 4N) belongs to the sequence 1, 1 + 2, 1 + 2 + 3, . . . . For example if N is 10 then P(20) is joined to P(21), P(23), P(26), P(30), P(35), P(1), P(8) and P(16).

*Figure 2.9*

***Example 2.6***
Emulate a Spirograph, in order to produce diagrams similar to figure 2.10.

*Figure 2.10*

A Spirograph consists of a cogged disk inside a cogged circle, which is placed on a piece of paper. Let the outer circle have integer radius A and the disk integer radius B. The disk is always in contact with the circle. There is a small hole in the disk at a distance D (also an integer) from the centre of the disk, through which is placed a sharp pencil point. The disk is moved around the circle in an anti-clockwise manner, but it must always touch the outer circle, the cogs ensure that there is no slipping. The pencil point traces out a pattern, which is complete when the pencil returns to its original position.

Initially we assume that the centres of the disk and the circle and also the hole all lie on the positive $x$-axis, the centre of the circle being the coordinate origin. In order to emulate the Spirograph we need to specify a general point on the track of the pencil point. We let $\alpha$ be the angle made with the positive $x$-axis by the line that joins the origin to the point where the circle and disk touch. The point of contact is therefore $(A\cos\alpha, A\sin\alpha)$ and the centre of the disk is $((A-B)\cos\alpha, (A-B)\sin\alpha)$. If $\beta$ is the angle made by the line that joins the hole to the centre of the disk with the $x$-direction, then the coordinates of the hole are

$$((A-B)\cos\alpha + D\cos\beta, (A-B)\sin\alpha + D\sin\beta)$$

The point of contact between the disk and circle will have moved through a distance $A\alpha$ around the circle, and a distance $-B\beta$ around the disk (the minus sign is because $\alpha$ and $\beta$ have opposite orientation). Since there is no slipping these distances must be equal and hence we have the equation $\beta = -(A/B)\alpha$. The pencil returns to its original position when both $\alpha$ and $\beta$ are integer multiples of $2\pi$. When $\alpha = 2N\pi$ then $\beta = -N(A/B)2\pi$, and hence the pencil point returns to its original position for the first time when $N(A/B)$ becomes an integer for the first time, that is when N is equal to B divided by the highest common factor of B and A. The function 'hcf' (listing 2.13) uses Euclid's algorithm (see Davenport, 1952) to calculate the highest common factor of two positive integers A and B.

This function is used in the procedure 'spiro' (listing 2.13) which calculates the value of N and then varies $\alpha$ (ALPHA) between 0 and $2N\pi$ in steps of $\pi/100$; for each $\alpha$, the value of $\beta$ (BETA) is calculated and then the general track is drawn. Figure 2.10 was drawn by a call to 'spiro' with A = 12, B = 7 and D = 5. The size of HORIZ and VERT must be chosen so that the figure fits on to the screen; in this case HORIZ = 28 and VERT = 21.

It is evident from this example that drawing patterns is not as straightforward as it appears. Even such a simple picture as figure 2.10 requires the mathematical backup of Euclid. As we progress through computer graphics, we shall discover more and more that it is essential to have at least an elementary knowledge of not only coordinate geometry but also calculus, algebra, Euclidean geometry and number theory. Be prepared to scour your local library (or pester your friendly neighbourhood mathematician) for the necessary information.

*Listing 2.13*

```
200 REM hcf - Euclid's algorithm
210 DEF FNhcf(A%,B%)
220 LOCAL I%,J%,R%
230 IF A%>B% THEN I%=A% : J%=B% ELSE I%=B% : J%=A%
240 R%=I% MOD J% : IF R%=0 THEN =J% ELSE I%=J%: J%=R% : GOTO 240

300 REM spiro
310 DEF PROCspiro(A%,B%,D%)
320 LOCAL I%,RAB%,ALPHA,BETA,ADIF,AOB,N%,NO%
330 RAB%=A%-B% : ALPHA=0 : ADIF=PI/50 : AOB=A%/B%
340 N%=B%/FNhcf(A%,B%) : NO%=100*N%
350 PROCmoveto(RAB%+D%,0)
360 FOR I%=1 TO NO%
370 ALPHA=ALPHA+ADIF : BETA=ALPHA*AOB
380 PROClineto(RAB%*COS(ALPHA)+D%*COS(BETA),RAB%*SIN(ALPHA)-D%*SIN(BETA))
390 NEXT I%
400 ENDPROC
```

---

**Complete Programs**

At this stage we shall group the listings 2.1 ('start'), 2.2 (two functions FNX and FNY), 2.3 ('setorigin'), 2.4 ('moveto'), 2.5 ('lineto') and 2.7 ('triangle') under the heading 'lib1'.

I 'lib1' and listing 2.6 ('drawing a square'). No INPUT data required.

II 'lib1' and listing 2.8 ('joining points of regular N-gon'). Data required: an integer $N \leqslant 30$.

III 'lib1' and listing 2.9 ('rose'). Data required: the values of M and N. Use $N \leqslant 30$ and for the best results set $M < N \leqslant 15$.

IV 'lib1' and listing 2.10 ('main program' and 'circle'). No data required.

V 'lib1' and listing 2.11 ('main program' and 'spiral'). No data required. When the spirals start to rotate you should stare at the screen for 30 seconds. The square appears to expand.

VI 'lib1' and listing 2.12 ('envelope'). Data required: an integer N. For best results take $2 \leqslant N \leqslant 30$.

VII 'lib1', listing 2.13 ('Euclid' and 'spiro') and your own main program (use listing 2.10 as a model). Data required: three integers A, B and D, where $A > B > D$. Choose HORIZ, VERT etc. so that the diagram fits on to the screen; that is, both HORIZ and VERT must be greater than $2 * (A - B + D)$. Try HORIZ = 28, VERT = 21, A = 12, B = 7, D = 5.

# 3 Two-Dimensional Coordinate Geometry

In chapter 2 we introduced the concept of the two-dimensional rectangular coordinate system, and defined points in space as vectors, whence we were able to draw line segments between pairs of points. To be strictly accurate, a *straight line* (or *line* for short) in two-dimensional space is not a finite segment, but stretches off to infinity in both directions, and so we need to introduce ways of representing a general point on such a line.

It is well known that the equation of a straight line is $y = mx + c$. This gives the relationship between the $x$-coordinate and the $y$-coordinate of a general point on a line, where $m$ is the tangent of the angle that the line makes with the positive $x$-axis, and $c$ is the point of intersection of the line with the $y$-axis, so that when $x = 0$ then $y = c$. This formula may be well known, but it is not very useful: if the line is vertical, then $m$ is infinite! A far better formula is

$$ay = bx + c$$

This allows for all possible lines: if the line is vertical $a$ is 0. $(b/a)$ is now the tangent of the angle that the line makes with the positive $x$-axis, and the line cuts the $y$-axis at $(c/a)$ provided that $a$ is not equal to zero, and the $x$-axis at $(-c/b)$ provided that $b$ is not equal to zero. The line is parallel to the $y$-axis if $a$ is zero, and to the $x$-axis if $b$ is zero.

We shall frequently use this formulation of a line in the following pages; however we now introduce another, possibly more useful, method for defining a line. Before we can describe this new method we must first define two operations on vectors (namely scalar multiple and vector addition) as well as describe how to calculate the absolute value of a vector. Suppose that we have two vectors $\boldsymbol{p}_1 \equiv (x_1, y_1)$ and $\boldsymbol{p}_2 \equiv (x_2, y_2)$ then

*scalar multiple*: we multiply the individual coordinates by a scalar (real) value $k$.

$$k\boldsymbol{p}_1 = (k \times x_1, k \times y_1)$$

*vector addition*: we add the $x$-coordinates together, and the $y$-coordinates together.

$$\boldsymbol{p}_1 + \boldsymbol{p}_2 = (x_1 + x_2, y_1 + y_2)$$

*absolute value*: the distance of the point $\boldsymbol{p}_1$ from the origin (this is also called the length, and the modulus of the vector).

$$|\boldsymbol{p}_1| = \sqrt{(x_1^2 + y_1^2)}$$

To define a line we first arbitrarily choose any two points on the line – again we call them $\boldsymbol{p}_1 \equiv (x_1, y_1)$ and $\boldsymbol{p}_2 \equiv (x_2, y_2)$. A general point $\boldsymbol{p}(\mu) \equiv (x, y)$ is given by the combination of scalar multiples and vector addition

$$(1 - \mu)\boldsymbol{p}_1 + \mu\boldsymbol{p}_2$$

for some real value of $\mu$; that is the vector $((1 - \mu) \times x_1 + \mu \times x_2, (1 - \mu) \times y_1 + \mu \times y_2)$. We place the $\mu$ in brackets after $\boldsymbol{p}$ to show the dependence of the vector on the value of $\mu$. Later when we understand the relationship more fully we shall leave out the $(\mu)$. If $0 \leqslant \mu \leqslant 1$ then $\boldsymbol{p}(\mu)$ lies on the line somewhere between $\boldsymbol{p}_1$ and $\boldsymbol{p}_2$. For any specified point $\boldsymbol{p}(\mu)$, the value of $\mu$ is given by the ratio

$$\frac{\text{distance of } \boldsymbol{p}(\mu) \text{ from } \boldsymbol{p}_1}{\text{distance of } \boldsymbol{p}_2 \text{ from } \boldsymbol{p}_1}$$

where the measure of distance is positive if $\boldsymbol{p}(\mu)$ is on the same side of $\boldsymbol{p}_1$ as $\boldsymbol{p}_2$, and negative otherwise. The positive distance between any two vector points $\boldsymbol{p}_1$ and $\boldsymbol{p}_2$ is given by (Pythagoras)

$$|\boldsymbol{p}_2 - \boldsymbol{p}_1| = \sqrt{\{(x_1 - x_2)^2 + (y_1 - y_2)^2\}}$$

Figure 2.1 shows a line segment between the points $(-3, -1) \equiv \boldsymbol{p}(0)$ and $(3, 2) \equiv \boldsymbol{p}(1)$: the point $(1, 1)$ lies on the line as $\boldsymbol{p}(2/3)$. Note that $(3, 2)$ is at a distance of $3\sqrt{5}$ from $(-3, -1)$ whereas $(1, 1)$ is at a distance of $2\sqrt{5}$. From now on we shall omit the $(\mu)$ from the point vector.

*Example 3.1*
We can further illustrate this idea by drawing the pattern shown in figure 3.1. At first sight it looks complicated, but on closer inspection it is seen to be simply a square, outside a square, outside a square etc. The squares are getting successively smaller and they are rotating through a constant angle. In order to draw the diagram we need a technique that, when given a general square, draws a smaller internal square rotated through this fixed angle. Suppose the general square has four corners $\{(x_i, y_i) \mid i = 1, 2, 3, 4\}$ and the $i^{\text{th}}$ side of the square is the line joining $(x_i, y_i)$ to $(x_{i+1}, y_{i+1})$ – assuming that additions of subscripts are modulo 4 (that is $4 + 1 \equiv 1$). A general point on this side of the square, $(x'_i, y'_i)$, is given by

$$((1 - \mu) \times x_i + \mu \times x_{i+1},\ (1 - \mu) \times y_i + \mu \times y_{i+1}) \text{ where } 0 \leqslant \mu \leqslant 1$$

In fact $\mu:1 - \mu$ is the ratio in which the side is bisected. If $\mu$ is fixed and the four points $\{(x'_i, y'_i) \mid i = 1, 2, 3, 4\}$ are calculated in the above manner, then the sides of the new square make an angle $\alpha = \tan^{-1} [\mu/(1 - \mu)]$ with the corresponding side of the outer square. So by keeping $\mu$ fixed for each new square, the angle between consecutive squares remains a constant $\alpha$. In listing 3.1, which generated figure 3.1, there are 21 squares and $\mu = 0.1$.

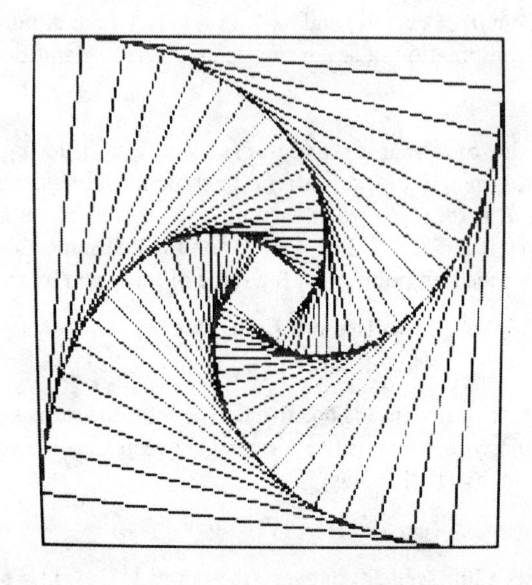

*Figure 3.1*

It is useful to note that the vector combination form of a line can be reorganised as

$$\boldsymbol{p}_1 + \mu(\boldsymbol{p}_2 - \boldsymbol{p}_1)$$

When given in this new representation the vector $\boldsymbol{p}_1$ may be called the *base vector*, and $(\boldsymbol{p}_2 - \boldsymbol{p}_1)$ the *directional vector*. In fact any point on the line can stand as a base vector; it simply acts as a point to anchor a line that is parallel to the directional vector. This concept of a vector acting as a direction needs some further explanation. We have already seen that a vector pair, $(x, y)$ say, may represent a point; a line that joins the coordinate origin to this point may be thought of as specifying a direction – any line in space that is parallel to this line is defined to have the same directional vector. We insist that the line goes from the origin towards $(x, y)$, the so-called positive *sense*; a line from $(x, y)$ towards the origin has negative sense.

This base and direction representation is also very useful for calculating the point of intersection of two lines, a problem that frequently crops up in two-dimensional graphics. For suppose we have two lines $\boldsymbol{p} + \mu\boldsymbol{q}$ and $\boldsymbol{r} + \lambda\boldsymbol{s}$, where

*Listing 3.1*

```
100 REM square in square etc.
110 MODE 1
120 HORIZ=2.8 : VERT=2.1
130 PROCstart(3,0)
140 PROCsetorigin(HORIZ/2,VERT/2)
150 DIM X(4),Y(4),XD(4),YD(4)
160 DATA 1,1, 1,-1, -1,-1, -1,1
169 REM setup coordinates of square
170 FOR I%=1 TO 4 : READ X(I%),Y(I%) : NEXT I%
180 MU=0.1 : UM=1-MU
189 REM loop through 21 squares
190 FOR I%=1 TO 21
200 PROCmoveto(X(4),Y(4))
209 REM draw square defined by arrays X and Y
    : find next square given by arrays XD and YD
210 FOR J%=1 TO 4
220 PROClineto(X(J%),Y(J%))
230 NJ%=(J% MOD 4)+1
240 XD(J%)=UM*X(J%)+MU*X(NJ%)
250 YD(J%)=UM*Y(J%)+MU*Y(NJ%)
260 NEXT J%
269 REM reset (X,Y) values to (XD,YD)
270 FOR J%=1 TO 4
280 X(J%)=XD(J%) : Y(J%)=YD(J%)
290 NEXT J%
300 NEXT I%
310 STOP
```

$p \equiv (x_1, y_1)$, $q \equiv (x_2, y_2)$, $r \equiv (x_3, y_3)$ and $s \equiv (x_4, y_4)$ for $-\infty < \mu, \lambda < \infty$. We need to find the unique values of $\mu$ and $\lambda$ such that

$$p + \mu q = r + \lambda s$$

that is, a point that is common to both lines. This vector equation can be written as two separate equations

$$x_1 + \mu \times x_2 = x_3 + \lambda \times x_4 \tag{3.1}$$

$$y_1 + \mu \times y_2 = y_3 + \lambda \times y_4 \tag{3.2}$$

Rewriting these equations we get

$$\mu \times x_2 - \lambda \times x_4 = x_3 - x_1 \tag{3.3}$$

$$\mu \times y_2 - \lambda \times y_4 = y_3 - y_1 \tag{3.4}$$

Multiplying equation (3.3) by $y_4$, equation (3.4) by $x_4$ and subtracting we get

$$\mu \times (x_2 \times y_4 - y_2 \times x_4) = (x_3 - x_1) \times y_4 - (y_3 - y_1) \times x_4$$

If $(x_2 \times y_4 - y_2 \times x_4) = 0$ then the lines are parallel and there is no point of intersection ($\mu$ does not exist), otherwise

$$\mu = \frac{(x_3 - x_1) \times y_4 - (y_3 - y_1) \times x_4}{(x_2 \times y_4 - y_2 \times x_4)} \tag{3.5}$$

and similarly

$$\lambda = \frac{(x_3 - x_1) \times y_2 - (y_3 - y_1) \times x_2}{(x_2 \times y_4 - y_2 \times x_4)} \tag{3.6}$$

The solution becomes even simpler if one of the lines is parallel to a coordinate axis. Suppose this line is $x = d$, then we can set $\boldsymbol{r} \equiv (d, 0)$ and $\boldsymbol{s} \equiv (0, 1)$, which when substituted in equation (3.5) gives

$$\mu = (d - x_1)/x_2$$

and similarly if the line is $y = d$

$$\mu = (d - y_1)/y_2$$

Naturally if the two lines are parallel then the denominator in these equations becomes zero and we get an infinite result, because two parallel lines cannot intersect.

*Example 3.2*

Find the point of intersection of the two lines that (a) join (1, −1) to (−1, −3) and (b) join (1, 2) to (3, −2).

The lines may be written as

$$(1 - \mu)(1, -1) + \mu(-1, -3) \qquad -\infty < \mu < \infty \tag{3.7}$$

$$(1 - \lambda)(1, 2) + \lambda(3, -2) \qquad -\infty < \lambda < \infty \tag{3.8}$$

or when placed in the base/directional vector form as

$$(1, -1) + \mu(-2, -2) \tag{3.9}$$

$$(1, 2) + \lambda(2, -4) \tag{3.10}$$

Substituting these values into equation (3.5) gives

$$\mu = \frac{(1 - 1) \times -4 - (2 + 1) \times 2}{(-2 \times -4 - (-2) \times 2)} = -1/2$$

whence the point of intersection is $(1, -1) - 1/2(-2, -2) \equiv (2, 0)$.

The general case is solved by the program given in listing 3.2.

*Exercise 3.1*

Experiment with this concept of vector representation of two-dimensional space. You can make up your own questions: it is easy to check that your answers are correct. Consider example 3.2. We know that (2, 0) lies on the first line because we used the value $\mu = -1/2$: our answer is correct if it also lies on the second line, which it does with $\lambda = 1/2$.

*Listing 3.2*

```
100 REM intersection of two lines
110 MODE 7
120 DIM X(4),Y(4)
130 PRINT TAB(8,3),"INTERSECTION OF LINES"
140 PRINT TAB(0,5),"LINE A FROM (X(1),Y(1)) TO (X(2),Y(2))"
150 PRINT TAB(0,6),"LINE B FROM (X(3),Y(3)) TO (X(4),Y(4))   "
159 REM INPUT vertices of lines A & B
160 FOR I%=1 TO 4
170 PRINT "X(";I%;"),Y(";I%;") "; : INPUT X(I%),Y(I%)
180 NEXT I%
190 CLS
199 REM PRINT information about lines
200 PRINT TAB(0,5);"Line A goes from"
210 PRINT"(";X(1);",";Y(1);") to (";X(2);",";Y(2);")"
220 PRINT TAB(0,8);"Line B goes from"
230 PRINT"(";X(3);",";Y(3);") to (";X(4);",";Y(4);")"
239 REM calculate (XINT,YINT) the point of intersection
240 X(2)=X(2)-X(1) : Y(2)=Y(2)-Y(1)
250 X(4)=X(4)-X(3) : Y(4)=Y(4)-Y(3)
260 DET=X(2)*Y(4)-Y(2)*X(4)
270 PRINT TAB(0,12);"Point of intersection ";
280 IF ABS(DET) < 0.00001 THEN PRINT "does not exist." : GOTO 320
290 MU=((X(3)-X(1))*Y(4)-(Y(3)-Y(1))*X(4))/DET
300 XINT=X(1)+MU*X(2) : YINT=Y(1)+MU*Y(2)
310 PRINT : PRINT"(";XINT;",";YINT;")."
320 PRINT TAB(0,22); : STOP
```

*Exercise 3.2*

Write a program that reads in data about two straight lines in the form of an equation and then calculates their point of intersection (if any).

Returning to the use of a vector ($\boldsymbol{q} \equiv (x, y) \neq (0, 0)$, say) that represents a direction, we note that any positive scalar multiple $k\boldsymbol{q}$, for $k > 0$, represents the *same direction* and sense as $\boldsymbol{q}$ (if $k$ is negative then the direction has its sense inverted). In particular, setting $k = 1/|\boldsymbol{q}|$ produces a vector $(x/\sqrt{(x^2 + y^2)}, y/\sqrt{(x^2 + y^2)})$ with unit absolute value.

Thus a general point on a line, $\boldsymbol{p} + \mu\boldsymbol{q}$, is a distance $\mu|\boldsymbol{q}|$ from the base point $\boldsymbol{p}$, and if $|\boldsymbol{q}| = 1$ (a unit vector) then the point is a distance $\mu$ from $\boldsymbol{p}$.

We now consider the angles made by directional vectors with various fixed directions. Suppose that $\alpha$ is the angle between the line joining $\boldsymbol{O}$ (the origin) to $\boldsymbol{q} \equiv (x, y)$, and the positive $x$-axis. Then $x = |\boldsymbol{q}| \times \cos\alpha$ and $y = |\boldsymbol{q}| \times \sin\alpha$ – see figure 3.2: there are similar figures for the three other quadrants.
If $\boldsymbol{q}$ is a unit vector (that is, $|\boldsymbol{q}| = 1$) then $\boldsymbol{q} \equiv (\cos\alpha, \sin\alpha)$. However, since $\sin\alpha = \cos(\alpha - \pi/2)$ for all values of $\alpha$, this expression can be rewritten as $\boldsymbol{q} \equiv (\cos\alpha, \cos(\alpha - \pi/2))$, where $\alpha - \pi/2$ is the angle that the vector makes with the positive $y$-axis. Hence the coordinates of a unit directional vector are called its *direction cosines*, since they are the cosines of the angle that the vector makes with the corresponding positive axes.

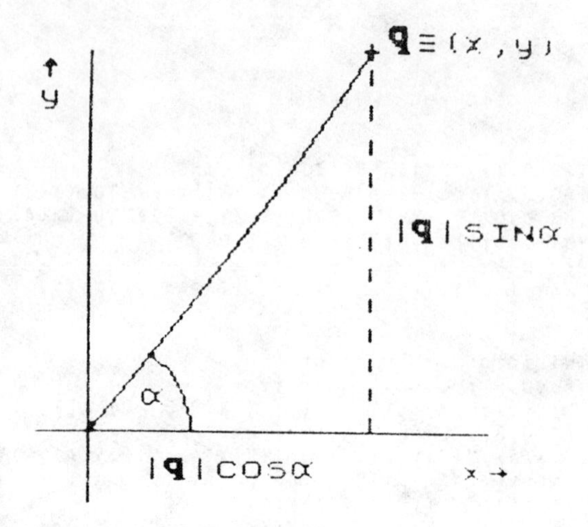


*Figure 3.2*

Before continuing we should take a look at the trigonometric functions available in BASIC: SIN and COS, and the inverse function ATN. SIN and COS are functions with one parameter (an angle given in radians) and one result (a value between −1 and +1). The ATN function takes any value and calculates the angle in radians (in the so-called *principal range* between $-\pi/2$ and $+\pi/2$) whose tangent is that value.

This leads us to the problem of finding the angle that a general direction $\boldsymbol{q} \equiv (x, y)$ makes with the positive $x$-axis, which is solved by the procedure 'angle' given in listing 3.3. 'angle' will be of great use in later chapters when we consider three-dimensional space.

*Listing 3.3*

```
8800 REM angle
8810 DEF FNangle(AX,AY)
8820 IF ABS(AX)>0.00001 THEN 8860
8830 IF ABS(AY)<0.00001 THEN =0
8840 IF AY<0 THEN =1.5*PI
8850 =PI/2
8860 IF AX<0 THEN =(ATN(AY/AX)+PI) ELSE =ATN(AY/AX)
```

Now suppose we have two directional vectors $(a, b)$ and $(c, d)$; for simplicity we can assume that they are both unit vectors and that they both pass through the origin (see figure 3.3). We wish to calculate the acute angle, $\alpha$, between these lines. From the figure we note that $OA = \sqrt{(a^2 + b^2)} = 1$ and $OB = \sqrt{(c^2 + d^2)} = 1$.

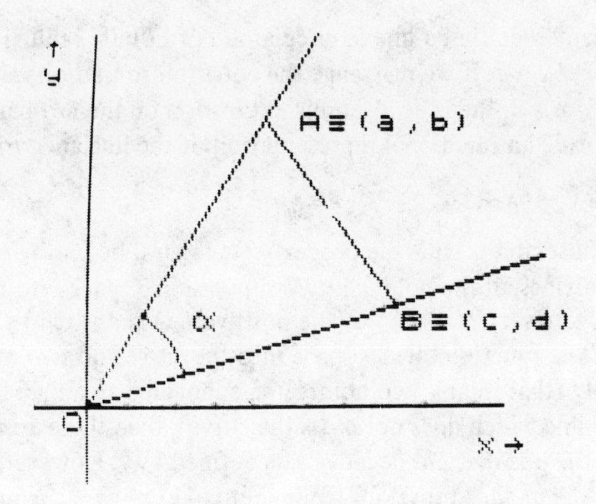


*Figure 3.3*

So by the Cosine Rule

$$AB^2 = OA^2 + OB^2 - 2 \times OA \times OB \times \cos\alpha = 2 \times (1 - \cos\alpha)$$

But also by Pythagoras

$$AB^2 = (a - c)^2 + (b - d)^2 = (a^2 + b^2) + (c^2 + d^2) - 2 \times (a \times c + b \times d)$$

$$= 2 - 2 \times (a \times c + b \times d)$$

Thus $a \times c + b \times \mathrm{d} = \cos\alpha$. It is possible that $a \times c + b \times d$ is negative in which case $\cos^{-1}(a \times c + b \times d)$ is obtuse and the required acute angle is $\pi - \alpha$. Since $\cos(\pi - \alpha) = -\cos\alpha$, then the acute angle is given immediately by $\cos^{-1}(|a \times c + b \times d|)$. For example, given the two lines with direction cosines $(\sqrt{3}/2, 1/2)$ and $(-1/2, -\sqrt{3}/2)$, we see that $a \times c + b \times d = -\sqrt{3}/2$ and thus $\alpha = \cos^{-1}(\sqrt{3}/2) = \pi/6$. This simple example was given in order to introduce the concept of a *scalar product* • of two vectors, $(a, b) \cdot (c, d) = a \times c + b \times d$. Scalar product is extendable into higher-dimensional space (see chapter 7 for a three-dimensional example) and it always has the property that it gives the cosine of the angle between any pair of lines whose directions are defined by the two vectors.

**Curves: Functional Representation versus Parametric Forms**

A curve in two-dimensional space can be considered as a relationship between $x$ and $y$ coordinate values, the so-called *functional relationship.* Alternatively the coordinates can be individually specified in terms of other variables or parameters, the *parametric form.*

We have already seen that a line (a circular arc of infinite radius) may be expressed as $ay = bx + c$. If we rearrange the equation so that one side is zero, that is $ay - bx - c = 0$, then the algebraic expression on the left-hand side of the equation is called a functional representation of the line and written as

$$f(x, y) \equiv ay - bx - c$$

All, but only, those points with the property $f(x, y) = 0$ lie on the curve. This representation divides all the points in two-dimensional space into three sets: $f(x, y) = 0$ (the zero set), $f(x, y) > 0$ (the positive set) and $f(x, y) < 0$ (the negative set). If the function divides space into the curve and two other *connected areas* only (that is, any two points in a connected area may be joined by a curvilinear line which does not cross the curve), then these areas may be identified with the positive and negative sets defined by $f$. However, be wary, there are many elementary functions (for example, $g(x, y) \equiv \cos(y) - \sin(x)$) that define not one but a series of curves and hence divide space into possibly an infinite number of connected areas (note that $g(x, y) \equiv g(x + 2m\pi, y + 2n\pi)$ for all integers $m$ and $n$). So it is possible that two unconnected areas can both belong to the positive set.

Note that the functional representation need not be unique. We could have put the line into an equivalent form

$$f'(x, y) \equiv bx + c - ay$$

in which case the positive set of this function is the negative set of our original, and vice versa.

The case where the curve does divide space into two connected areas is very useful in computer graphics, as we shall see in the study of two-dimensional and (especially) three-dimensional graphics algorithms. Take for example the straight line

$$f(x, y) \equiv ay - bx - c$$

where a point $(x_1, y_1)$ is on the same side of the line as $(x_2, y_2)$ if and only if $f(x_1, y_1)$ has the same non-zero sign as $f(x_2, y_2)$. The functional representation tells us more about a point $(x_1, y_1)$ than just on which side of a line it lies – it also enables us to calculate the distance of the point from the line.

Suppose we have the above line, then its direction vector is $(a, b)$. A line perpendicular to this will have the direction vector $(-b, a)$. (Why? Because the product of the tangents of two mutually perpendicular lines is $-1$; see McCrae, 1953.) So the point $\boldsymbol{q}$ on the line closest to the point $\boldsymbol{p} \equiv (x_1, y_1)$ is of the form

$$\boldsymbol{q} \equiv (x_1, y_1) + \mu(-b, a)$$

Therefore, a new line that joins $\boldsymbol{p}$ to $\boldsymbol{q}$ is perpendicular to the original line. Since $\boldsymbol{q}$ lies on this original line, then

$$f(\boldsymbol{q}) = f((x_1, y_1) + \mu(-b, a)) = 0$$

that is

$$a \times (y_1 + \mu \times a) - b \times (x_1 - \mu \times b) - c = f(x_1, y_1) + \mu (a^2 + b^2) = 0$$

Hence

$$\mu = -f(x_1, y_1)/(a^2 + b^2)$$

The point $\boldsymbol{q}$ is a distance $\mu \times |(-b, a)|$ from $(x_1, y_1)$ which naturally means that the distance of $(x_1, y_1)$ from the line is $\mu \times \sqrt{(a^2 + b^2)} = -f(x_1, y_1)/\sqrt{(a^2 + b^2)}$: the sign denotes on which side of the line the point is lying. If $a^2 + b^2 = 1$ then $|f(x_1, y_1)|$ gives the distance of the point $(x_1, y_1)$ from the line.

This idea leads us directly to a way of implementing *convex areas*; these areas are such that a straight line segment that joins any two points within the area lies totally inside the area. We shall limit our study to convex polygons, however, since it is obvious that any convex area may be approximated by a polygon, providing that it has enough sides.

Suppose we have a convex polygon with $n$ vertices $\{\boldsymbol{p} \equiv (x_i, y_i) | i = 1, 2, \ldots, n\}$ taken in order around the polygon (either clockwise or anticlockwise) -- we shall call such a description of a convex polygon an *oriented convex set* of vertices. The problem of finding whether such a set is clockwise or anticlockwise is considered in chapter 7. The $n$ boundary edges of the polygon are segments of the lines

$$f_i(x, y) \equiv (x_{i+1} - x_i) \times (y - y_i) - (y_{i+1} - y_i) \times (x - x_i)$$

where $i = 1, \ldots, n$, and the addition in the subscripts is modulo $n$ (that is, $n + j \equiv j$ for $1 \leqslant j \leqslant n$). Try to explain why these formulae do actually describe the line segments!

This systematic definition of the lines enables us to define the *inside* of the convex area. Any given line segment, say the one joining $\boldsymbol{p}_i$ to $\boldsymbol{p}_{i+1}$ for some $i$, is such that the points inside the body must lie on the same side of this line as the remaining vertices of the polygon, in particular $\boldsymbol{p}_{i+2}$. So the inside is given by

$$\{(x, y) | \text{sign of } f_i(x, y) = \text{sign of } f_i(x_{i+2}, y_{i+2}) \neq 0 \text{: } i = 1, \ldots, n\}$$

A point on the boundary is given by

$$\{(x, y) | \text{there exists one } j \text{, or two if } (x, y) \text{ is a corner}$$
$$\text{where } 1 \leqslant j \leqslant n \text{ such that } f_j(x, y) = 0 \text{ and}$$
$$\text{sign of } f_i(x, y) = \text{sign of } f_i(x_{i+2}, y_{i+2}) \neq 0 \text{: } i \neq j \text{ and } 1 \leqslant i \leqslant n\}$$

A point outside the area is defined by

$$\{(x, y) | \text{there exists one } j, 1 \leqslant j \leqslant n \text{ such that}$$
$$0 \neq \text{sign of } f_j(x, y) \neq \text{sign of } f_j(x_{j+2}, y_{j+2}) \neq 0\}$$

Naturally the additions of subscripts are all modulo $n$. This technique of 'inside and outside' is fundamental to the hidden surface algorithm of chapter 12.

*Example 3.3*
Suppose we are given the convex polygon with vertices (1, 0), (5, 2), (4, 4) and (−2, 1): see figure 3.4. In this order the vertices obviously have an anticlockwise orientation. Are the points (3, 2), (1, 4), (3, 1) inside, outside or on the boundary of the polygon? What is the distance of (4, 4) from the first line?

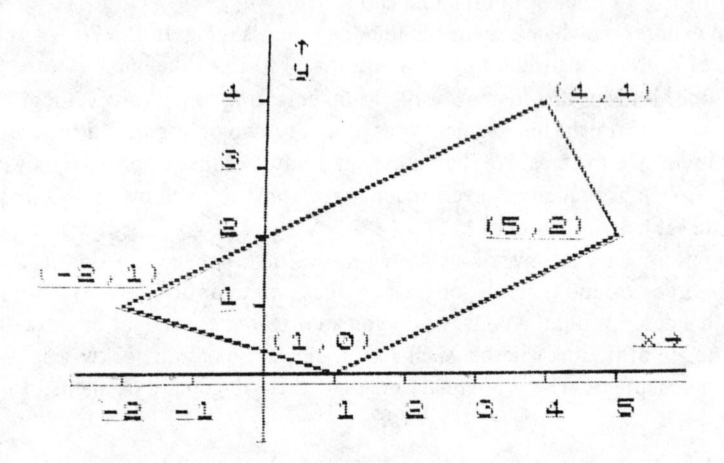


Figure 3.4

$$f_1(x, y) \equiv (5-1) \times (y-0) - (2-0) \times (x-1) \equiv 4y - 2x + 2$$

$$f_2(x, y) \equiv (4-5) \times (y-2) - (4-2) \times (x-5) \equiv -y - 2x + 12$$

$$f_3(x, y) \equiv (-2-4) \times (y-4) - (1-4) \times (x-4) \equiv -6y + 3x + 12$$

$$f_4(x, y) \equiv (1+2) \times (y-1) - (0-1) \times (x+2) \equiv 3y + x - 1$$

Hence point (3, 2) is inside the body because $f_1(3, 2) = 4$ and $f_1(4, 4) = 10$; $f_2(3, 2) = 4$ and $f_2(-2, 1) = 15$; $f_3(3, 2) = 9$ and $f_3(1, 0) = 15$; $f_4(3, 2) = 8$ and $f_4(5, 2) = 10$ – all with the same positive signs.
Point (1, 4) is outside the body because $f_3(1, 4) = -9$ and $f_3(1, 0) = 15$ – opposite signs.
Point (3, 1) is on the boundary because $f_1(3, 1) = 0$, $f_2(3, 1) = 5$, $f_3(3, 1) = 15$ and $f_4(3, 1) = 5$.

In fact there is no need to work out $f_i(x_{i+2}, y_{i+2})$ for every $i$ – since they all have the same sign, once we have calculated $f_1(x_3, y_3)$ then we can work with this value throughout.

(4, 4) is a distance $(f_1(4, 4)/\sqrt{(4^2 + 2^2)} = 10/\sqrt{20}) = \sqrt{5}$ from line 1

*Exercise 3.3*
Imagine two convex polygons that intersect one another. The area of intersection is also a convex polygon. Use the methods that are mentioned in this chapter to calculate the vertices of the new polygon.

Having dealt with the functional representation of a line, what about the parametric form? We noted that this form is one where the $x$-coordinate and $y$-coordinate of a general point on the curve are given in terms of parameter(s) (which could be the $x$ or $y$ values themselves), together with a range for the parameter. So we have already seen a parametric form of a line, it is simply the base and directional representation

$$b + \mu d \equiv (x_1, y_1) + \mu(x_2, y_2)$$

$$\equiv (x_1 + \mu \times x_2, y_1 + \mu \times y_2) \qquad \text{where } -\infty < \mu < \infty$$

Here $\mu$ is the parameter, and $x_1 + \mu \times x_2$ and $y_1 + \mu \times y_2$ are the respective $x$ and $y$ values, which depend only on variable $\mu$.

We can also produce functional representations and parametric forms for most well-behaved curves. For example a sine curve is given by $f(x, y) \equiv y - \sin(x)$ in functional representation, and by $(x, \sin(x))$ with $-\infty < x < \infty$ in its parametric form. The general conic section (ellipse, parabola and hyperbola) is represented by the general function

$$f(x, y) \equiv a \times x^2 + b \times y^2 + h \times x \times y + f \times x + g \times y + c$$

where the coefficients $a, b, c, f, g, h$ uniquely identify a curve. A circle centred at the origin of radius $r$ has $a = b = 1, f = g = h = 0$ and $c = -r^2$, whence $f(x, y) \equiv x^2 + y^2 - r^2$. All the points $(x, y)$ on the circle are such that $f(x, y) = 0$, the inside of the circle has $f(x, y) < 0$, and the outside of the circle $f(x, y) > 0$. The parametric form of this circle is $(r \times \cos \alpha, r \times \sin \alpha)$ where $0 \leqslant \alpha \leqslant 2\pi$. (We have already met the parametric form of a circle, ellipse and spiral in chapter 2.)

It is very useful to experiment with these (and other) concepts in two-dimensional geometry. There will be many occasions when it is necessary to include these ideas in programs, as well as the ever-present need when we are generating coordinate data for diagrams.

*Example 3.4*
Suppose we wish to draw a circular ball (radius $r$) that is disappearing down an elliptical hole (major axis $a$, minor axis $b$) – see figure 3.5. Parts of both the ellipse and circle are obscured.

Let the ellipse be centred on the origin with the major axis horizontal, and the centre of the circle a distance $d$ vertically above the origin. The ellipse has the functional representation

$$f_e(x, y) \equiv x^2/a^2 + y^2/b^2 - 1$$

and in parametric form

$$(a \times \cos\alpha, b \times \sin\alpha) \text{ with } 0 \leqslant \alpha \leqslant 2\pi$$

For the circle

$$f_c(x, y) \equiv x^2 + (y - d)^2 - r^2$$

and in parametric form

$$(r \times \cos\lambda,\ d + r \times \sin\lambda) \text{ where } 0 \leqslant \lambda \leqslant 2\pi$$

To generate the picture we must find the points $(x, y)$ common to the circle and ellipse (if any). As a useful demonstration we shall mix the representations in searching for a solution, by using the functional representation for the circle and the parametric form of the ellipse.

So we are searching for the points $(x, y) \equiv (a \times \cos\alpha, b \times \sin\alpha)$ on the ellipse that also satisfy $f_c(x, y) = 0$. That is

$$a^2 \times \cos^2\alpha + (b \times \sin\alpha - d)^2 - r^2 = 0$$

or

$$a^2 \times \cos^2\alpha + b^2 \times \sin^2\alpha - 2 \times b \times d \times \sin\alpha + d^2 - r^2 = 0$$

And since $\cos^2\alpha = 1 - \sin^2\alpha$, then

$$(b^2 - a^2) \times \sin^2\alpha - 2 \times b \times d \times \sin\alpha + a^2 + d^2 - r^2 = 0$$

This is a simple quadratic equation in the unknown $\sin\alpha$, which is easily solved (the quadratic equation $Ax^2 + Bx + C = 0$ has two roots given by $(-B \pm\sqrt{(B^2 - 4 \times A \times C)})/(2 \times A))$. For each value of $\sin\alpha$ we can find values for $\alpha$ with $0 \leqslant \alpha \leqslant 2\pi$ (if they exist) and we can then calculate the points of intersection $(a \times \cos\alpha, b \times \sin\alpha)$.

There is no hard and fast rule about which representation to use in any given situation – a *feel* for the method is required and that only comes with experience.

*Exercise 3.4*
Write a program that will draw figure 3.5.

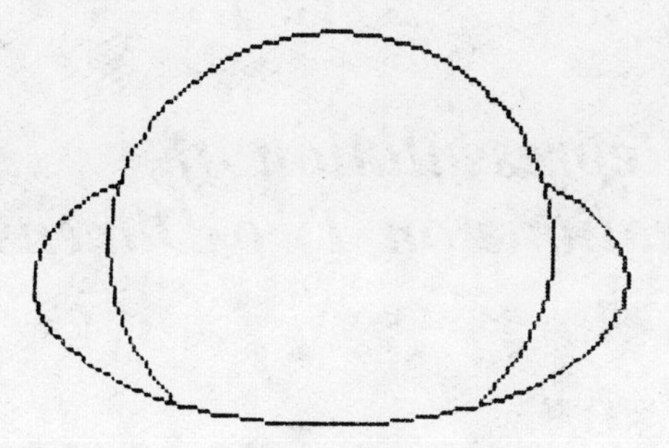

*Figure 3.5*

---

**Complete Programs**

I 'lib1' and listing 3.1: no data required.

II Listing 3.2. Data required: four coordinate pairs (X1, Y1), (X2, Y2), (X3, Y3) and (X4, Y4).

# *4 Matrix Representation of Transformations on Two-Dimensional Space*

In chapter 2 we saw the need to translate pictures of objects about the screen. Rather than perpetually to change the screen coordinate system, it is conceptually much easier to define an object in the simplest terms possible (as vertices in the form of pixel or coordinate values, together with line and area information that is related to the vertices), and then transform the object to various parts of the screen but keeping the screen coordinate system fixed. We shall restrict ourselves to linear transformations (see below). It will often be necessary to transform a large number of vertices, and to do this efficiently we use *matrices*. Before looking at such matrix representations we should explain exactly what we mean by a matrix, and also by a *column vector*. In fact we restrict ourselves to square matrices: to 3 × 3 (said 3 by 3) for the study of two-dimensional space, and later we use 4 × 4 matrices when considering three-dimensional space. Such a 3 × 3 matrix (A say) is simply a group of real numbers placed in a block of 3 rows by 3 columns: a column vector (D say) is a group of numbers placed in a column of 3 rows:

$$\begin{pmatrix} A_{11} & A_{12} & A_{13} \\ A_{21} & A_{22} & A_{23} \\ A_{31} & A_{32} & A_{33} \end{pmatrix} \quad \text{and} \quad \begin{pmatrix} D_1 \\ D_2 \\ D_3 \end{pmatrix}$$

A general entry in the matrix is usually written $A_{ij}$; the first subscript denotes the $i^{th}$ row, and the second subscript the $j^{th}$ column (for example, $A_{23}$ represents the value in the second row of the third column). The entry in the column vector, $D_i$, denotes the value in the $i^{th}$ row. All these named entries will be explicitly replaced by numerical values and it is important to realise that the *information* stored in a matrix or column vector is not just the individual values but it is also the position of these values within the matrix or vector. Naturally BASIC programs are written along a line (no subscripts or superscripts) and hence matrices and vectors are implemented as arrays and the subscript values appear inside round brackets following the array identifier.

Matrices can be added. Matrix C = A + B, the sum of two matrices A and B, is defined by the general entry $C_{ij}$ thus:

$$C_{ij} = A_{ij} + B_{ij} \quad 1 \leqslant i, j \leqslant 3$$

Matrix A can be multiplied by a scalar $k$ to form a matrix B:

$$B_{ij} = k \times A_{ij} \quad 1 \leqslant i, j \leqslant 3$$

We can multiply a matrix A by a column vector D to produce another column vector E thus

$$E_i = A_{i1} \times D_1 + A_{i2} \times D_2 + A_{i3} \times D_3 = \sum_k A_{ik} \times D_k \quad \text{where } 1 \leqslant i, k \leqslant 3$$

The $i^{\text{th}}$ row element of the new column vector is the sum of the products of the corresponding elements of the $i^{\text{th}}$ row of the matrix with those in the column vector.

Furthermore, we can calculate the product (matrix) C = A × B of two matrices A and B:

$$C_{ij} = A_{i1} \times B_{1j} + A_{i2} \times B_{2j} + A_{i3} \times B_{3j} = \sum_k A_{ik} \times B_{kj} \quad \text{where} \quad 1 \leqslant i, j, k \leqslant 3$$

We take the sum (in order) of the elements in the $i^{\text{th}}$ row of the first matrix multiplied by the elements in the $j^{\text{th}}$ column of the second. It should be noted that the product of matrices is not necessarily *commutative*, that is A × B need not be the same as B × A. For example

$$\begin{pmatrix} 0 & 1 & 0 \\ 0 & 0 & 1 \\ 1 & 0 & 0 \end{pmatrix} \times \begin{pmatrix} 0 & 0 & 1 \\ 0 & 1 & 0 \\ 1 & 0 & 0 \end{pmatrix} = \begin{pmatrix} 0 & 1 & 0 \\ 1 & 0 & 0 \\ 0 & 0 & 1 \end{pmatrix} \text{ but } \begin{pmatrix} 0 & 0 & 1 \\ 0 & 1 & 0 \\ 1 & 0 & 0 \end{pmatrix} \times \begin{pmatrix} 0 & 1 & 0 \\ 0 & 0 & 1 \\ 1 & 0 & 0 \end{pmatrix} = \begin{pmatrix} 1 & 0 & 0 \\ 0 & 0 & 1 \\ 0 & 1 & 0 \end{pmatrix}$$

Experiment with these ideas until you have enough confidence to use them in the theory that follows. For those who want more details about the theory of matrices we recommend books by Finkbeiner (1978) and by Stroud (1982).

There is a special matrix called the *identity matrix* I (sometimes called the unit matrix):

$$I = \begin{pmatrix} 1 & 0 & 0 \\ 0 & 1 & 0 \\ 0 & 0 & 1 \end{pmatrix}$$

Also for every matrix A we can calculate its *determinant* det(A):

$$\det(A) = A_{11} \times (A_{22} \times A_{33} - A_{23} \times A_{32}) + A_{12} \times (A_{23} \times A_{31} - A_{21} \times A_{33}) + A_{13} \times (A_{21} \times A_{32} - A_{22} \times A_{31})$$

Any matrix whose determinant is non-zero is called *non-singular*, and those whose determinant is zero are called *singular*. All non-singular matrices A have an *inverse*

$A^{-1}$, which has the property that $A \times A^{-1} = I$ and $A^{-1} \times A = I$. For methods of calculating an inverse of a matrix see Finkbeiner (1978); also see listing 7.4 in chapter 7 which uses the Adjoint method.

We shall now consider the transformation of points in space. Suppose a point $(x, y)$ – 'before' – is transformed to $(x', y')$ – 'after'. We shall completely understand the transformation if we can find equations that relate the 'before' and 'after' points. A linear transformation is one that defines the 'after' point in terms of linear combinations of the coordinates of the 'before' point (that is, the equations contain only multiples of $x$, $y$ and additional real values); the transformation includes neither non-unit powers, nor multiples of $x$ and $y$, nor other variables. Such equations may be written as

$$x' = A_{11} \times x + A_{12} \times y + A_{13}$$

$$y' = A_{21} \times x + A_{22} \times y + A_{23}$$

The A values are called the *coefficients* of the equation. As we can see, the result of the transformation is a combination of multiples of $x$-values, $y$-values and unity. We may add another equation:

$$1 = A_{31} \times x + A_{32} \times y + A_{33}$$

For this to be true for all values of $x$ and $y$, we see that $A_{31} = A_{32} = 0$ and $A_{33} = 1$. Although this may seem a pointless exercise, we shall see that it is in fact very useful. For if we set each point vector $(x, y)$ (also called a *row vector* for obvious reasons) in the form of a three-dimensional column vector

$$\begin{pmatrix} x \\ y \\ 1 \end{pmatrix}$$

then the above three equations can be written in the form of a matrix multiplied by a column vector:

$$\begin{pmatrix} x' \\ y' \\ 1 \end{pmatrix} = \begin{pmatrix} A_{11} & A_{12} & A_{13} \\ A_{21} & A_{22} & A_{23} \\ A_{31} & A_{32} & A_{33} \end{pmatrix} \times \begin{pmatrix} x \\ y \\ 1 \end{pmatrix}$$

So if we store the transformation as a matrix, we can transform every required point by considering it to be a column vector and premultiplying this by the matrix.

Many writers of books on computer graphics do not like the use of column vectors. They prefer to extend the row vector, that is $(x, y)$, to $(x, y, 1)$ and post-multiply the row vector by the matrix so that the above equations in matrix form become

$$(x', y', 1) = (x, y, 1) \times \begin{pmatrix} A_{11} & A_{21} & A_{31} \\ A_{12} & A_{22} & A_{32} \\ A_{13} & A_{23} & A_{33} \end{pmatrix}$$

Note that this matrix is the *transpose* of the matrix of coefficients in the equations. This causes a great deal of confusion among those who are not confident in the use of matrices. It is for this reason that we keep to the column vector notation in this book. As you get more practice in the use of matrices it is a good idea to rewrite some (or all) of the following transformation procedures in the other notation. It is not really important which method you finally use *as long as you are consistent*. (Note that the transpose B of a matrix A is given by $B_{ij} = A_{ji}$, where $1 \leqslant i, j \leqslant 3$.)

**Combination of Transformations**

A very useful property of this matrix representation of transformations is that if we wish to combine two transformations, say transformation (= matrix) A followed by transformation B, then the combined transformation is represented by their product $C = B \times A$. Note the order of multiplication – the matrix that represents the first transformation is *premultiplied* by the second. This is because the final matrix will be used to premultiply a column vector that represents a point, and so the first transformation matrix must appear on the right of the product and the last on the left. (If we had used the row vector method then the product would appear in the *natural order* from left to right – this is the price we pay for identifying the transformation matrix with the coefficients of the equation.)

So we need to introduce a procedure 'mult2' (see listing 4.1) which forms the product of two matrices. The BASIC computer language does not allow the transmission of array parameters into procedures, so we must invent an efficient means of coping with this limitation. We assume that all matrix multiplication operates on matrices A and R to give the product matrix B, and when the product is obtained B is copied back into R. The reason for the choice of identifiers and the final copy will become evident as we progress. We also need a procedure 'idR2' (see listing 4.1) which sets R to the identity matrix. Should we need to form the product of a sequence of matrices we first set R = I and then for each of the matrices, from right to left, we name each A and call the procedure 'mult2' in turn. At the end of the process R contains the matrix product of the sequence.

All natural transformations may be reduced to a combination of three basic forms of linear transformation: translation, scaling and rotation about the coordinate origin. It should also be noted that all valid applications of these transformations return non-singular matrices. The procedures that follow generate

*Listing 4.1*

```
9100 REM mult2
9110 DEF PROCmult2
9120 LOCAL I%,J%,K%
9130 FOR I%=1 TO 3
9140 FOR J%=1 TO 3
9150 AR=0
9160 FOR K%=1 TO 3
9170 AR=AR+A(I%,K%)*R(K%,J%)
9180 NEXT K%
9190 B(I%,J%)=AR
9200 NEXT J%
9210 NEXT I%
9220 FOR I%=1 TO 3
9230 FOR J%=1 TO 3
9240 R(I%,J%)=B(I%,J%)
9250 NEXT J%
9260 NEXT I%
9270 ENDPROC

9300 REM idR2
9310 DEF PROCidR2
9320 LOCAL I%,J%
9330 FOR I%=1 TO 3
9340 FOR J%=1 TO 3
9350 R(I%,J%)=0
9360 NEXT J%
9370 R(I%,I%)=1
9380 NEXT I%
9390 ENDPROC
```

a matrix called A for each of the three types of transformation, so that each transformation procedure can be used in conjunction with 'mult2' to produce combinations of transformations.

**Translation**

A 'before' point $(x, y)$ is moved by a vector (TX, TY) to $(x', y')$ say. This produces the equations

$$x' = 1 \times x + 0 \times y + \mathrm{TX}$$

$$y' = 0 \times x + 1 \times y + \mathrm{TY}$$

so the matrix that describes this transformation is

$$\begin{pmatrix} 1 & 0 & \mathrm{TX} \\ 0 & 1 & \mathrm{TY} \\ 0 & 0 & 1 \end{pmatrix}$$

A procedure, 'tran2', for generating such a matrix A given the values TX and TY is given in listing 4.2.

*Listing 4.2*

```
9000 REM tran2
9010 DEF PROCtran2(TX,TY)
9020 LOCAL I%,J%
9030 FOR I%=1 TO 3
9040 FOR J%=1 TO 3
9050 A(I%,J%)=0
9060 NEXT J% : A(I%,I%)=1
9070 NEXT I%
9080 A(1,3)=TX : A(2,3)=TY
9090 ENDPROC
```

## Scaling

The $x$-coordinate of a point in space is scaled by a factor SX, and the $y$-coordinate by SY, thus

$$x' = \mathrm{SX} \times x + 0 \times y + 0$$

$$y' = 0 \times x + \mathrm{SY} \times y + 0$$

giving the matrix

$$\begin{pmatrix} \mathrm{SX} & 0 & 0 \\ 0 & \mathrm{SY} & 0 \\ 0 & 0 & 1 \end{pmatrix}$$

Usually SX and SY are both positive, but if one or both are negative this creates a reflection as well as a scaling. In particular, if SX = –1 and SY = 1 then the point is reflected about the $y$-axis. A program segment, 'scale2', to produce such a scaling matrix A given SX and SY is given in listing 4.3.

*Listing 4.3*

```
8900 REM scale2
8910 DEF PROCscale2(SX,SY)
8920 LOCAL I%,J%
8930 FOR I%=1 TO 3
8940 FOR J%=1 TO 3
8950 A(I%,J%)=0
8960 NEXT J%
8970 NEXT I%
8980 A(1,1)=SX : A(2,2)=SY : A(3,3)=1
8990 ENDPROC
```

**Rotation about the Origin**

If we rotate a point in an anticlockwise direction (the normal mathematical orientation) about the origin by an angle $\theta$ then the equations are

$$x' = \cos\theta \times x - \sin\theta \times y + 0$$

$$y' = \sin\theta \times x + \cos\theta \times y + 0$$

and the matrix is

$$\begin{pmatrix} \cos\theta & -\sin\theta & 0 \\ \sin\theta & \cos\theta & 0 \\ 0 & 0 & 1 \end{pmatrix}$$

The procedure, 'rot2', to produce a rotation matrix, A, for an angle $\theta$ is given in listing 4.4.

*Listing 4.4*

```
8600 REM rot2
8610 DEF PROCrot2(THETA)
8620 LOCAL I%,J%
8630 FOR I%=1 TO 3
8640 FOR J%=1 TO 3
8650 A(I%,J%)=0
8660 NEXT J%
8670 NEXT I%
8680 A(3,3)=1
8690 CT=COS(THETA) : ST=SIN(THETA)
8700 A(1,1)=CT : A(2,2)=CT
8710 A(1,2)=-ST : A(2,1)=ST
8720 ENDPROC
```

**Inverse Transformations**

For every transformation there is an inverse transformation that will restore the points in space to their original position. If a transformation is represented by a matrix A, then the inverse transformation is represented by the inverse matrix $A^{-1}$. There is no need to calculate this inverse by using listing 7.4, we can find it directly by using listings 4.2, 4.3 and 4.4, with parameters derived from the parameters of the original transformation:

(1) A translation by (TX, TY) is inverted by a translation by (−TX, −TY).
(2) A scaling by SX and SY is inverted by a scaling by 1/SX and 1/SY (naturally both SX and SY are non-zero, for otherwise the two-dimensional space would contract into a line or a point).
(3) A rotation by an angle $\theta$ is inverted by a rotation by an angle $-\theta$.

(4) If the transformation matrix is a product of a number of translation, scaling and rotation matrices $A \times B \times C \times \ldots \times L \times M \times N$ (say), then the inverse transformation matrix is

$$N^{-1} \times M^{-1} \times L^{-1} \times \ldots \times C^{-1} \times B^{-1} \times A^{-1}$$

Note the order of multiplication!

**The Placing of an Object**

We are often required to draw a given object at various points on the screen, and at arbitrary orientations. It would be very inefficient to calculate by hand the coordinates of vertices for each position of the object and input them to the program. Instead we first define an arbitrary but fixed coordinate system for two-dimensional space, which we shall call the ABSOLUTE system. Then we give the coordinates of the vertices of the object in some simple way, usually about the origin, which we call the SETUP position. Lines and areas within the object are defined in terms of the vertices. We can then use matrices to move the vertices of the object from the SETUP to the ACTUAL position in the ABSOLUTE system. The lines and areas maintain their relationship with the now transformed vertices. The matrix that relates the SETUP to the ACTUAL position will be called P throughout this book (we sometimes give it a letter subscript to identify it uniquely from other such matrices). Because of the restriction of not passing arrays as parameters into subprograms, we shall not normally explicitly generate array P, instead it will be implicitly used to update the array R.

**Looking at the Object**

Thus objects in a scene can be moved relative to the ABSOLUTE coordinate axes. When observing such a scene, the eye is assumed to be looking directly at point (DX, DY) of the ABSOLUTE system and the head tilted through an angle $\alpha$ (ALPHA). It would be convenient to assume that it is looking at the origin and there is no tilt of the head (we call this the OBSERVED position). Therefore we generate another matrix that will transform space so that the eye is moved from its ACTUAL position to this OBSERVED position. The ACTUAL to OBSERVED matrix is named Q throughout this book, and is achieved by first translating all points in space by a vector (−DX, −DY), matrix A, and then rotating them by an angle $-\alpha$, matrix B (note the minus signs!). Thus $Q = B \times A$, which is generated in procedure 'look2', given as listing 4.5. Normally we do not calculate Q explicitly since, as usual, it is used to update R; however, if it is necessary to use the values of the matrix repeatedly then obviously it is sensible to store Q.

*Listing 4.5*

```
8200 REM Look2
8210 DEF PROCLook2
8220 CLS : INPUT"(DX,DY) ",DX,DY
8230 INPUT"ALPHA ",ALPHA
8240 PROCtran2(-DX,-DY) : PROCmult2
8250 PROCrot2(-ALPHA) : PROCmult2
8260 ENDPROC
```

## Drawing an Object

Combining the SETUP to ACTUAL matrix P, with the ACTUAL to OBSERVED matrix Q, we get the SETUP to OBSERVED matrix R = Q × P (we shall always use R to denote this matrix – and remember R is always the result of our 'mult 2' procedure). transforming all the SETUP vertices by R, with the corresponding movement of line and area information, means that the coordinates of the object are given relative to the observer who is looking at the origin of the ABSOLUTE coordinate system with head upright, and who is in fact really looking at a graphics screen. So we identify the ABSOLUTE coordinate system with the system of the screen to find the position of the vertices on the screen, and then draw the vertices, lines and areas that compose the object. In practice this is achieved by a *construction procedure* which uses matrix R. It will set up the vertex, line and area information, transform the vertices by using R, and perhaps finally draw the object; see example 4.1 below. Later we shall see that there are certain situations where it is more efficient to store the vertex, line and area information. For example, the vertex coordinates can be stored in arrays X and Y, line information in a two-dimensional array LIN or area information in a two-dimensional array FACET. Vertices may be stored in their SETUP, ACTUAL or OBSERVED position – it really depends on the context of the program. This SETUP to ACTUAL to OBSERVED method will enable us to draw a dynamic series of scenes – objects can move relative to the ABSOLUTE axes, and to themselves, while simultaneously the observer can move independently around the scene. To start with, however, we shall consider the simplest case of a fixed scene.

## Complicated Pictures – the 'Building Block' Method

We can draw pictures that contain a number of similar objects. There is no need to produce a new procedure for each occurrence of the object, all we do each time is to calculate a new SETUP to OBSERVED matrix and enter this into the same procedure. Naturally we shall require one procedure for each new type of object in the picture. The final picture is achieved by the execution of a procedure that is named 'scene2' which will be called from the standard main program (listing 4.6). This main program defines the MODE of the picture, centres the graphics area after having input HORIZ and VERT, and then calls 'scene2'.

*Listing 4.6*

```
100 REM MAIN PROGRAM
110 INPUT"Which mode "MOWD : MODE MOWD
120 INPUT"HORIZ,VERT",HORIZ,VERT
130 PROCstart(3,0)
140 PROCsetorigin(HORIZ/2,VERT/2)
150 PROCscene2
160 STOP
```

'scene2' declares all the necessary arrays and then, if required, calls 'look2' to generate Q; if more than one object is to be drawn then we store Q. For each individual object (or *block*) we calculate a matrix P and call the required construction procedure using R = Q × P. All the blocks finally build into the finished picture. To distinguish between different occurrences of these matrices in what follows, we sometimes add a subscript to the names P and R.

This modular approach for solving the problem of defining and drawing a picture may not be the most efficient, but from our experience it does greatly clarify the situation for beginners, enabling them to ask the right questions about constructing a required scene. Also when dealing with animation we shall see that this approach minimises problems in scenes where not only are the objects moving relative to one another, but also the observer himself is moving. Naturally if the head is upright then matrix Q can be replaced by a call to 'setorigin' which changes the screen coordinate system. Or if the eye is looking at the origin, head upright, then Q is the identity matrix I, so it plays no part in transforming the picture and the 'look2' procedure may be ignored. We shall make no such assumptions and work with the most general situation: it is a useful exercise throughout this book for the reader to *cannibalise* our programs in order to make them more efficient for specific cases. It is our aim to explain these concepts in the most general and straightforward terms, even if it is at the expense of efficiency and speed. The reader can return to these programs when he is ready and fully understands the ideas of transforming space. Later we shall give some hints on how to make these changes, but at the moment this would only confuse the issue.

However, the most important reason for this modular approach will be seen when we come to drawing pictures of three-dimensional objects. We shall define these three-dimensional constructions as an extension of the ideas above and full understanding of two-dimensional transformations is essential before we can go on to higher dimensions.

***Example 4.1***

Consider a simple *flag* SETUP that consists of three coloured areas and two lines that are defined by vertices (labelled 1 to 12) taken from the set (5, 5), (−5, 5),

(–5, –5), (5, –5), (4, 5), (–4, 5), (–5, 4), (–5, –4), (–4, –5), (4, –5), (5, –4) and (5, 4). The three areas (or *facets*) are given by vertices 1, 2, 3, 4 (facet 1), 1, 5, 8, 3, 9, 12 (facet 2) and 2, 7, 10, 4, 11, 6 (facet 3). The two lines are given by vertices 1, 3 (line 1) and 2, 4 (line 2). This information is stored in a DATA statement and recalled when required. See figure 4.1, which shows a flag that was drawn on a screen 16 units by 12 units; the SETUP to ACTUAL matrix is the identity and the ACTUAL to OBSERVED matrix is such that the observer is looking at the origin with head upright. Listing 4.7 gives the necessary procedure 'scene2' which moves the object into position and takes a general view, and listing 4.8 is the required construction procedure 'flag'. Note that 'flag', which uses matrix R to transform the vertices (and hence the object) into their OBSERVED position, does not store the vertex values for this position in a permanent data-base. Instead the values are kept in arrays X and Y for the duration of the procedure and if the procedure is re-entered to draw another flag then these array locations are used again.

*Figure 4.1*

*Listing 4.7*

```
6000 REM scene2 / flag not stored, single view
6010 DEF PROCscene2
6020 DIM X(12),Y(12),A(3,3),B(3,3),R(3,3)
6030 PROCidR2 : PROClook2
6040 PROCflag
6050 ENDPROC
```

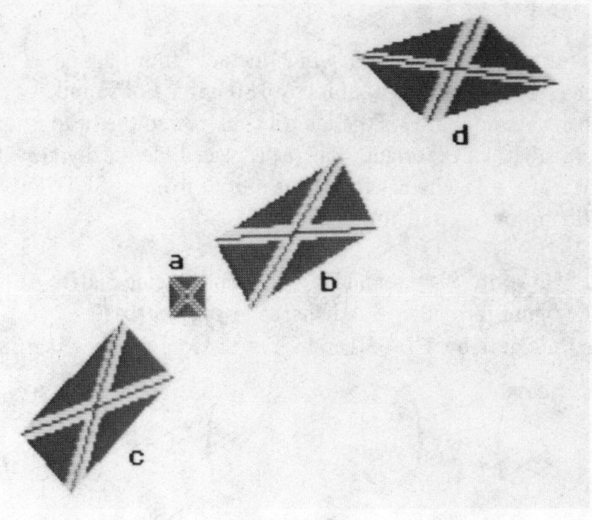


*Figure 4.2*

*Listing 4.8*

```
6500 REM flag / data not stored
6510 DEF PROCflag
6520 LOCAL I%,XX,YY
6530 RESTORE 6540
6540 DATA 5,5, -5,5, -5,-5, 5,-5, 4,5, -4,5, -5,4, -5,-4, -4,-5,
         4,-5, 5,-4, 5,4
6549 REM READ vertex data and place in position using matrix R
6550 FOR I%=1 TO 12 : READ XX,YY
6560 X(I%)=R(1,1)*XX+R(1,2)*YY+R(1,3)
6570 Y(I%)=R(2,1)*XX+R(2,2)*YY+R(2,3)
6580 NEXT I%
6589 REM draw red base of flag
6590 GCOL0,1
6600 MOVE FNX(X(2)),FNY(Y(2)) : MOVE FNX(X(1)),FNY(Y(1))
6610 PLOT85,FNX(X(3)),FNY(Y(3)) : PLOT85,FNX(X(4)),FNY(Y(4))
6619 REM draw two yellow diagonal stripes
6620 GCOL0,2
6630 MOVE FNX(X(1)),FNY(Y(1)) : MOVE FNX(X(5)),FNY(Y(5))
6640 PLOT85,FNX(X(12)),FNY(Y(12)) : PLOT85,FNX(X(8)),FNY(Y(8))
6650 PLOT85,FNX(X(9)),FNY(Y(9)) : PLOT85,FNX(X(3)),FNY(Y(3))
6660 MOVE FNX(X(2)),FNY(Y(2)) : MOVE FNX(X(6)),FNY(Y(6))
6670 PLOT85,FNX(X(7)),FNY(Y(7)) : PLOT85,FNX(X(11)),FNY(Y(11))
6680 PLOT85,FNX(X(10)),FNY(Y(10)) : PLOT85,FNX(X(4)),FNY(Y(4))
6689 REM draw two red diagonal lines
6690 GCOL0,1
6700 MOVE FNX(X(1)),FNY(Y(1)) : DRAW FNX(X(3)),FNY(Y(3))
6710 MOVE FNX(X(2)),FNY(Y(2)) : DRAW FNX(X(4)),FNY(Y(4))
6720 ENDPROC
```

*Example 4.2*
Suppose we wish to draw figure 4.2, which includes four flags labelled (a), (b), (c) and (d) on a screen that is 240 units by 180 units. For simplicity in this picture we shall assume that Q is the identity matrix, so the head is upright and the eye looks at the SETUP origin. Flag (a) is placed identically at its SETUP position (that is, $R_a = I$) whereas flag (b) is moved from its SETUP to ACTUAL position by the following transformations:

(1) Scale the figure with SX = 4 and SY = 2, so producing matrix A.
(2) Rotate the figure through $\pi/6$ radians, so giving matrix B.
(3) Translate the figure by TX = 30 and TY = 15, so producing matrix C.

$$A = \begin{pmatrix} 4 & 0 & 0 \\ 0 & 2 & 0 \\ 0 & 0 & 1 \end{pmatrix} \quad B = \begin{pmatrix} \sqrt{3}/2 & -1/2 & 0 \\ 1/2 & \sqrt{3}/2 & 0 \\ 0 & 0 & 1 \end{pmatrix} \quad C = \begin{pmatrix} 1 & 0 & 30 \\ 0 & 1 & 15 \\ 0 & 0 & 1 \end{pmatrix}$$

The complete transformation is given by $R_b = Q \times P_b = I \times P_b = P_b = C \times B \times A$ (note the order of matrix multiplication, and that the subscript distinguishes the placing of flag (b) from the others).

If instead we used the order $A \times B \times C$ (giving matrix $P_d$), then

$$P_b = \begin{pmatrix} 2\sqrt{3} & -1 & 30 \\ 2 & \sqrt{3} & 15 \\ 0 & 0 & 1 \end{pmatrix} \quad P_d = \begin{pmatrix} 2\sqrt{3} & -2 & 60\sqrt{3} - 30 \\ 1 & \sqrt{3} & 15\sqrt{3} + 30 \\ 0 & 0 & 1 \end{pmatrix}$$

which are obviously two different transformations. Matrix $R_d = Q \times P_d = I \times P_d$ produces flag (d). Note how this flag is not symmetrical about two mutually perpendicular axes as are the other three flags; be very careful with the use of the scaling transformation – remember scaling is defined about the origin and this will cause distortions in the shape of an object that is moved away from the origin!

To illustrate this example further we shall show how to calculate the ACTUAL position of the four corners of flag (b) on the screen by setting the coordinates in the form of a column vector and premultiplying it by matrix $R_b = I \times P_b$. For example

$$\begin{pmatrix} 2\sqrt{3} & -1 & 30 \\ 2 & \sqrt{3} & 15 \\ 0 & 0 & 1 \end{pmatrix} \times \begin{pmatrix} 5 \\ 5 \\ 1 \end{pmatrix} = \begin{pmatrix} 10\sqrt{3} + 25 \\ 5\sqrt{3} + 25 \\ 1 \end{pmatrix} \quad \text{etc.}$$

When returned to normal vector form we see that the four vertices (5, 5), (–5, 5), (–5, –5) and (5, –5) have been transformed to $(10\sqrt{3} + 25, 5\sqrt{3} + 25)$, $(-10\sqrt{3} + 25, 5\sqrt{3} + 5)$, $(-10\sqrt{3} + 35, -5\sqrt{3} + 5)$ and $(10\sqrt{3} + 35, -5\sqrt{3} + 25)$ respectively.

Flag (c) is flag (b) reflected in the line $3y = -4x - 9$. This line cuts the $y$-axis at $(0, -3)$ and makes an angle $\alpha = \cos^{-1}(-3/5) = \sin^{-1}(4/5) = \tan^{-1}(-3/4)$ with the positive $x$-axis. If we move space by a vector $(0, 3)$, matrix D say, this line will go through the origin. Furthermore, if we rotate space by $-\alpha$, matrix E say, the line is now identical with the $x$-axis. Matrix F can reflect the flag in the $x$-axis, $E^{-1}$ puts the line back at an angle $\alpha$ with the $x$-axis, and finally $D^{-1}$ returns the line to its original position. Matrix $G = D^{-1} \times E^{-1} \times F \times E \times D$ will therefore reflect all the ACTUAL vertices of flag (b) about the line $3y = -4x - 9$, and $R_c = I \times P_c = G \times P_b$ can therefore be used to draw flag (c). That is we use matrix $P_b$ to move the flag to position (b) and then G to place it in position (c):

$$D = \begin{pmatrix} 1 & 0 & 0 \\ 0 & 1 & 3 \\ 0 & 0 & 1 \end{pmatrix} \quad E = \begin{pmatrix} -3/5 & 4/5 & 0 \\ -4/5 & -3/5 & 0 \\ 0 & 0 & 1 \end{pmatrix} \quad F = \begin{pmatrix} 1 & 0 & 0 \\ 0 & -1 & 0 \\ 0 & 0 & 1 \end{pmatrix}$$

and

$$P_c = \frac{1}{25} \begin{pmatrix} -48 - 14\sqrt{3} & 7 - 24\sqrt{3} & -642 \\ 14 - 48\sqrt{3} & 24 + 7\sqrt{3} & -669 \\ 0 & 0 & 25 \end{pmatrix}$$

Figure 4.2 is drawn by using the new 'scene2' procedure of listing 4.9: note that this 'scene2' does not call 'look2', since it is assumed that the eye is looking at the origin with the head erect. The main program and the 'flag' procedure, as well as all the other graphics package procedures, stay unchanged.

*Listing 4.9*

```
6000 REM scene2 / 4 flags not stored, fixed view
6010 DEF PROCscene2
6020 DIM X(12),Y(12),A(3,3),B(3,3),R(3,3)
6029 REM flag a)
6030 PROCidR2 : PROCflag
6039 REM flag b)
6040 PROCscale2(4,2) : PROCmult2
6050 PROCrot2(PI/6) : PROCmult2
6060 PROCtran2(30,15) : PROCmult2
6070 PROCflag
6080 PROCtran2(0,3) : PROCmult2
6089 REM flag c)
6090 THETA=FNangle(-3,4)
6100 PROCrot2(-THETA) : PROCmult2
6110 PROCscale2(1,-1) : PROCmult2
6120 PROCrot2(THETA) : PROCmult2
6130 PROCtran2(0,-3) : PROCmult2
6140 PROCflag
6149 REM flag d)
6150 PROCidR2
6160 PROCtran2(30,15) : PROCmult2
6170 PROCrot2(PI/6) : PROCmult2
6180 PROCscale2(4,2) : PROCmult2
6190 PROCflag
6200 ENDPROC
```

*Exercise 4.1*
In order to convince yourself that this program may be used to deal with the general situation, you should run this program using non-zero values of DX, DY or $\alpha$ so that the ACTUAL to OBSERVED matrix Q is not the identity matrix. Your 'scene2' procedure should call 'look2' to calculate Q, which must be stored. Then for each object in the scene, in turn, calculate the SETUP to ACTUAL matrix P (which 'mult2' places in R), premultiply it by Q (which has to be copied into matrix A for use with 'mult2') and finally enter the construction procedure with the product matrix $R = Q \times P$.

*Exercise 4.2*
Use the above procedures to draw diagrams that are similar to figure 4.2, but where the number, position and direction of the flags are read in from the keyboard. You can produce procedures to draw more complicated objects, we have chosen a very simple example so that the algorithms would not be obscured by the complexity of objects. The above method can deal with as many vertices, lines and coloured areas as the Model B can handle within time and storage limitations.

*Exercise 4.3*
By using loops in the program we can draw ordered sequences of the objects; for example, they may all have the same orientation but their points of reference (the origin in the SETUP position) may be equally spaced along any line $\boldsymbol{p} + \mu\boldsymbol{q}$. We can set up a loop with index parameter $\mu$ and draw one flag for each pass through the loop. For each value of $\mu$ we can alter the parameters of translation in a regular way within the loop (using $\mu$, $\boldsymbol{p}$ and $\boldsymbol{q}$). The new values of these parameters are used to calculate a different SETUP to ACTUAL matrix for each occurrence, and this moves the object into a new ACTUAL position. $R = Q \times P = I \times P$ is used to observe and draw each object on the screen. With these ideas, construct a line of flags on the screen.

## Efficient Use of Matrices

It is obvious that whatever combination of transformations we use, the third row of every matrix will always be (0 0 1). If we work with only the top two rows of the matrix this will make our procedures much more efficient. We still keep $3 \times 3$ rather than $2 \times 3$ matrices (which is really all we need), because we may have previously written other procedures that assume $3 \times 3$ matrices. ReDIMensioning the arrays could lead to array bound errors in the earlier procedures – the cost of a few extra real numbers per matrix is a small price to pay to avoid errors. It is also more efficient to use explicit statements rather than loops. Listings 4.1, 4.2, 4.3 and 4.4 are rewritten as listings 4.1a, 4.2a, 4.3a and 4.4a, respectively, to make use of these facts.

*Listing 4.1a*

```
9100 REM mult2
9110 DEF PROCmult2
9120 LOCAL I%,J%,K%
9130 FOR I%=1 TO 2
9140 FOR J%=1 TO 3
9150 B(I%,J%)=A(I%,1)*R(1,J%)+A(I%,2)*R(2,J%)
9160 NEXT J%
9170 B(I%,3)=B(I%,3)+A(I%,3)
9210 NEXT I%
9220 FOR I%=1 TO 2
9230 FOR J%=1 TO 3
9240 R(I%,J%)=B(I%,J%)
9250 NEXT J%
9260 NEXT I%
9270 ENDPROC

9300 REM idR2
9310 DEF PROCidR2
9320 R(1,1)=1 : R(1,2)=0 : R(1,3)=0
9330 R(2,1)=0 : R(2,2)=1 : R(2,3)=0
9340 ENDPROC
```

*Listing 4.2a*

```
9000 REM tran2
9010 DEF PROCtran2(TX,TY)
9020 A(1,3)=TX : A(2,3)=TY
9030 A(1,1)= 1 : A(1,2)= 0
9040 A(2,1)= 0 : A(2,2)= 1
9050 ENDPROC
```

*Listing 4.3a*

```
8900 REM scale2
8910 DEF PROCscale2(SX,SY)
8920 A(1,1)=SX : A(2,2)=SY
8930 A(1,2)= 0 : A(1,3)= 0
8940 A(2,1)= 0 : A(2,3)= 0
8950 ENDPROC
```

*Listing 4.4a*

```
8600 REM rot2
8610 DEF PROCrot2(THETA)
8620 CT=COS(THETA) : ST=SIN(THETA)
8630 A(1,1)= CT : A(2,2)=CT
8640 A(1,2)=-ST : A(2,1)=ST
8650 A(1,3)=  0 : A(2,3)= 0
8660 ENDPROC
```

The construction of figure 4.2 may seem rather contrived since the position of the objects was chosen in an arbitrary way. However, in most diagrams the positioning of objects will be well defined, the values being implicit in the diagram required. Example 4.3 illustrates this.

*Example 4.3*

Write a program to draw an ellipse that has major axis A and minor axis B, and that is centred at the point (CX, CY). The major axis makes an angle $\theta$ (THETA) with the positive $x$-direction. Note that the order of transformations is important: first rotate and then translate. If we wish to draw ellipses with major axis horizontal then we need not use matrices, we can stay with the procedure set in exercise 2.5 and use ideas that are similar to those in listing 2.9. Listing 4.10 gives a 'scene2' procedure that reads in data about the ellipse, calculates the SETUP to OBSERVED matrix and then calls the construction procedure 'ellipse' to draw the ellipse.;

*Listing 4.10*

```
6000 REM scene2 / ellipse not stored : fixed view
6010 DEF PROCscene2
6020 DIM A(3,3),B(3,3),R(3,3)
6029 REM major axis A, minor axis B, centre (CX,CY),
     angle THETA
6030 INPUT"A,B,CX,CY,THETA",A,B,CX,CY,THETA
6040 PROCidR2 : PROCrot2(THETA) : PROCmult2
6050 PROCtran2(CX,CY) : PROCmult2
6060 PROCellipse(A,B)
6070 ENDPROC

6500 REM ellipse / points not stored
6510 DEF PROCellipse(A,B)
6520 LOCAL I%,ALPHA,ADIF,XX,YY,XPT,YPT
6529 REM find points (XX,YY) on the ellipse with
      major axis A, minor axis B and placed in
      position using matrix R
6530 XPT=R(1,1)*A+R(1,3) : YPT=R(2,1)*A+R(2,3)
6540 PROCmoveto(XPT,YPT)
6550 ALPHA=0 : ADIF=PI/50
6560 FOR I%=1 TO 100
6570 ALPHA=ALPHA+ADIF
6580 XX=A*COS(ALPHA) : YY=B*SIN(ALPHA)
6590 XPT=R(1,1)*XX+R(1,2)*YY+R(1,3)
6600 YPT=R(2,1)*XX+R(2,2)*YY+R(2,3)
6610 PROClineto(XPT,YPT)
6620 NEXT I%
6630 ENDPROC
```

*Exercise 4.4*

Write a procedure for drawing an individual matrix-transformable object (in this case the *astroid* shown in figure 4.3a) and then use the matrix techniques to draw combinations of these objects (as in figure 4.3b). An astroid is a closed curve with the parametric form (R × $\cos^3\theta$, R × $\sin^3\theta$) where $0 \leqslant \theta \leqslant 2\pi$ and R is the radius (the maximum distance from the centre of the object). The parameters needed by this procedure are the radius of the astroid and the transforming matrix. Figure 4.3b is the combination of a large number of two different forms of the astroid. One has radius 1 and is not rotated, the other has radius $\sqrt{2}$ and is rotated through $\pi/4$ radians.

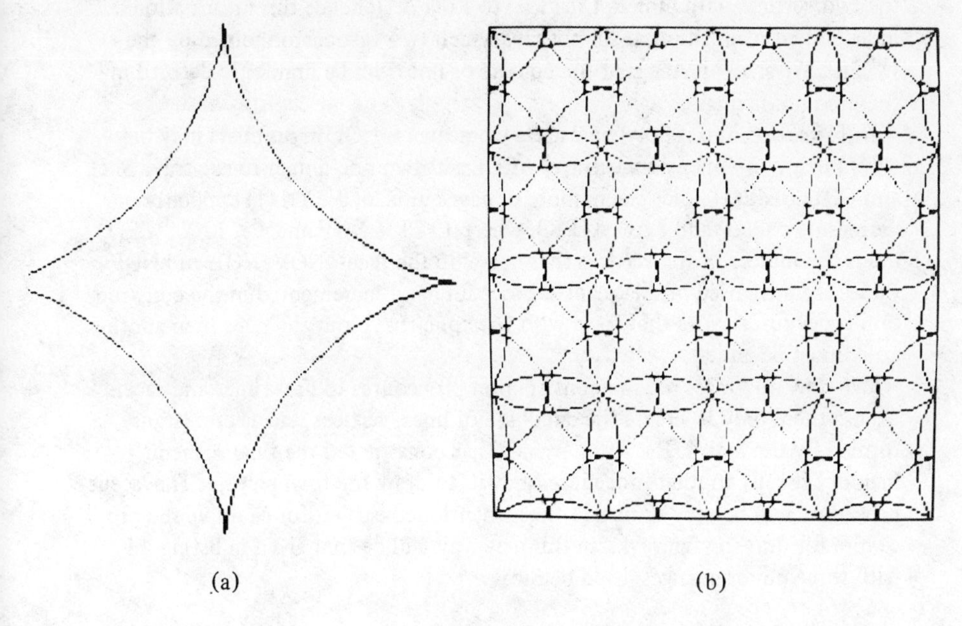

(a) (b)

*Figure 4.3*

*Exercise 4.5*

Experiment with these matrix techniques. Write a procedure to generate the matrix that is needed to rotate points in space by an angle $\theta$ about an arbitrary point (X, Y) in space (not necessarily the origin). Also produce another procedure to generate the matrix that will reflect points about the general line $ay = bx + c$ (use the ideas given in example 4.2 for the production of flag (c)).

**Storing Information about Scenes**

It was mentioned earlier that certain situations arise when we need to store all the information about a scene in a large data-base rather than lose the information on leaving the construction procedure. Our data-base will consist of vertices, lines and facets, together with information on colour which can be explicitly or implicitly stored. Vertices are stored as arrays X and Y, of size greater than or equal to NOV, the final number of vertices to be stored (these vertices can be stored in the SETUP, ACTUAL or OBSERVED position: it depends on the context of the problem).

Line information is stored in a two-dimensional array LIN whose first index is 1 or 2, and whose second index is a number between 1 and a value greater than or equal to NOL, the final number of lines in the scene. The $I^{th}$ line joins the two vertices with indices LIN(1, I) to LIN(2, I); hence this information is independent of position, it simply says which two vertices are joined by the $I^{th}$ line. We shall assume that the colours of lines will be implicitly defined in the program listings.

Information about polygonal areas or facets ($\leqslant$ NOF in number) may be stored in a two-dimensional array FACET and two one-dimensional arrays SIZE and COL. SIZE(J) holds the number of edges in facet J, COL(J) explicitly defines its colour, and FACET(J,K), where $1 \leqslant J \leqslant$ NOF and $1 \leqslant K \leqslant$ SIZE(J), holds the indices of the vertices that make up the facet. NOV, NOL and NOF values are initialised in the 'scene2' procedure and incremented in the construction procedures. Note that if we wish to explicitly colour the lines then another array must be added.

We now no longer require construction procedures to draw lines and facets, we use them only to create the data-base of lines, vertices, facets etc. (transformed by the matrix R). After 'scene2' has constructed the final scene in memory it calls another procedure 'drawit' to draw the final picture. The 'scene2' procedure will be very similar to those mentioned earlier; for example the procedure for drawing figure 4.2 in this new way will be that given in listing 4.9 with three minor changes listed below:

```
6020 DIM X(48), Y(48), LIN(2, 8) FACET(6, 12), SIZE(12), COL(12),
     A(3, 3), B(3, 3), R(3, 3)

6030 NOV = 0 : NOL = 0 : NOF = 0 : PROCidR2 : PROCflag

6200 PROCdrawit : ENDPROC
```

This is used in conjunction with listing 4.11 which gives the 'flag' construction procedure (which now merely sets up the data) and the 'drawit' procedure.

Suppose we wish to produce different views of the same scene (again we shall use figure 4.2 as an example), that is, with the same SETUP to ACTUAL matrices P, but different ACTUAL to OBSERVED matrices Q. The obvious solution is to create a data-base for the scene with the vertices in the ACTUAL position (we can use the 'flag' procedure of listing 4.11). Now for each new OBSERVED position we calculate Q and enter it into another 'drawit' procedure (see listing 4.12 – which is different from listing 4.11) which transfers each vertex from its ACTUAL to its OBSERVED position using Q, stores them in arrays XD and YD so as not to corrupt the X, Y data-base, and recalls them when they are required

*Listing 4.11*

```
6500 REM flag / placed in position by matrix R and stored
6510 DEF PROCflag
6520 LOCAL I%,J%,XX,YY,L1,L2,FVAL
6530 RESTORE 6540
6540 DATA 4,1,1,2,3,4,  6,2,1,5,8,3,9,12,  6,2,2,7,10,4,11,6
6550 DATA 1,3, 2,4
6560 DATA 5,5, -5,5, -5,-5, 5,-5, 4,5, -4,5, -5,4, -5,-4, -4,-5,
          4,-5, 5,-4, 5,4
6569 REM READ facet information
6570 FOR I%=1 TO 3 : NOF=NOF+1 : READ SIZE(NOF),COL(NOF)
6580 FOR J%=1 TO SIZE(NOF) : READ FVAL : FACET(J%,NOF)=FVAL+NOV
6590 NEXT J% : NEXT I%
6599 REM READ line information
6600 FOR I%=1 TO 2 : NOL=NOL+1 : READ L1,L2
6610 LIN(1,NOL)=L1+NOV : LIN(2,NOL)=L2+NOV
6620 NEXT I%
6629 REM READ vertex information and move it into position
6630 FOR I%=1 TO 12 : READ XX,YY : NOV=NOV+1
6640 X(NOV)=R(1,1)*XX+R(1,2)*YY+R(1,3)
6650 Y(NOV)=R(2,1)*XX+R(2,2)*YY+R(2,3)
6660 NEXT I%
6670 ENDPROC

7000 REM drawit / using flag data base
7010 DEF PROCdrawit
7020 LOCAL I%,J%,K% : CLG
7029 REM draw the NOF facets : explicit colours in array COL
7030 FOR I%=1 TO NOF
7040 GCOL 0,COL(I%)
7050 K%=FACET(2,I%) : MOVE FNX(X(K%)),FNY(Y(K%))
7060 FOR J%=3 TO SIZE(I%)
7070 K%=FACET(1,I%) : MOVE FNX(X(K%)),FNY(Y(K%))
7080 K%=FACET(J%,I%) : PLOT 85,FNX(X(K%)),FNY(Y(K%))
7090 NEXT J% : NEXT I%
7099 REM draw the NOL lines implicit colour 1 (red)
7100 GCOL0,1
7110 FOR I%=1 TO NOL
7120 K%=LIN(1,I%) : PROCmoveto(X(K%),Y(K%))
7130 K%=LIN(2,I%) : PROClineto(X(K%),Y(K%))
7140 NEXT I%
7150 ENDPROC
```

for drawing. When using this method to construct different views of figure 4.2 only the 'scene2' and 'drawit' procedures differ from their earlier manifestations, and then only slightly. We give them in listing 4.12.

*Exercise 4.6*
Construct a 'drawit' procedure for a flag which uses the 'triangle' procedure (listing 2.7).

*Exercise 4.7*
Construct a dynamic scene. With each new view the flags will move relative to one another in some well-defined manner. The observer should also move in

*Listing 4.12*

```
6000 REM scene2 / 4 flags stored, variable view
6010 DEF PROCscene2
6020 DIM X(48),Y(48),XD(48),YD(48),LIN(2,8),FACET(6,12),
       SIZE(12),COL(12),A(3,3),B(3,3),R(3,3)
6028 REM create a data base of flags in ACTUAL position
6029 REM flag a)
6030 NOV=0 : NOL=0 : NOF=0 : PROCidR2 : PROCflag
6039 REM flag b)
6040 PROCscale2(4,2) : PROCmult2
6050 PROCrot2(PI/6) : PROCmult2
6060 PROCtran2(30,15) : PROCmult2
6070 PROCflag
6079 REM flag c)
6080 PROCtran2(0,3) : PROCmult2
6090 THETA=FNangle(-3,4)
6100 PROCrot2(-THETA) : PROCmult2
6110 PROCscale2(1,-1) : PROCmult2
6120 PROCrot2(THETA) : PROCmult2
6130 PROCtran2(0,-3) : PROCmult2
6140 PROCflag
6149 REM flag d)
6150 PROCidR2
6160 PROCtran2(30,15) : PROCmult2
6170 PROCrot2(PI/6) : PROCmult2
6180 PROCscale2(4,2) : PROCmult2
6190 PROCflag
6199 REM loop through different views
6200 PROCidR2 : PROClook2
6210 PROCdrawit
6220 GOTO 6200
6230 ENDPROC

7000 REM drawit
7010 DEF PROCdrawit
7020 LOCAL I%,J%,K% : CLG
7029 REM move vertices to OBSERVED position using matrix R
7030 FORI%=1 TO NOV
7040 XD(I%)=R(1,1)*X(I%)+R(1,2)*Y(I%)+R(1,3)
7050 YD(I%)=R(2,1)*X(I%)+R(2,2)*Y(I%)+R(2,3)
7060 NEXT I%
7069 REM draw facets
7070 FOR I%=1 TO NOF
7080 GCOL 0,COL(I%)
7090 K%=FACET(2,I%) : MOVE FNX(XD(K%)),FNY(YD(K%))
7100 FOR J%=3 TO SIZE(I%)
7110 K%=FACET(1,I%) : MOVE FNX(XD(K%)),FNY(YD(K%))
7120 K%=FACET(J%,I%) : PLOT 85,FNX(XD(K%)),FNY(YD(K%))
7130 NEXT J% : NEXT I%
7140 GCOL0,1
7149 REM draw lines
7150 FOR I%=1 TO NOL
7160 K%=LIN(1,I%) : PROCmoveto(XD(K%),YD(K%))
7170 K%=LIN(2,I%) : PROClineto(XD(K%),YD(K%))
7180 NEXT I%
7190 ENDPROC
```

some simple way, for example the eye could start looking at the origin, twenty views later it could be looking at the point (100, 100), and with each view the head could tilt a further 0.1 radian. You no longer need to INPUT the values of (DX, DY) and ALPHA into 'look2', instead they should be calculated by the program.

*Exercise 4.8*

Construct a scene that is a diagrammatic view of a room in your house – with schematic two-dimensional drawings of tables, chairs etc. placed in the room. Each different type of object has its own construction procedure, and the 'scene2' procedure should read in data to place these objects around the room. Once the scene is set produce a variety of views, looking from various points and orientations. Use the menu technique of chapters 5 and 6 to input information.

Or you can set up a line-drawing picture of a map, and again view it from various orientations. The number of possible choices of scene is enormous!

We can choose small values for HORIZ and VERT, which has the effect of the observer zooming up close to parts of a scene, and all external lines will be conveniently clipped off.

---

**Complete Programs**

We group the listings 3.3 ('angle'), 4.1a ('mult2' and 'idR2'), 4.2a ('tran2'), 4.3a ('scale2'), 4.4a ('rot2'), 4.5 ('look2') and 4.6 ('main program') under the heading 'lib2'.

I 'lib1', 'lib2', listings 4.7 ('scene2') and 4.8 ('flag'). Data required: mode, HORIZ, VERT, DX, DY and ALPHA. Try 1, 24, 18, 1, 1, 0.5. Keep any five of these values fixed and systematically make small changes in the other data value.

II 'lib1', 'lib2', listings 4.9 ('scene2') and 4.8 ('flag'). Data required: mode, HORIZ, VERT. Try 1, 240, 180; 1, 160, 120; 1, 80, 60.

III 'lib1', 'lib2' and listings 4.10 ('scene2' and 'ellipse'). Data required: mode, HORIZ, VERT, A, B, CX, CY, THETA. Try 1, 30, 20, 12, 9, 1, 1, 0.5. Again fix all but one of the values and change the remaining value systematically.

IV 'lib1', 'lib2', listings 4.9 ('scene2' adjusted as described in the text) and 4.11 ('flag' and 'drawit'). Data required: as II above. LOAD with PAGE = &1100.

V 'lib1', 'lib2', listings 4.11 ('flag' but not 'drawit') and 4.12 ('scene2' and 'drawit'). Data required: mode, HORIZ, VERT, DX, DY, ALPHA. Try 1, 240, 180, 5, 5, 1. Systematically change each of the data values in turn. LOAD with PAGE = &1100.

# 5 *Character Graphics on the BBC Microcomputer*

In all the MODEs except mode 7 each character to be drawn in two colours is made up of a set of eight by eight pixels and may be printed as any foreground colour. Such a block of pixels is known as a *character block*. The BBC micro has a 95 character *standard* set, and also has the capability of displaying *user-defined characters*. Both types of characters may be placed on the screen by the PRINT command, so we must look closely at this operation.

PRINT allows us to place characters at any text position on the screen. Such a position is specified by column and row numbers. The column number lies between 0 on the left of the screen, and on the right either 19 (in modes 2 and 5), 39 (modes 1, 4 and 6) or 79 (modes 0 and 3). The row or line position on this screen is one of the 32 lines (or 25 lines in modes 3 and 6), from top (0) to bottom (31 or 24). For each character position on the screen there are corresponding (mode-dependent) locations in the screen memory: 8 for two-colour modes, 16 for four-colour modes and 32 for sixteen-colour modes. In the two-colour mode each 8-pixel line of an 8 by 8 character block on the screen corresponds to an 8-bit binary memory location, one bit per pixel. If the binary digit is a 1 then the corresponding pixel will be drawn in the foreground colour, and if the digit is a 0 it will be drawn in the background colour. There is a table of data stored in the memory which defines the shape of each character. For any given character the PRINT command finds the corresponding eight 8-bit values from the table and copies them into the appropriate screen memory locations. This has the effect of displaying the character on the screen. Obviously if we are using four-colour or sixteen-colour modes and two-colour characters (background and foreground) then this method will not work; however PRINT automatically takes the 8 binary numbers from the table and converts them to the 16 or 32 numbers required for the multi-colour modes.

### The Standard Character Set

The table of data for the standard character set is stored in ROM, the permanent Read Only Memory of the computer. There are eight pieces of data for each of the 95 characters, thus the table consists of 760 (95 * 8) consecutive locations and starts at &C000. Each character has a unique ASCII code number, see the user manual. The table contains the data for each of the characters in turn starting with the space character (ASCII code 32) and ending with the pound symbol £ (ASCII code 126). In order to PRINT a character the command requires the eight pieces of data for that character. To find the location in the table it subtracts 32 decimal (20 hexadecimal) from the ASCII code of the character, multiplies the result by eight and finally adds &C000. If a two-colour mode is in use with default colours then PRINT simply copies the data (foreground logical colour 1 and background 0) into the screen memory and the character appears on the screen. (We can invert the colours by setting the background to 1 and the foreground to 0.) However if a four-colour mode is being used then PRINT must calculate the two eight-bit values from each of the eight pieces of table data in order to produce eight pixels in the appropriate colours. In the sixteen-colour mode the PRINT command must translate each piece of data into four eight-bit values, but more of this in a moment.

*Example 5.1*
First run listing 5.1 which demonstrates how this process works in a two-colour mode with foreground 1 and background 0 by showing the calculations as they are performed. A detailed explanation of how the screen memory locations are arranged is given later in this chapter, but for the moment we will limit ourselves to block (0, 0). Figure 5.1 is an example run of this program using '*' as INPUT data (see the user guide for information about indirection operators). Note that this program makes no permanent change to the characters in the table, and also that all numbers are given in hexadecimal notation.

```
  "*" SELECTED.   ASC("*") = 2A

CALCULATION OF DATA LOCATION

START OF TABLE =              C000
 ASC("*") - 20 = A
   A * 8        =               50
                            ------
DATA STARTS AT                C050
                            ------

SCREEN LOCATION   DATA   TABLE LOCATION

        5800         0       C050
        5801        18       C051
        5802        7E       C052
        5803        3C       C053
        5804        7E       C054
        5805        18       C055
        5806         0       C056
        5807         0       C057

N.B. ALL NUMBERS IN HEXADECIMAL

PRESS SPACE TO CONTINUE
```

*Figure 5.1*

*Listing 5.1*

```
 1Ø MODE 4
 2Ø BORED=FALSE
 3Ø REPEAT : CLS
 4Ø REPEAT
 5Ø PRINT TAB(Ø,2);SPC(3Ø);TAB(Ø,2);
 6Ø INPUT "Which character ? "A$
 7Ø UNTIL LEN(A$)=1
 8Ø CLS
 9Ø A=ASC(A$) : A$=""""+A$+""""
1ØØ PRINT TAB(1,4);A$;" SELECTED.  ASC(";A$;") = ";~A'
11Ø PRINT "CALCULATION OF DATA LOCATION"'
12Ø PRINT "START OF TABLE = ",~&CØØØ
13Ø B=A-ASC(" ") : C=B*8
14Ø PRINT " ASC(";A$;") - 2Ø = ";~B
15Ø PRINT "      ";~B;" * 8       = ",~C
16Ø D=&CØØØ+C
17Ø PRINT SPC(25);"------"
18Ø PRINT "DATA STARTS AT ",~D
19Ø PRINT SPC(25);"------"'
2ØØ PRINT "SCREEN LOCATION  DATA  TABLE LOCATION"'
21Ø S=HIMEM
219 REM transfer eight pieces of data from table to screen
22Ø FOR I%=Ø TO 7
23Ø DAT=D?I%
239 REM change value of DAT here for solution of exercise 5.1
24Ø S?I%=DAT
25Ø PRINT ~(S+I%),~DAT,~(D+I%)
26Ø NEXT I%
27Ø PRINT '"N.B. ALL NUMBERS IN HEXADECIMAL"
28Ø PRINT '"PRESS SPACE TO CONTINUE"
29Ø REPEAT UNTIL INKEY(-99)
3ØØ UNTIL BORED
```

***Exercise 5.1***

Rewrite listing 5.1 so that it will give you the option of accepting or replacing by INPUT each of the eight data values before it is stored in the screen memory. Experiment by changing one or two values from a standard character.

We now give a method for taking values from the character table and drawing these characters on the screen for multi-colour modes. We start by defining a value $n$ that equals 1, 2 or 4 for the two-colour, four-colour or sixteen-colour modes respectively, and we let $m = 8/n$. Suppose f and b are the $n$-bit binary numbers that represent the logical foreground and background colours respectively. We calculate a new value F, a foreground mask, by replacing each digit in f by $m$ occurrences of the same digit (for example if $n = 2$ and f = 01, then $m = 4$ and F = 00001111). The background mask B can be created in the same way from b. For each 8-bit number V from the character table, we need to transform it into $n$ 8-bit numbers $S_i$ $(1 \leqslant i \leqslant n)$ so that one line of a character may be drawn in two colours (f and b) on the screen. First we break V into $n$ $m$-bit pieces $p_i$ $(1 \leqslant i \leqslant n)$, that is $V = p_1 \ldots p_n$. Then we create $n$ 8-bit numbers

$A_i = (p_i)^n$, which means that the $m$ digits of $p_i$ are repeated $n$ times, for example, $(01)^4 = 01010101$. From there we calculate the $S_i$ by:

$$S_i = (A_i \text{ AND F}) \text{ OR } (\bar{A}_i \text{ AND B}) \quad 1 \leqslant i \leqslant n$$

where $\bar{A}_i = A_i$ EOR 11111111. We give three examples.

(a) Mode 2: $n = 4$ then $m = 2$.
Suppose f = 0001, b = 0100 and V = 00010111, then

F = 00000011 and B = 00110000

$p_1 = 00 \quad A_1 = 00000000 \quad \bar{A}_1 = 11111111$

$p_2 = 01 \quad A_2 = 01010101 \quad \bar{A}_2 = 10101010$

$p_3 = 01 \quad A_3 = 01010101 \quad \bar{A}_3 = 10101010$

$p_4 = 11 \quad A_4 = 11111111 \quad \bar{A}_4 = 00000000$

$S_1 = 00000000$ OR $00110000 = 00110000$

$S_2 = 00000001$ OR $00100000 = 00100001$

$S_3 = 00000001$ OR $00100000 = 00100001$

$S_4 = 00000011$ OR $00000000 = 00000011$

Bits 7, 5, 3 and 1 represent the first colour from the word and bits 6, 4, 2, 0 the second: see chapter 1. Thus using / to represent the relative position of colours and f for foreground and b for background:

$S_1 = 00110000 \rightarrow$ 0100/0100, that is b/b

$S_2 = 00100001 \rightarrow$ 0100/0001, that is b/f

$S_3 = 00100001 \rightarrow$ 0100/0001, that is b/f

$S_4 = 00000011 \rightarrow$ 0001/0001, that is f/f

Thus the four values combine to give the eight colours b/b/b/f/b/f/f/f which correspond directly to our original line 00010111.

(b) Mode 1: $n = 2$ then $m = 4$.
Suppose f = 01, b = 11 and V = 00010111, then

F = 00001111 and B = 11111111

$p_1 = 0001 \quad A_1 = 00010001 \quad \bar{A}_1 = 11101110$

$p_2 = 0111 \quad A_2 = 01110111 \quad \bar{A}_2 = 10001000$

$S_1 = 00000001$ OR $11101110 = 11101111$

$S_2 = 00000111$ OR $10001000 = 10001111$

Bits 7 and 3, 6 and 2, 5 and 1, and 4 and 0 give the four colours from each byte.

$S_1$ = 11101111 → 11/11/11/01, that b/b/b/f

$S_2$ = 10001111 → 11/01/01/01, that is b/f/f/f

Thus the two values combine to give the eight colours b/b/b/f/b/f/f/f which correspond directly to our original line 00010111.

(c) Mode 0: $n = 1$ then $m = 8$.
Suppose f = 0, b = 1 and V = 00010111, then

F = 00000000 and B = 11111111

$p_1$ = 00010111 $A_1$ = 00010111 $\overline{A}_1$ = 11101000

$S_1$ = 00000000 OR 11101000 = 11101000

Bits correspond directly to the eight pixels from the byte.

$S_1$ = 11101000 → 1/1/1/0/1/0/0/0, that is b/b/b/f/b/f/f/f.

Thus the value gives the eight colours b/b/b/f/b/f/f/f which correspond directly to our original line 00010111.

This logic is programmed in listing 5.2. At this early stage you need not make a great effort to understand the effect of each logical operation, unless you intend to study in detail the assembly language programs in this book.

*Listing 5.2*

```
 10 BORED=FALSE : REPEAT
 20 INPUT "Which mode ",M : MODE M
 30 REPEAT
 40 PRINT TAB(0,2);SPC(30);TAB(0,2);
 50 INPUT"Which character ",A$
 60 UNTIL LEN(A$)=1
 69 REM same calculation as in 5.1
 70 A=ASC(A$)
 80 B=A-ASC(" ")
 90 C=B*8
100 D=&C000+C
110 S=HIMEM
120 INPUT"Which background ",BC
130 INPUT"Which foreground ",FC
140 ON M+1 GOTO 150,230,380,150,150,230,150
150 REM section for 2␣colour modes
160 COLF=&FF*FC : COLB=&FF*BC
170 FOR I%=0 TO 7
180 FMASK=D?I%
190 BMASK=FMASK EOR &FF
200 S?I%=(COLF AND FMASK) OR (COLB AND BMASK)
210 NEXT I%
220 GOTO 570
230 REM section for 4␣colour modes
240 COLF=(FC AND 2)/2*&F0 + (FC AND 1)*&0F
```

```
250 COLB=(BC AND 2)/2*&F0 + (BC AND 1)*&0F
260 FOR I%=0 TO 7 : N%=D?I%
270 FMASK1=0 : FMASK2=0
279 REM check each bit of N% and put double-bit in the
        foreground mask for that half if on.
280 FOR J%=0 TO 3
290 IF (N% AND 2^(J%+4)) THEN FMASK1=FMASK1 + &11*2^J%
300 IF (N% AND 2^J%) THEN FMASK2=FMASK2+ &11*2^J%
310 NEXT J%
320 BMASK1=FMASK1 EOR &FF : BMASK2=FMASK2 EOR &FF
329 REM mix the colours with masks to find two values and put
        2nd value eight bytes on i.e. next to first value.
330 I8%=I%+8
340 S?I%=(COLF AND FMASK1) OR (COLB AND BMASK1)
350 S?I8%=(COLF AND FMASK2) OR (COLB AND BMASK2)
360 NEXT I%
370 GOTO 570
380 REM section for 16␣colour mode
390 COLF=(FC AND 8)/8*&C0 + (FC AND 4)/4*&30
    + (FC AND 2)/2*&0C + (FC AND 1)*&03
400 COLB=(BC AND 8)/8*&C0 + (BC AND 4)/4*&30
    + (BC AND 2)/2*&0C + (BC AND 1)*&03
410 FOR I%=0 TO 7 : N%=D?I%
420 FMASK1=0 : FMASK2=0 : FMASK3=0 : FMASK4=0
429 REM check each bit of N% and put quadruple-bit in the mask
        for that quarter if on.
430 FOR J%=0 TO 1
440 IF (N% AND 2^(J%+6)) THEN FMASK1=FMASK1 + &55*2^J%
450 IF (N% AND 2^(J%+4)) THEN FMASK2=FMASK2 + &55*2^J%
460 IF (N% AND 2^(J%+2)) THEN FMASK3=FMASK3 + &55*2^J%
470 IF (N% AND 2^J%) THEN FMASK4=FMASK4 + &55*2^J%
480 NEXT J%
490 BMASK1=FMASK1 EOR &FF : BMASK2=FMASK2 EOR &FF
500 BMASK3=FMASK3 EOR &FF : BMASK4=FMASK4 EOR &FF
509 REM mix the colours with masks to find four values and put each
        value eight bytes on i.e. next to the previous value.
510 I8%=I%+8 : I16%=I%+16 : I24%=I%+24
520 S?I%=(COLF AND FMASK1) OR (COLB AND BMASK1)
530 S?I8%=(COLF AND FMASK2) OR (COLB AND BMASK2)
540 S?I16%=(COLF AND FMASK3) OR (COLB AND BMASK3)
550 S?I24%=(COLF AND FMASK4) OR (COLB AND BMASK4)
560 NEXT I%
570 UNTIL BORED
```

*Exercise 5.2*

Write a program that does the inverse of this process and can recognise a character that is printed at block (0, 0) in any foreground and background colours, in modes 0, 1 or 2. This will mean calculating the eight pieces of data used to construct the character and comparing them with each set of eight in the character table until you find a match. Note that you will need to know the logical colour of the background, which will be equivalent to zero bits in our eight numbers, everything else must be foreground and 'ones'. Remember that when using the OSBYTE call with A% = &87 (see the user guide) it is essential to ensure that the background COLOUR is set to the appropriate value (as is done in the worm game in chapter 1).

**User-defined Characters: VDU 23**

This second type of character is treated in exactly the same way as the ordinary character set, but the table that holds the data for these characters is in RAM. When the machine is turned on, there is an area reserved for a table that defines the 32 characters with ASCII codes from 128 to 159. This table consists of the 256 bytes stored in memory from &C00 to &CFF. From OS 1.0 onwards the red user-definable function keys at the top of the keyboard (the *soft keys*) will produce some of these characters when used with the shift and/or control keys (see the user guide). The data in the table for these characters can be changed by the user, so that any required character can be typed into a BASIC PRINT text string directly from the keyboard. The VDU 23 command is used to redefine these keys, and is entered in the format

VDU 23, ASCII code, eight (8-bit) numbers

*Example 5.2*

The program in listing 5.3 allows you to redefine a character with ASCII code between 128 and 159, by typing all eight 8-bit binary numbers for a character. After redefining a character, the program also prints out the data in a hexadecimal form for inclusion as DATA statements in future programs (for example, listing 5.4). This information can be copied into a program by using the COPY key. The 'display' procedure may also be used to print out the data for a character in the ASCII range 128 to 159 in binary notation.

*Exercise 5.3*

Use listing 5.3 to generate a character that consists of a chequer-board pattern of pixels (for example, &85, &170, &85 etc.). Experiment with this program by using various background and foreground colours in order to make new colours (for example, red and yellow give orange).

*Exercise 5.4*

Use the procedures from listing 5.3 to make an elementary character editor. Move the text cursor around the 'display'ed data and recognise each binary digit, altering it where desired. When you wish to replace the character you will need a method of reconstructing a decimal or hexadecimal number from the binary strings for each line so that they can be stored in the memory.

*Example 5.3*

Listing 5.4, which contains DATA generated by listing 5.3, can be used to create 'thin' numbers for modes 1 and 2 and to store them as characters that are equivalent to the ASCII codes 128 to 137 and 144 to 146. Hence shift and the soft keys f0 to f9 give the 'thin' digits, and control with f0, f1 and f2 give 'thin' '+', '–' and '.'. It also contains a procedure to print a string of 'thin' digits on the screen. These characters will be particularly useful for labelling data diagrams

*Listing 5.3*

```
 1Ø MODE 4
 2Ø DIM A(7)
 3Ø REPEAT
 4Ø PRINT TAB(Ø,1);SPC(39);TAB(Ø,1);
 5Ø INPUT "Which ASCII code ",CHAR
 6Ø UNTIL CHAR>127 AND CHAR<16Ø
 7Ø PRINT "TYPE IN EIGHT, 8-BIT BINARY NUMBERS"
 8Ø PRINT '" --------"
 9Ø FOR I%=Ø TO 7
1ØØ REPEAT
11Ø PRINT TAB(Ø,I%+5);SPC(39);TAB(Ø,I%+5);
12Ø INPUTA$ : A=FNT(A$)
13Ø UNTIL A>=Ø AND A<=255
14Ø A(I%)=A
15Ø NEXT I%
16Ø VDU 23,CHAR
17Ø FOR I%=Ø TO 7
18Ø VDU A(I%)
19Ø NEXT I%
2ØØ PRINT ''"ASCII CODE ";CHAR;" NOW REDEFINED";
             '"TO REPRESENT ";CHR$(CHAR)
21Ø PRINT '"DATA ";
22Ø FOR I%=Ø TO 7
23Ø PRINT "&";~A(I%);",";
24Ø NEXT I%
249 REM 'delete' to erase last comma
25Ø VDU 127
26Ø PRINT
27Ø END

3ØØ REM base ten to binary conversion
31Ø DEF FNB(N)
32Ø LOCAL I%,B$
33Ø B$="":I%=N
34Ø REPEAT
35Ø IF I% DIV 2=I%/2 THEN B$="Ø"+B$ ELSE B$="1"+B$
36Ø I%=I% DIV 2 : UNTIL I%=Ø
37Ø =B$

4ØØ REM binary to base ten conversion
41Ø DEF FNT(B$)
42Ø LOCAL T,I%
43Ø T=Ø : I%=1 : REPEAT
44Ø T=T*2+VAL(MID$(B$,I%,1))
45Ø I%=I%+1 : UNTIL I%>LEN(B$)
46Ø =T

5ØØ REM display
51Ø DEF PROCdisplay(C)
519 REM print binary values defining a character
      (see also OSWORD call with A=&ØA)
52Ø IF C<128 OR C>159 THEN ENDPROC
53Ø D=(C-128)*8+&CØØ
54Ø FOR I%=Ø TO 7
55Ø K=D?I% : B$=FNB(K) : PRINT LEFT$("ØØØØØØØØ",8-LEN(B$));B$
56Ø NEXT I%
57Ø ENDPROC
```

in mode 1 and for printing the score in games in mode 2. Note how in this case the PRINT procedure starts at a text block position but subsequently places the characters by using the graphics cursor.

*Listing 5.4*

```
 10 MODE 1
 20 FOR I%=128 TO 137
 30 PROCread(I%)
 40 NEXT I%
 50 DATA &40,&A0,&A0,&A0,&A0,&A0,&40,0
 60 DATA &40,&C0,&40,&40,&40,&40,&E0,0
 70 DATA &40,&A0,&20,&40,&80,&80,&E0,0
 80 DATA &40,&A0,&20,&40,&20,&A0,&40,0
 90 DATA &20,&60,&A0,&A0,&E0,&20,&20,0
100 DATA &E0,&80,&C0,&20,&20,&A0,&40,0
110 DATA &40,&A0,&80,&C0,&A0,&A0,&40,0
120 DATA &E0,&20,&20,&40,&40,&80,&80,0
130 DATA &40,&A0,&A0,&40,&A0,&A0,&40,0
140 DATA &40,&A0,&A0,&60,&20,&A0,&40,0
150 FOR I%=144 TO 146
160 PROCread(I%)
170 NEXT I%
180 DATA &0,&40,&40,&E0,&40,&40,&0,&0
190 DATA &0,&0,&0,&E0,&0,&0,&0,&0
200 DATA &0,&0,&0,&40,&40,&0,&0,&0
209 REM test 'thin' with a string
210 PROCthin(1,10,10,"0.123+456-789")
220 END

230 REM read
240 DEF PROCread(I%)
249 REM redefine character I% using eight pieces of data
250 VDU 23,I%
260 FOR J%=1 TO 8
270 READ K : VDU K
280 NEXT J%
290 ENDPROC

300 REM thin
310 DEF PROCthin(M,X,Y,A$)
319 REM this only gives correct size for modes < 3
320 A%=2^(4+M)
329 REM use graphics cursor to place each character of string
330 VDU 5
340 MOVE X*A%,1023-Y*32
350 FOR I%=1 TO LEN(A$) : P$=MID$(A$,I%,1)
360 IF P$>="0" AND P$<="9" THEN VDU (80+ASC(P$)) : GOTO 380
369 REM deal with special symbols
370 IF P$="+" THEN VDU 144 ELSE IF P$="-" THEN VDU 145 ELSE VDU 146
380 MOVE (X+I%/2)*A%,1023-Y*32
390 NEXT I%
399 REM separate text and graphics
400 VDU 4
410 ENDPROC
```

*Example 5.4*
Defined characters can be directly incorporated into your programs to enhance the speed of display construction. The equivalent character could be constructed by a series of DRAW and PLOT commands but this would take longer in most cases. For instance we can build up tessellated patterns on the screen with characters in a very quick time compared to the length of time it would take to PLOT or DRAW the same pattern. Listing 5.5 shows how this can be done by using combinations of the user-defined characters with ASCII codes 128 to 131 that were constructed by using listing 5.3.

*Listing 5.5*

```
  9 REM tessellation pattern
 10 MODE 4
 20 CLS : INPUT "TWO ACTUAL COLOURS ",FC,BC : CLS
 30 GCOL 0,128 : GCOL 0,1 : MOVE 0,1023
 40 VDU 19,0,BC,0,0,0 : VDU 19,1,FC,0,0,0
 49 REM use graphics cursor as text cursor so that display
       doesn't scroll
 50 VDU 5
 60 A=128 : B=129 : C=130 : D=131
 70 FOR Y%=0 TO 31
 80 FOR X%=0 TO 39 STEP 4
 90 VDU A,B,C,D
100 NEXT X%
109 REM shift characters around
110 T=A : A=B : B=C : C=D : D=T
120 NEXT Y%
130 VDU 4
140 REPEAT UNTIL INKEY(-99)
```

*Exercise 5.5*
Experiment with various possible symmetries of characters and patterns for placement of characters on the screen (that is, the order in which groups of characters are drawn on the screen). Alter the program so that it tries all the possible combinations of foreground and background colours within two nested FOR. . .NEXT loops.

We have seen that the amount of work that goes into constructing even one character is enough to imply that the construction of a complete new set of characters would be a very arduous task. So we need a program that will simplify this task, and that will also allow us to alter characters that have already been created. The following program is such a character generation and editing program for ASCII codes from 32 to 255, and was designed for use in the development of graphical display programs.

*Listing 5.6*

```
 10 MODE 4
 19 REM ensure all blocks can be used
 20 *FX20,6
 30 DIM B(8),A(7),S(7,7),R(7,7)
 40 DIM M$(6)
 50 FOR I%=1 TO 6 : READ M$(I%) : NEXT I%
 60 DATA 1  ... DISPLAY CHARACTERS,2  ... DISPLAY ALL CHARACTERS
       ,3  ... EDITOR,4 ... SAVE CHARACTERS,5  ... LOAD CHARACTERS
       ,6  ... TEST PROGRAM
 70 FOR I%=1 TO 7 : READ A(I%)
 80 IF A(I%)<&C00 THEN A(I%)=A(I%)+PAGE-&600
 90 NEXT I%
100 DATA &300,&400,&500,&C00,&0,&100,&200
110 QUIT=FALSE
120 REPEAT : PROCmenu : UNTIL QUIT
130 PROCtestprog
140 END

200 REM menu
210 DEF PROCmenu : VDU 19,1,2,0,0,0
220 COLOUR 128 : CLS : COLOUR 1
229 REM display options and wait for selection
230 PRINT TAB(6,3);"*** CHARACTER GENERATOR ***"''
240 FOR I%=1 TO 6
250 PRINT SPC(6);M$(I%)''
260 NEXT I%
270 PRINT "Which option ? ";
280 REPEAT : A$=GET$ : UNTIL A$>"0" AND A$<"7"
290 VDU19,1,7,0,0,0
300 IF A$="1" THEN PROCdisplay
310 IF A$="2" THEN PROCdisall
320 IF A$="3" THEN PROCedit
330 IF A$="4" THEN PROCfile("SAVE")
340 IF A$="5" THEN PROCfile("LOAD")
350 IF A$="6" THEN QUIT=TRUE : ENDPROC
360 PRINT TAB(0,31);"PRESS SPACE TO RETURN TO MENU";
370 REPEAT UNTIL INKEY(-99)
380 ENDPROC

400 REM display OPTION 1
410 DEF PROCdisplay
419 REM display one block of 32 characters with their codes.
420 COLOUR 129 : CLS : COLOUR 0
430 PRINT TAB(0,1);"Which block ?";
440 REPEAT
450 B$=GET$ : B=VAL(B$)
460 UNTIL B<8 AND B>0
470 PRINT B : C=32*B
480 FOR I%=0 TO 31
490 PRINT TAB((I% MOD 2)*20,I% DIV 2+6);
499 REM remember 127 is 'delete'
500 PRINT I%+C;"= "; : IF I%<>127 THEN VDU I%+C
510 NEXT I%
520 ENDPROC

600 REM disall OPTION 2
610 DEF PROCdisall
620 COLOUR 129 : CLS : COLOUR 0
630 PRINT ''
```

```
639 REM show all characters except 'delete'
640 FOR I%=32 TO 255
650 IF I%<> 127 THEN VDU 32,I%
660 NEXT I%
670 ENDPROC

700 REM edit OPTION 3
710 DEF PROCedit
719 REM set cursor keys for use
720 *FX4,1
729 REM give submenu options and draw grid for editing
730 COLOUR 129 : CLS : COLOUR 0
740 PRINT '"     1) COLOUR 1    0) COLOUR 0"
750 PRINT "    <SPACE> TO COLOUR SQUARE"
760 PRINT "    CURSOR KEYS MOVE THE CROSS"
770 PRINT "    X)-AXIS      Y)-AXIS      R)OTATE"
780 PRINT "    U)NPACK      P)ACK        M)ERGE"
790 FOR I=0 TO 7 : FOR J=0 TO 7
    : PROCsquare(I,J,0) : NEXT J : NEXT I
800 LX=320 : RX=LX+640 : BY=128 : TY=BY+640
810 GCOL0,0 : MOVE LX,BY
    : DRAW LX,TY : DRAW RX,TY : DRAW RX,BY : DRAW LX,BY
820 I=0 : J=0 : C=0 : PROCmark(I,J)
829 REM remove cursor cross and scan keyboard for commands
830 REPEAT : PROCmark(I,J)
840 IF INKEY(-42) AND J>0 THEN J=J-1
850 IF INKEY(-58) AND J<7 THEN J=J+1
860 IF INKEY(-26) AND I>0 THEN I=I-1
870 IF INKEY(-122) AND I<7 THEN I=I+1
880 IF INKEY(-99) THEN PROCsquare(I,J,C)
889 REM replace cross and check for rest of commands
890 PROCmark(I,J)
900 A$=INKEY$(0)
910 IF A$="1" OR A$="0" THEN C=VAL(A$) ELSE 930
920 COLOUR 0 : PRINT TAB(0,0);"COLOUR = ";C;
    : COLOUR C:PRINT " ** " : COLOUR 0
930 IF A$="R" THEN PROCrotate
940 IF A$="X" THEN PROCx_axis
950 IF A$="Y" THEN PROCy_axis
959 REM all final three options use an ASCII value so input it
960 IF NOT (A$="U" OR A$="P" OR A$="M") THEN 1040
970 REPEAT
980 PRINT TAB(0,30);SPC(39);TAB(0,30);
990 INPUT "Which character ",CHAR
1000 UNTIL CHAR<256 AND CHAR>31
1010 IF A$="U" THEN PROCunpack : PROCr_to_s : PROCmark(I,J)
1020 IF A$="M" THEN PROCmerge : PROCmark(I,J)
1030 IF A$="P" THEN PROCpack
1040 UNTIL A$="P"
1049 REM return cursor keys to normal
1050 *FX4,0
1060 ENDPROC

1100 REM square
1110 DEF PROCsquare(X,Y,IN) : GCOL0,IN
1119 REM colour square in on grid
1120 LX=640+80*(X-4)+4 : RX=LX+72 : BY=Y*80+132 : TY=BY+72
1130 MOVE LX,BY : MOVE LX,TY : PLOT 85,RX,BY : PLOT 85,RX,TY
1139 REM plot point on small character
1140 S(X,Y)=IN : PLOT 69,1027+X*4,320+Y*4
1150 ENDPROC
```

```
12ØØ REM mark
121Ø DEF PROCmark(X,Y) : GCOL 3,7
1219 REM eor cross onto a square for use as cursor
122Ø LX=65Ø+8Ø*(X-4) : RX=LX+6Ø : BY=Y*8Ø+138 : TY=BY+6Ø
123Ø MOVE LX,BY : DRAW RX,TY : MOVE RX,BY : DRAW LX,TY
124Ø ENDPROC

13ØØ REM pack
131Ø DEF PROCpack
1319 REM redefine character using data direct from screen
132Ø VDU 23,CHAR
133Ø FOR I%=Ø TO 7
134Ø VDU (I%?&734Ø)
135Ø NEXT
136Ø ENDPROC

14ØØ REM unpack
141Ø DEF PROCunpack
1419 REM place character on screen and read data directly
        from its position.
142Ø COLOUR 128 : COLOUR 1 : PRINT TAB(32,21); : VDU CHAR
143Ø FOR I%=Ø TO 7 : B(I%)=I%?&734Ø : NEXT I%
1439 REM convert bytes in B() to bits in R(,)
144Ø FOR B=Ø TO 7
145Ø Y=7-(B MOD 8)
146Ø FOR X=Ø TO 7
147Ø IF B(B) AND 2^(7-X) THEN R(X,Y)=1 ELSE R(X,Y)=Ø
148Ø NEXT X : NEXT B
149Ø COLOUR 129 : COLOUR Ø
15ØØ ENDPROC

16ØØ REM rotate
161Ø DEF PROCrotate
1619 REM shift bits around into R
162Ø FOR I%=Ø TO 7
163Ø FOR J%=Ø TO 7
164Ø R(I%,J%)=S(J%,7-I%)
165Ø NEXT J% : NEXT I%
166Ø PROCr_to_s
167Ø ENDPROC

17ØØ REM r_to_s
171Ø DEF PROCr_to_s
1719 REM put bits from R into S and update screen display
172Ø FOR I%=Ø TO 7
173Ø FOR J%=Ø TO 7
174Ø S(I%,J%)=R(I%,J%)
175Ø PROCsquare(I%,J%,S(I%,J%))
176Ø NEXT J% : NEXT I%
177Ø ENDPROC

18ØØ REM y_axis
181Ø DEF PROCy_axis
1819 REM flip bits around into R
182Ø FOR I%=Ø TO 7
183Ø FOR J%=Ø TO 7
184Ø R(I%,J%)=S(7-I%,J%)
185Ø NEXT J% : NEXT I%
186Ø PROCr_to_s
187Ø ENDPROC
```

```
1900 REM x_axis
1910 DEF PROCx_axis
1919 REM flip bits around into R
1920 FOR I%=0 TO 7
1930 FOR J%=0 TO 7
1940 R(I%,J%)=S(I%,7-J%)
1950 NEXT J% : NEXT I%
1960 PROCr_to_s
1970 ENDPROC

2000 REM file OPTIONS 4 AND 5
2010 DEF PROCfile(B$)
2020 CLS : INPUT "WHAT FILE NAME",A$ : IF A$="" THEN ENDPROC
2030 PRINT "WHAT BLOCK ?";
2040 REPEAT : C$=GET$ : UNTIL C$>"0" AND C$<"8"
2050 C=VAL(C$) : VDU22,7
2059 REM change to mode 7 and print command into memory
2060 PRINT B$;" ";A$;" ";~A(C); : IF B$="SAVE" THEN PRINT " +100";
2069 REM put a carriage return into the memory to finish command
2070 PRINT : ?&7C28=&D
2079 REM set pointers to screen and use CLI to execute command
2080 X%=0 : Y%=&7C : CALL&FFF7
2089 REM switch back to mode 4
2090 VDU22,4
2100 ENDPROC

2200 REM merge
2210 DEF PROCmerge
2220 PROCunpack
2229 REM mix incoming character in R with existing one in S
2230 FOR I%=0 TO 7
2240 FOR J%=0 TO 7
2250 R(I%,J%)=S(I%,J%) OR R(I%,J%)
2260 NEXT J% : NEXT I%
2270 PROCr_to_s
2280 COLOUR 129 : COLOUR 0
2290 ENDPROC

2300 REM tessellation testprog
2310 DEF PROCtestprog
2320 CLS : INPUT "TWO ACTUAL COLOURS ",FC,BC : CLS
2330 GCOL 0,128 : GCOL 0,1 : MOVE 0,1023
2340 VDU 19,0,BC,0,0,0 : VDU 19,1,FC,0,0,0
2349 REM use graphics cursor as text cursor so that display
     doesn't scroll
2350 VDU 5
2360 A=128 : B=129 : C=130 : D=131
2370 FOR Y%=0 TO 31
2380 FOR X%=0 TO 39 STEP 4
2390 VDU A,B,C,D
2400 NEXT X%
2409 REM shift characters around
2410 T=A : A=B : B=C : C=D : D=T
2420 NEXT Y%
2430 VDU 4
2440 REPEAT UNTIL INKEY(-99)
2450 ENDPROC
```

The CHARACTER GENERATOR 1 (listing 5.6) procedures are intended to take all the hard work out of preparing and using defined characters: they allow you to edit and to manipulate characters, to save and to reload defined characters, and to use them with your own programs. The characters are split into seven groups each of 32 characters, that is codes 32 to 63, 64 to 95 etc. (see the user guide for a discussion of OSHWM, and *FX20, 1: although with some systems it is necessary to use *FX20, 6(!)). Because so much space is needed for the characters it is necessary to move the BASIC programs along the store. You must set the PAGE value to &600 greater than normal; that is, for an OS 0.1 type PAGE = &1400, and for OS 1.0 and above (from now on referred to as OS ⩾ 1.0) PAGE = &1F00.

The program offers a choice of six options.

(1) The first option is DISPLAY CHARACTERS. On selecting this option you will be asked which of the seven blocks of 32 consecutive characters you wish to view. The screen will then display the 32 ASCII codes followed by the characters currently defined for those codes in black on a white background.
(2) The second option is DISPLAY ALL CHARACTERS. On selecting this option the screen will display all the characters for ASCII codes from 32 to 255 in black on a white background.
(3) The third option is the editor, which is the most complicated option and has a large set of commands that are accessed by typing a single key.

In edit mode a character will be displayed as black blocks in an 8 by 8 grid, with a cross (or edit cursor) initially placed in the bottom left-hand corner. The cursor is controlled by the standard cursor keys either singly or in pairs.

Pressing the space bar will change a square in the character grid to the currently selected colour (1 or 0). White is equivalent to a binary one and black is zero. The current colour is displayed in the top left-hand corner of the screen and may be altered at any time by pressing either 1 or 0.

The next two commands are UNPACK and PACK, which are activated by typing their initial letters. UNPACK takes the piece of data for a character from the memory and converts it into separate binary digits for display in the grid as well as PRINTing it at normal size on the screen alongside the grid. Pack takes the piece of data from the grid and uses it to redefine the character. By plotting the character at normal size during the editing, we are in fact creating the eight bytes of data in the screen memory and so it is simple to read the piece of data from the screen and place it directly into the character table. Should we use this program with an optional extra processor (see the user guide) we would have to replace the PACK procedure with one that calculated the data from the S array by the type of logical functions given in listing 5.4.

The next three commands all specify transformations similar to those that were used to perform on two-dimensional objects in chapter 4. ROTATE turns the character through 90 degrees anticlockwise about its centre. X-AXIS reflects the character about the horizontal axis and Y-AXIS reflects the character about the vertical. These commands can be used to create character sets for any orientation.

Finally we have MERGE. This allows any character to be merged into the grid on top of what is already being edited. This is very useful for creating foreign language sets, for example, to place a slash through an O in the Scandinavian languages, or to add accents to letters in French etc.

(4) and (5) The fourth option allows characters to be SAVEd in blocks of 32 characters, either on disk or on tape and the fifth option allows them to be reLOADed. For both options we must reply to the question 'WHICH SET' with a number between 1 and 7, in which case that particular block is SAVEd or reLOADed.

To allow other programs to load and to use alternate sets of characters created in this way, then the 'file' procedure must be included in the new program.

(6) The sixth option simply calls up procedure 'testprog' which can either contain a short test program or simply end the procedure.

In order to familiarise yourself with the 'CHARACTER GENERATOR 1' carry out the following instructions. Create a character like a spidery ink-blot pattern and SAVE it as ASCII code 128. Unpack this character. Rotate and SAVE it as ASCII code 129. Edit 129, use X-AXIS reflection and SAVE it as code 130. Edit 130, use Y-AXIS reflection, and SAVE it as 131. Now use option (6) to run the 'testprog' procedure which contains a tessellation program from listing 5.5, and see what pattern emerges.

*Exercise 5.6*

Write a routine that affects a whole block of characters one after another and uses some of the editor routines from the 'CHARACTER GENERATOR 1' to perform transformations on each character. Figure 5.2 shows a listing that was produced with characters that have been ROTATED.

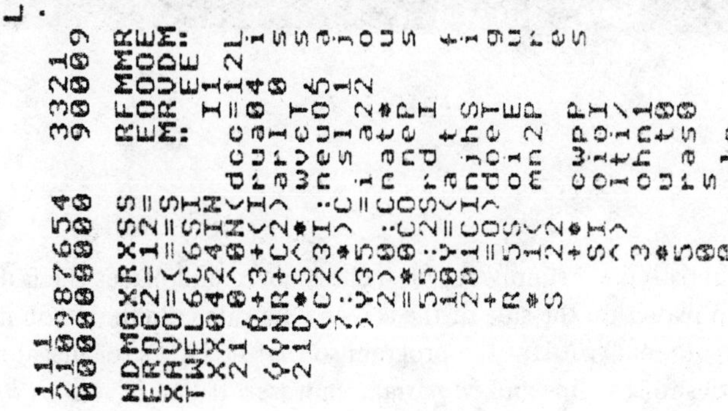

*Figure 5.2*

*Example 5.5*
We now give an example of a complete program (listing 5.7) which uses the characters developed with 'CHARACTER GENERATOR 1'. The following program (loaded at &1F00 for OS ⩾ 1.0 and &1400 for OS 0.1) simulates a chess board. A picture of a typical display is shown in figure 5.3. Each chess piece is constructed from 9 characters and placed 3 by 3 on the screen. The 56 characters required for the display were created as ASCII codes 160 to 215, subsequently stored as two blocks in locations starting at &1900 and &1A00 (disc) or &E00 and &F00 (tape), and placed as files CHESSP1 and CHESSP2 on backing store. You may have to strip the REMarks from the program in order to have enough store to run it.

*Figure 5.3*

*Exercise 5.7*
The program in listing 5.7 simply acts as a chess board and places the last 20 moves for each player on the side of the screen: the side columns scroll if more than 20 moves are made. Adapt the program so that it checks for illegal moves, and add facilities for castling and *en passant* captures. If you have a *lot of time!!* to spare then add routines to make the computer play against you (see Liffick, 1979).

*Listing 5.7*

```
  9 REM data for chesspieces
 1Ø *LOAD CHESSP1 19ØØ
 2Ø *LOAD CHESSP2 1AØØ
 3Ø MODE 1 : VDU23,1,Ø;Ø;Ø;Ø;
 4Ø VDU19,2,4,Ø,Ø,Ø : *FX2Ø,6
 5Ø DIMB(8,8),C(8,8),N$(1,1ØØ)
 6Ø PRINT TAB(Ø,2);"WHITE";SPC(3Ø);"BLACK"
 69 REM underline WHITE and BLACK with red blocks
 7Ø GCOL Ø,1
 8Ø MOVE Ø,911 : MOVEØ,919
 9Ø PLOT 85,16Ø,911 : PLOT 85,16Ø,919
1ØØ MOVE 1279,911 : MOVE 1279,919
11Ø PLOT 85,1119,911 : PLOT 85,1119,919
119 REM draw tablecloth under board
12Ø GCOLØ,3
13Ø MOVE 176,8Ø : MOVE 11Ø3,8Ø
14Ø PLOT 85,176,1ØØ7 : PLOT 85,11Ø3,1ØØ7
15Ø COLOUR 131 : COLOUR Ø
16Ø FOR I%=1 TO 8
169 REM print letters along bottom and numbers up the side
17Ø PRINT TAB(I%*3+6,28);CHR$(64+I%)
18Ø PRINT TAB(33,(8-I%)*3+4);I%
189 REM put pawns on row 2 and make them white
19Ø B(I%,2)=6 : C(I%,2)=3
199 REM put pawns on row 7
2ØØ B(I%,7)=6
2Ø9 REM read order of pieces for back rows
21Ø READ A
219 REM white back row
22Ø B(I%,1)=A : C(I%,1)=3
229 REM black back row
23Ø B(I%,8)=A
24Ø NEXT I%
249 REM draw each square including any piece on the square
25Ø FOR I%=1 TO 8
26Ø FOR J%=1 TO 8
27Ø PROCsquare(I%,J%,1)
28Ø NEXT J%
29Ø NEXT I%
299 REM input players moves in turn
3ØØ FOR N%=1 TO 1ØØ
31Ø PROCinput("WHITE") : N$(Ø,N%)=N$ : N$(1,N%)="-----"
32Ø PROClist
33Ø PROCinput("BLACK") : N$(1,N%)=N$
34Ø PROClist
35Ø NEXT N%
36Ø DATA 1,2,3,4,5,3,2,1
37Ø END

4ØØ REM flash
4Ø9 REM IN : coordinates of start and end of move
        OUT: A$="Y" if move accepted
41Ø DEF PROCflash(X1,Y1,X2,Y2)
42Ø COLOUR 128 : COLOUR 3
429 REM give player a chance to check input and/or reconsider move
43Ø PRINT TAB(Ø,3Ø);SPC(39);TAB(1Ø,3Ø);"ACCEPT (Y,N) ? "
439 REM flash two squares involved while waiting for reply
44Ø REPEAT
45Ø PROCsquare(X1,Y1,Ø) : PROCsquare(X2,Y2,Ø)
```

```
460 A$=INKEY$(20) : IF A$<>"" THEN 490
470 PROCsquare(X1,Y1,1) : PROCsquare(X2,Y2,1)
480 A$=INKEY$(20)
490 UNTIL A$<>""
500 IF A$<> "Y" THEN 530
509 REM if move is accepted then put piece in new position and
        erase at old position
510 B(X2,Y2)=B(X1,Y1) : C(X2,Y2)=C(X1,Y1)
520 B(X1,Y1)=0 : C(X1,Y1)=0
530 PROCsquare(X1,Y1,1) : PROCsquare(X2,Y2,1)
540 ENDPROC

600 REM square
609 REM X,Y coordinates of square M<>1 for inverse display
610 DEF PROCsquare(X,Y,M)
620 LOCAL I%,J%
630 P=B(X,Y) : C=C(X,Y)
640 PRINT TAB(X*3+5,(8-Y)*3+3);
650 IF M=1 THEN COLOUR 129+((X+Y) MOD 2) ELSE COLOUR 128+C
660 IF M=1 THEN COLOUR C ELSE COLOUR 1+((X+Y) MOD 2)
669 REM if square has no piece on it then output blanks
670 IF P=0 THEN VDU 32,32,32,10,8,8,8,32,32,32,10,8,8,8,32,32,32
    : GOTO 710
680 J%=&A0+9*(P-1)
689 REM for each row of square output the 3 characters of piece
        then go down and back three spaces
690 FOR I%=1 TO 3 : VDU J%,J%+1,J%+2,10,8,8,8
700 J%=J%+3 : NEXT I%
710 ENDPROC

800 REM input
810 DEF PROCinput(B$)
819 REM prompts one of players to enter move returns N$ with
        accepted move
820 REPEAT
830 COLOUR 128 : COLOUR 3
840 PRINT TAB(0,30);SPC(39);TAB(0,30);B$;"'S MOVE NO. ";N%;" : ";
850 OK=TRUE : INPUT N$
859 REM check input is valid
860 IF LEN(N$)<>5 THEN OK=FALSE
870 F$=LEFT$(N$,1)
    : IF F$<"A" OR F$>"H" THEN OK=FALSE ELSE X1=ASC(F$)-64
880 F$=MID$(N$,2,1)
    : IF F$<"1" OR F$>"8" THEN OK=FALSE ELSE Y1=VAL(F$)
890 F$=MID$(N$,4,1)
    : IF F$<"A" OR F$>"H" THEN OK=FALSE ELSE X2=ASC(F$)-64
900 F$=MID$(N$,5,1)
    : IF F$<"1" OR F$>"8" THEN OK=FALSE ELSE Y2=VAL(F$)
910 UNTIL OK
920 N$=LEFT$(N$,2)+"-"+RIGHT$(N$,2)
929 REM offer move for acceptance
930 PROCflash(X1,Y1,X2,Y2)
940 IF A$="Y" THEN ENDPROC ELSE 820

1000 REM list
1010 DEF PROClist
1020 COLOUR 128 : COLOUR 3
1029 REM show last 21 moves made
1030 IF N%<20 THEN J%=0 ELSE J%=N%-20
1040 FOR I%=1 TO 21
1050 PRINT TAB(0,I%+5);N$(0,I%+J%);TAB(35,I%+5);N$(1,I%+J%);
1060 NEXT I%
1070 ENDPROC
```

We have seen how characters created in this way can be printed in different colours, however we can still have only two colours in any one character-sized area. There are obvious advantages if we had the ability to print multi-coloured characters quickly at any position on the screen. To do this we must have a small machine-code routine which takes the data that relate to such a 'character' (with mult-colour information already encoded, rather than the two-colour format) and transfers them to the screen. We therefore need to understand the way in which the memory positions of the screen are arranged. As we saw in chapter 1, when a mode is first selected the top left-hand corner of the screen is represented by the first byte of the screen memory. The next seven bytes represent the lines vertically below this initial byte. This makes it very easy to place the data for a two-colour character into the correct display locations. The byte at location HIMEM + 8 is horizontally adjacent to the first byte (that is, HIMEM) and is then underscored by the next seven bytes and so on along the row of characters. When we get to the end of the row the next location is the top of the first character on the second line. The complete screen memory is organised in rows in this way, from top (row 0) to bottom (row 31), and from left to right within each row. In a two-colour mode this means that the display holds the information for the first character followed by the second set of data etc., through all the characters displayed in order. Of course in a four-colour mode two columns of bytes will be required to hold the data for one character (left half and right half) and in the sixteen-colour mode we need four columns (far left, middle left, middle right and far right), but this is still fairly simple to calculate since the next column of bytes is always the next eight bytes in the memory.

Simple! It would be if the screen stayed still; furthermore what we have said above is not strictly true. When the screen scrolls up (or down) by one row some odd things happen. The BBC micro uses *hardware scrolling*. This means that the computer can decide which of the 32 (or so) rows in the memory corresponds to the top of the screen (it need not be row 0), and the rest follow in order down the screen with line zero following line thirty-one. When the display scrolls up (or down) it is a simple matter of redefining which row in the memory is the top line of the screen, and the line that disappears from the top (or bottom) is blanked out by the operating system and reallocated to the bottom (or top). This is much faster than *software scrolling*, where rows on the screen have a fixed correspondence with areas of memory, and a program is needed to move all the data from row 1 to row 0, row 2 to row 1 etc. until all the data from the bottom line has been copied to the line above so that the bottom line is ready for use again.

We shall avoid scrolling the screen since this will only confuse our calculations of positions (unless we carefully count the number of scrolling movements and allow for them), and instead make a new print routine which we shall call 'prynt'. This routine (listing 5.8) is loaded with PAGE = &3000 to keep it out of harm's way, and the machine code it generates is placed at the locations that follow &2300 and stored in backing store as file PRYNT. If we now 'prynt' off the bottom of the screen the information will *wrap around* and reappear at the top. The assembly language program (listing 5.7) uses the memory locations from &2400 onwards to store tables of multi-colour character definitions. The characters will have code numbers between 32 and 127 and may be accessed in a program by referring to the standard character with the same ASCII code. The program is designed to print characters in any of modes 0, 1 or 2, so it must know how many bytes make up the character. This is passed into the routine by the variable A% (which is transferred to the A-register) which should be set to either 8, 16 or 32 for the respective modes. If you use the wrong value of A% for a given mode you can produce half-width or double-width characters printing. This can be very useful if you want to print half-width 'thin' numbers in mode 2 or double-width jet-plane characters for games in mode 1. The 'prynt' position for the character is calculated from the values of X% and Y%. These are equivalent to the TAB(X, Y) values of the PRINT command. In order to 'prynt' a string of such characters we generate a string (B$ say) of normal ASCII characters with codes corresponding to the characters to be drawn, and then call the routine:

CALLprynt, B$

Note that the values of X% and Y% will not change unless they are reset in subsequent 'prynt's.

*Listing 5.8*

```
 10 REM assembly code for prynt
        assign names to locations for use by the routine
 19 REM table of screen line starts
 20 HI=&23E0
 29 REM data pointer for characters
 30 DLO=&80 : DHI=&81
 39 REM screen pointer for position
 40 SLO=&82 : SHI=&83
 49 REM pointer to string info
 50 PLO=&84 : PHI=&85
 59 REM address of string
 60 ALO=&86 : AHI=&87
 69 REM no. of chars. : temp y store
 70 NUM=&88 : TY=&89
 79 REM print position for string
 80 TABX=&8A : TABY=&8B
 89 REM size of character in bytes
 90 SIZE=&8C
 99 REM data table address hi byte
100 TABLE=&8D
109 REM length of line in chars.
110 WIDE=&8E
120 VDU 14
130 FOR O%=0 TO 3 STEP 3
140 P%=&2300
150 [
160 OPT O%    ;Set char size
```

```
170 STA SIZE  ;from A% and
180 STX TABX  ;print position
190 STY TABY  ;from X% and Y%
200 LDA &600  ;Check only one
210 CMP #1    ;parameter in
220 BNE BAD   ;call or error.
230 LDA &603  ;Check string
240 CMP #129  ;variable
250 BNE BAD   ;or error.
260 LDA &601  ;Copy pointer
270 STA PLO   ;to variable
280 LDA &602  ;into zero page
290 STA PHI   ;pointer.
300 LDY #0    ;Initialise Y
310 STY TY    ;for indirects.
320 LDA (PLO),Y
330 STA ALO   ;Copy address
340 INY       ;of string from
350 LDA (PLO),Y
360 STA AHI   ;variable data.
370 INY       ;Move pointer
380 INY       ;to get length
390 LDA (PLO),Y
400 STA NUM   ;of string.
410 JSR START ;Initialise mode
420 .OUT
430 LDY TY    ;output loop
440 LDA (ALO),Y
450 INY       ;move pointer
460 STY TY    ;store counter
470 JSR CHAR  ;prynt character
480 DEC NUM   ;last character?
490 BNE OUT   ;no, do next one
500 RTS       ;end of prynt.
510 .BAD
520 BRK       ;Error section
530 ]
540 ?P%=99:$(P%+1)="Misprynt":P%=P%+10
550 [OPT O%
560 BRK       ;end of error.
570 .CHAR
580 LDX #0    ;prynt one char.
590 STX SHI   ;use SHI and SLO
600 STA SLO   ;multiply ascii
610 JSR MULT  ;to get offset
620 LDA SHI   ;move result
630 CLC       ;to data pointer
640 ADC TABLE ;adding in
650 STA DHI   ;start of table
660 LDA SLO   ;to complete
670 STA DLO   ;data address
680 LDA TABX  ;multiply x
690 STX SHI   ;to get offset
700 STA SLO   ;from start of
710 JSR MULT  ;line.
720 LDX TABY  ;add lo-byte
730 TXA       ;for screen line
740 ROR A     ;odd lines have
750 BCC EVEN  ;&80 extra for
760 LDA SLO   ;their address
770 CLC       ;mod 256.
780 ADC #&80  ;even line is
```

```
 790 STA SLO   ;zero lo-byte
 800 .EVEN
 810 LDA HI,X  ;Get hi-byte
 820 ADC SHI   ;of screen line
 830 STA SHI   ;= screen point
 840 LDX SIZE  ;Move X bytes
 850 LDY #0    ;of data to
 860 .TRANS
 870 LDA (DLO),Y
 880 STA (SLO),Y
 890 INY       ;screen in
 900 DEX       ;loop.
 910 BNE TRANS ;When done add
 920 INC TABX  ;one to x pos.
 930 LDA TABX  ;and check for
 940 CMP WIDE  ;end of line
 950 BCC OK    ;If gone over
 960 STX TABX  ;zero x pos.
 970 INC TABY  ;and add to
 980 LDA TABY  ;y pos. If y
 990 CMP #32   ;is off bottom
1000 BCC OK    ;then put it
1010 STX TABY  ;back to top.
1020 .OK
1030 RTS       ;end of char.
1040 .MULT
1050 LDA SIZE  ;Multiply by
1060 CMP #8    ;appropriate
1070 BEQ M8    ;amount for
1080 CMP #16   ;size of data
1090 BEQ M16   ;block in use
1100 ASL SLO   ;Multiply
1110 ROL SHI   ;shi,slo by 2
1120 .M16
1130 ASL SLO   ;times 2 again
1140 ROL SHI
1150 .M8
1160 ASL SLO   ;times 2
1170 ROL SHI   ;three more
1180 ASL SLO   ;times
1190 ROL SHI
1200 ASL SLO
1210 ROL SHI
1220 RTS       ;end of mult.
1230 .START
1240 LDA SIZE  ;get values of
1250 LDX #&2C  ;table hi-byte
1260 LDY #80   ;line length
1270 CMP #8    ;which are
1280 BEQ NSTAR ;appropriate
1290 LDX #&28  ;to size of
1300 LDY #40   ;character
1310 CMP #16   ;being used
1320 BEQ NSTAR ;and store
1330 LDX #&20  ;for future
1340 LDY #20   ;reference
1350 .NSTAR
1360 STX TABLE ;table hi-byte
1370 STY WIDE  ;width of line
1380 RTS       ;end of start.
1390 ]
1400 NEXT O%
```

```
1409 REM construct table of hi-bytes for screen line addresses
1410 M%=&3000
1420 FOR I%=0 TO 31
1430 M=M%+640*I%
1440 HI?I%=M DIV 256
1450 NEXT I%
1459 REM save code after assembly
1460 *SAVE PRYNT 2300 +100
```

We now give 'CHARACTER GENERATOR 2' (listing 5.9), which is an elementary character editor that uses routine 'prynt' from file PRYNT. It has been deliberately kept short so that it can operate normally on all operating systems, however its size is such that it has to be loaded after the PAGE has been reset to &1100. The selection of a mode automatically sets the screen to display a grid of the correct relative dimensions for that mode, and gives you options equivalent to those of 'CHARACTER GENERATOR 1'. The available commands, which are called by typing their initial letter, are detailed below.

Pack and Unpack: as before these will display or store a character.
Save and Load: these are the same as options (4) and (5) above, but are now used to save or load the complete character data area (&2400 to &2FFF).

The choice of colours is made by typing the single hexadecimal digit of the required logical colour (for example, press A for colour 10). We are naturally limited to the number of logical colours that are available in any one mode, however there is nothing to stop us reassigning the logical–actual colour relationships within a program that uses these characters.

As before the cursor keys are used to move around the grid and the space bar is used to colour in squares.

From the assembler listing 5.8 we can see that the table of characters apparently starts from either &2000 (for the 32-byte long characters), &2800 (for the 16-byte characters) or &2C00 (for the 8-byte characters). In fact these are the positions where the data for the character with code 0 would have been found, although the real table does not start until the data for the character that is coded 32 is reached. In this way it is not necessary to subtract 32 from the ASCII-equivalent code for each character in order to find its position in the table.

*Example 5.6*

Listing 5.10 will allow you to type in redefined characters directly from the keyboard (strictly speaking you type the ASCII-equivalent characters) and 'prynt' them on the screen. First you need to create some characters in order to use this program. The two parts of figure 5.4 (a and b) are 'painting-by-numbers' charts (in hexadecimal) for two characters in mode 2. Use 'CHARACTER GENERATOR 2' to create the equivalent multi-coloured characters. Save

*Listing 5.9*

```
 10 DIM B(32),T(2),S(7,7),R(7,7) : T(0)=&2C00 : T(1)=&2800
                                  : T(2)=&2000
 20 DIM H(23) : FOR I=0 TO 23 : READ H(I) : NEXT I
 30 DATA 0,1,4,5,16,17,20,21,64,65,68,69,80,81,84,85
        ,&88,&44,&22,&11,0,1,16,17
 40 INPUT "MODE ",M : MODE M
 50 A%=2^(M+3) : B%=2^(2^M) : D%=2^(M+1) : M%=2^(3-M)
 60 SX=20*D%
 70 COLOUR 135 : CLS
 80 FOR I=0 TO 7 : FOR J=0 TO 7
 90 PROCsquare(I,J,0)
100 NEXT J : NEXT I
110 LX=640-4*SX-D% : RX=LX+SX*8 : BY=196 : TY=838
120 GCOL 0,0 : MOVE LX,BY : DRAW LX,TY : DRAW RX,TY
    : DRAW RX,BY : DRAW LX,BY
130 I=0 : J=0 : C=0 : PROCmark(I,J)
140 *FX4,1
150 REPEAT : PROCmark(I,J)
160 IF INKEY(-42) AND J>0 THEN J=J-1
170 IF INKEY(-58) AND J<7 THEN J=J+1
180 IF INKEY(-26) AND I>0 THEN I=I-1
190 IF INKEY(-122) AND I<7 THEN I=I+1
200 IF INKEY(-99) THEN PROCsquare(I,J,C)
210 PROCmark(I,J)
220 COLOUR 0
230 A$=INKEY$(0) : IF A$="" THEN 350
240 IF VAL(A$)=0 AND A$<>"0" AND (A$<"A" OR A$>"F") THEN 270
250 C=EVAL("&"+A$)
260 PRINT TAB(0,0);"COLOUR ";~C; : COLOUR C : PRINT " **"
270 IF A$="S" THEN PROCfile("SAVE")
280 IF A$="L" THEN PROCfile("LOAD")
290 IF A$<>"P" AND A$<>"U" THEN 350
300 REPEAT : PRINT TAB(0,29);SPC(39);TAB(0,29);
310 INPUT"Which character ",CHAR
320 UNTIL CHAR>31 AND CHAR <127
330 IF A$="U" THEN PROCunpack : PROCmark(I,J)
340 IF A$="P" THEN PROCpack
350 UNTIL A$="Q"
360 *FX4,0
370 END

400 REM square
410 DEF PROCsquare(X,Y,IN) : GCOL 0,IN
420 LX=640+SX*(X-4) : RX=LX+SX-D%*2 : BY=Y*80+200 : TY=BY+72
430 MOVE LX,BY : MOVE LX,TY : PLOT 85,RX,BY : PLOT 85,RX,TY
440 S(X,Y)=IN : PLOT 69,1031+D%*X,960+4*Y
450 ENDPROC

500 REM mark
510 DEF PROCmark(X,Y) : GCOL 3,7
520 LX=650+SX*(X-4) : RX=LX+SX-30 : BY=Y*80+210 : TY=BY+52
530 MOVE LX,BY : DRAW RX,TY : MOVE RX,BY : DRAW LX,TY
540 ENDPROC

600 REM pack
610 DEF PROCpack
620 FOR X=0 TO 7 : FOR Y=0 TO 7
630 B=8*(X DIV M%)+7-Y
640 ON M+1 GOTO 650,660,690
```

```
650 N%=2^(7-X) : B(B)=B(B) AND (255 EOR N%) OR N%*S(X,Y) : GOTO 700
660 HI=X MOD 4 : B(B)=B(B) AND (255 EOR H(HI+16))
670 B(B)=B(B) OR H(S(X,Y)+20)*2^(3-HI)
680 GOTO 700
690 HI=2-(X MOD 2) : B(B)=B(B) AND (&AA/HI) OR (H(S(X,Y))*HI)
700 NEXT Y : NEXT X
710 MEM=T(M)+CHAR*A%
720 FOR I%=0 TO A%-1 : MEM?I%=B(I%) : NEXT I%
730 ENDPROC

800 REM unpack
810 DEF PROCunpack
820 MEM=T(M)+CHAR*A%
830 FOR I%=0 TO A%-1 : B(I%)=MEM?I% : NEXT I%
840 FOR B=0 TO A%-1
850 Y=7-(B MOD 8)
860 ON M+1 GOTO 870,890,920
870 FOR X=0 TO 7 : IF B(B) AND 2^(7-X) THEN S(X,Y)=1 ELSE S(X,Y)=0
880 NEXT X : GOTO 950
890 FOR I%=0 TO 3 : X=I%+4*(B DIV 8)
    : HI=(B(B) AND H(16+I%))/2^(3-I%)
900 S(X,Y)=(HI AND &F0)/8+(HI AND &F)
910 NEXT I% : GOTO 950
920 FOR I%=1 TO 2 : X=2-I%+2*(B DIV 8) : HI=(B(B) AND (&55*I%))/I%
930 J%=-1 : REPEAT : J%=J%+1 : UNTIL H(J%)=HI
940 S(X,Y)=J% : NEXT I%
950 NEXT B
960 FOR I%=0 TO 7
970 FOR J%=0 TO 7
980 PROCsquare(I%,J%,S(I%,J%))
990 NEXT J% : NEXT I%
1000 ENDPROC

1100 REM file
1110 DEF PROCfile(B$)
1120 PRINT TAB(0,29);
1130 INPUT "WHAT FILE NAME",A$ : IF A$="" THEN ENDPROC
1140 A$=B$+" "+A$+" 2400" : IF B$="SAVE"THEN A$=A$+" 3000"
1150 $&3000=A$ : X%=0 : Y%=&30 : CALL&FFF7
1160 ENDPROC
```

these (and any other characters) on tape or disk, and then use the program from listing 5.9 to reload the file and display the characters on the screen. If you are feeling fit and healthy you can fill the screen with the callisthenic character from figure 5.4a and then join in.

You will find that this type of character is used in the video game in chapter 15.

| F | 0 | 0 | 7 | 7 | 0 | 0 | F |
|---|---|---|---|---|---|---|---|
| 0 | F | 0 | 7 | 7 | 0 | F | 0 |
| 8 | 8 | 7 | 7 | 7 | 7 | 8 | 8 |
| 0 | 0 | 7 | 7 | 7 | 7 | 0 | 0 |
| 0 | 0 | 7 | 7 | 7 | 7 | 0 | 0 |
| 0 | 0 | 7 | 0 | 0 | 7 | 0 | 0 |
| 0 | F | 8 | 0 | 0 | 8 | F | 0 |
| F | 0 | 8 | 0 | 0 | 8 | 0 | F |

(a)

| 0 | 0 | 0 | 0 | 0 | 0 | 0 | 0 |
|---|---|---|---|---|---|---|---|
| 0 | 0 | 6 | 6 | 6 | 6 | 0 | 0 |
| 0 | 6 | 8 | F | 8 | F | 6 | 0 |
| 6 | 6 | 6 | 6 | 6 | 6 | 6 | 6 |
| 6 | 6 | 6 | 9 | E | 6 | 6 | 6 |
| 6 | 6 | 6 | 6 | 6 | 6 | 6 | 6 |
| 6 | 6 | 6 | 6 | 6 | 6 | 6 | 6 |
| 6 | 0 | 6 | 0 | 6 | 0 | 6 | 0 |

(b)

*Figure 5.4*

*Listing 5.10*

```
   9 REM program to test PRYNT routine
  1Ø *LOAD PRYNT
  2Ø INPUT"MODE",M : MODE M : A%=2^(3+M)
  3Ø WIDE=8Ø/2^M : PRYNT=&23ØØ : HIMEM=&23ØØ
  39 REM load in a set of characters
  4Ø PROCfile("LOAD")  : X%=Ø : Y%=Ø
  49 REM PRYNT any characters typed and alter prynt position
  5Ø REPEAT : A$=GET$
  6Ø CALL PRYNT,A$
  7Ø X%=X%+1 : IF X%=WIDE THEN Y%=(Y%+1) MOD 32 : X%=Ø
  8Ø UNTIL FALSE

11ØØ REM file
111Ø DEF PROCfile(B$)
112Ø PRINT TAB(Ø,29);
113Ø INPUT "WHAT FILE NAME",A$:IFA$=""THEN ENDPROC
114Ø A$=B$+" "+A$+" 24ØØ" : IF B$="SAVE"THEN A$=A$+" 3ØØØ"
115Ø $&3ØØØ=A$ : X%=Ø : Y%=&3Ø : CALL&FFF7
116Ø ENDPROC
```

In the next chapter we shall consider how character graphics and our knowledge of two-dimensional geometry can be combined to form data displays for use in the office or the laboratory.

---

**Complete Programs**

I Listing 5.1. Data required: any character. Try #.

II Listing 5.2. Data required: a data mode (try 1), a character (#) and background and foreground colours (try 1 and 2).

III Listing 5.3. Data required: an ASCII code (try 128) and eight 8-bit binary numbers (try 10101010, 01010101, 10101010, 01010101, 10101010, 01010101, 10101010 and 01010101).

IV Listing 5.4. No data required.

V Listing 5.5. Use listing 5.3 to create characters with ASCII codes 128, 129, 130 and 131 before running the program. It requires actual background and foreground colours (try 1 and 2).

VI Listing 5.6 and PAGE set to &1400 for OS 0.1 and &1F00 for OS $\geqslant$ 1.0. Use option (3) of the CHARACTER GENERATOR 1 to create characters 128, 129, 130 and 131 and run option (6) (listing 5.5). Type 1 (to specify that you wish to draw in white) and move the cross around the screen with the cursor keys: the space bar will colour in a pixel (type 0 to plot pixels in black). Pack the characters in codes 128 etc.

VII Listing 5.7 loaded at PAGE = &1400 (OS 0.1) or &1F00 (OS $\geqslant$ 1.0). You may have to strip it of REMarks. Characters must be created in blocks CHESSP1 and CHESSP2 on backing store. The chess program needs each move of the game to be specified (such as E2 to E4) and the question Accept? to be answered as Yes or No.

VIII Listing 5.8 and 5.9. Run listing 5.8 with PAGE = &3000, which saves a file PRYNT for future use. Listing 5.9, PAGE = &1100, calls for a mode (try 2); then move the cross about the screen with the cursor keys, add colours with the space bar, and change colour by typing a hexadecimal digit (0 to F). Pack the new characters into locations equivalent to the ASCII codes 32 to 126. When you have generated the required symbols Save a file called TESTC. Try placing new characters in locations equivalent to ASCII 32 (normally a space), 33 (!), 34 (") and 35 (#).

IX Listing 5.10 with PAGE = &1100. This needs to load PRYNT. Then type on the keyboard !, # etc. and watch the equivalent character being drawn.

# 6 Diagrams and Data Graphs

More information is available to more people than ever before. Businessmen are being overwhelmed by massive documents that contain reams of statistics on every subject from capital expenditure to market research. Worst of all, computers are pouring out printouts of dreary data that cover every topic from Astrology to Zoology. Obviously something must be done! Computers have helped to create the problem and they can also help to solve it. The data must be presented in a more digestible manner: as pie-charts, histograms, scientific graphs or just plain diagrams. With the advent of desktop computers the increasing sales of programs that produce these displays has made this one of the major growth areas in computer graphics. In this chapter we shall see how such diagrams can be constructed with ease, given just a few tools to aid our draughtsmanship.

There are so many different types of diagrams that it is impossible to cover every possibility. We shall concentrate on the drawing of histograms, pie-charts and data graphs as well as giving a simple method for labelling and adjusting general types of diagram. Hence we give four major listings, which contain interactive programs for producing these diagrams, as examples of how to approach the general problem of data diagram construction. Naturally each individual program will require vastly differing data, although they will have some common input, display menus and prompts. Furthermore during the execution of a program the data being read may depend on previous responses (the program must not ask you for a radius before you ask to draw a circle!). Therefore we have organised the responses and displays (and the equivalent procedures) as part of a *question and answer* program that is based on the *level* concept. In our case level 0 will be common to all four programs, whereas lower levels will be unique to each of the four types of program.

To cope with the need for displaying both diagrams and prompts, the screen is divided into two areas: the graphics area which holds the diagram, and a text area for menus and prompts. In the top of the text areas we place five coloured blocks (normally logical colour 1: default red) and marked f0, f1, f2, f3 and f4 X, Y. Also, by pressing f9 when the machine requires input will cause a termination of the program. We call these the pseudo-soft keys because they correspond to the soft keys at the top of the keyboard. At any given moment during the execution of the program the machine can write character strings beneath each pseudo-soft key to demonstrate the option that is currently available with that key. Other prompts that request normal INPUT can also be printed in this text area beneath the blocks. When a soft key has been pressed then the colour of the equivalent pseudo-key turns yellow. Key f4 controls a crosswire cursor which, when activated, can be moved about the screen using cursor keys. However if you type f4 (when the corresponding pseudo-key is red) then a new position of the cursor can be explicitly INPUT as the coordinates of an addressable point. The present cursor position is written under the f4 pseudo-key.

The level 0 prompts consist of five options: SAVE (f0) to 'save' a picture on disk or tape, LOAD (f1) to re'load' it from such a backing store, ERASE (f2) to erase the present picture (after double checking), the red f4 key for cursor control, and ETC. (f3). The latter option leads on to level 1, which naturally depends on which one of the four main programs has been loaded. The procedures for this level are given in listing 6.1.

There are five procedures which 'init'ialise various variables that are used by the procedures on all levels. The first, 'initdims', initialises any DIMensions that are required for any of the procedures. The 'inikeys' procedure sets up the variables that are needed for reading the soft keys and for the display of soft-key prompts at the bottom of the screen. The procedure also uses the Command Line Interpreter (see the user guide) to clear any definitions off the first five soft keys so that no garbage is inadvertently entered into the programs. 'init-prompt' sets up the strings that correspond to the red key prompts that are displayed in the text area. The fourth 'init' procedure, 'initdiag', sets up the graphics window that is used for drawing and clears the background to a colour, in this case logical 0. Finally 'initcursor' sets the crosswire cursor at its start position and initialises the variables that are used in the main cursor procedure.

Next we have a set of three procedures that can be used to display the set of simulated function keys. The 'prompt' procedure displays any one of a set of options for the key assignments: it uses the 'text' procedure to control the number of lines available at the bottom of the screen. A non-zero parameter for 'text' specifies the number of lines, and then it clears the screen, whereas a zero parameter sets the text window to cover the whole screen but does *not* clear the screen. The 'light' procedure lights up the pseudo-soft keys in specified background and foreground colours (defaulting to red, yellow or white).

Our construction of a 'cursor' requires a little further discussion. The need for accurately controlling the position of objects on the screen is self-evident. This is achieved on most graphics displays by a crosshair (crosswire) cursor, which may be controlled either from the keyboard or in more expensive devices from an external joystick, lightpen or similar analogue input device. Not wishing to put the reader to any further expense we shall use the keyboard to control movements: it achieves the same effect as a joystick anyway. The 'cursor' procedure that is contained in listing 6.1 overlays the existing picture with crosswires by using the EOR option of GCOL. These crosswires specify the point at their intersection. The cursor is moved in any one of eight directions by the standard cursor keys either singly or in pairs. If you have a joystick or similar peripheral attached to your computer then alter the 'cursor' procedure so that it receives information from your device rather than from the keyboard.

The 'cursor' procedure may be called to initiate a single movement by using the parameter 1 in the call (externally initiated by pressing the f4 key when the equivalent pseudo-key shows red and explicitly typing the coordinates, as in the 'sketch' procedure), or a continuous sequence of moves using parameter 0 (externally initiated by pressing the cursor keys). The coordinate values of the present cursor position are requested by the program when the pseudo-key f4 shows (default) white, and they are entered by pressing soft key f4. When a cursor key is held down the speed of movement gradually increases (a cursor that always moves just one addressable point per key depression is tedious to use!). To aid in positioning the cursor there is a grid which is switched on and off by pressing G. If operative then it is automatically removed when you press f4 to enter a point.

*Listing 6.1*

```
 10 MODE 1 : VDU23,1,0;0;0;0;
 20 PROCinitdims
 30 PROCinitkeys
 40 PROCinitprompt
 50 PROCinitdiag(0)
 60 PROCinitcursor(640,512)
 70 LEVEL=0 : OL=-1
 80 BC=0 : OC=1 : TC=2 : GC=3
100 REM main loop
110 REPEAT
120 IF LEVEL<>OL THEN PROCprompt(LEVEL) : OL=LEVEL
130 IF INKEY(K(0)) THEN PROCkey0
140 IF INKEY(K(1)) THEN PROCkey1
150 IF INKEY(K(2)) THEN PROCkey2
160 IF INKEY(K(3)) THEN PROCkey3
170 IF INKEY(K(4)) THEN PROCkey4
180 UNTIL INKEY(-120)
190 STOP

200 REM initdiag
210 DEF PROCinitdiag(BACK)
219 REM set window and clear graphics to BACKground colour
220 VDU 24,0;65;1279;1023;
230 GCOL0,128+BACK : CLG
240 ENDPROC

300 REM initkeys
310 DEF PROCinitkeys
320 DIM K$(4),K(4) : RESTORE 380
329 REM remove key definitions from key 0 to key 4
330 FOR I%=0 TO 4 : A$="KEY"+STR$(I%)
340 $32512=A$ : X%=0 : Y%=127 : CALL &FFF7
350 NEXT I%
359 REM set up arrays of INKEY values and strings for display
360 FOR I%=0 TO 4 : READ K$(I%),K(I%)
370 NEXT I%
380 DATA"  f0  ",-33,"  f1  ",-114,"  f2  ",-115,"  f3  ",-116
      ,"  f4 X,Y ",-21
390 ENDPROC
```

```
 400 REM prompt
 410 DEF PROCprompt(A)
 419 REM clear the bottom two lines
 420 PROCtext(2) : PROCtext(0)
 429 REM display keys with appropriate prompts for level A
 430 FOR I%=0 TO 3
 440 PROClight(I%,1,3)
 450 PRINT TAB(I%*7,31);P$(A,I%);
 460 NEXT I%
 470 PROClight(4,1,3)
 480 PRINT TAB(30,31);X; : PRINT TAB(34,31);",";Y;
 490 ENDPROC

 500 REM light
 510 DEF PROClight(KEY,BACK,TEXT)
 519 REM print key in BACK colour with label in TEXT colour
 520 COLOUR 128+BACK : COLOUR TEXT
 530 PRINT TAB(KEY*7,30);K$(KEY);
 540 COLOUR 128 : COLOUR 3
 549 REM make sure key is not still being held down
 550 REPEAT : UNTIL NOT INKEY(K(KEY))
 560 ENDPROC

 600 REM text
 610 DEF PROCtext(N)
 619 REM set text window of N lines up from bottom and clear buffers
 620 IF N<>0 THEN N=32-N
 630 VDU 28,0,31,39,N : *FX15,0
 639 REM if N=0 then window is whole of screen so don't clear it
 640 IF N<>0 THEN CLS
 650 ENDPROC

 700 REM initcursor
 710 DEF PROCinitcursor(XPOS,YPOS)
 719 REM set starting point for cursor
 720 X=XPOS : Y=YPOS : OX=-1 : OY=-1
 730 ENDPROC

 800 REM cursor
 810 DEF PROCcursor(M)
 819 REM M=0 means continue till f4 is pressed. M=1 is single step.
 820 GCOL3,3 : IF M=0 THEN S=1 ELSE S=4
 829 REM if cursor has moved then use PROCcross to change display
 830 IF OX<>X OR OY<>Y THEN PROCcross : OX=X : OY=Y
 840 IF INKEY(-122) AND X<1280-S THEN X=X+S
 850 IF INKEY(-26) AND X>=S THEN X=X-S
 860 IF INKEY(-42) AND Y>=65+S THEN Y=Y-S
 870 IF INKEY(-58) AND Y<1024-S THEN Y=Y+S
 879 REM if cursor is moving then add to step size and update the
         display of coordinates
 880 IF OX=X AND OY=Y THEN S=1 ELSE S=S+1 : PRINT TAB(30,31);"  ";
     : PRINT TAB(30,31);X; : PRINTTAB(34,31);",";Y;
 889 REM if not single step mode then keep monitoring cursor keys
         unless f4 has been pressed while cursor is stationary
 890 IF M=0 AND ( S>1 OR NOT INKEY(-21) ) THEN 830
 899 REM in continuous mode cursor is removed when point is entered
 900 IF M=0 THEN OX=-1 : OY=-1 : PROCcross
 910 ENDPROC

1000 REM cross
1010 DEF PROCcross
1019 REM erase cross at OldX and OldY place new cross at X and Y
```

```
1020 MOVE 0,OY : DRAW 1280,OY : MOVE 0,Y : DRAW 1280,Y
1030 MOVE OX,0 : DRAW OX,1024 : MOVE X,0 : DRAW X,1024
1040 ENDPROC

1100 REM fill
1110 DEF PROCfill(X1,Y1,X2,Y2,X3,Y3)
1120 IF ((Y1 DIV 4)=(Y2 DIV 4) AND (Y1 DIV 4)=(Y3 DIV 4))
       THEN MOVE X1,Y1 : DRAW X2,Y2 : DRAW X3,Y3 : ENDPROC
1130 MOVE X1,Y1 : MOVE X2,Y2 : PLOT 85,X3,Y3
1140 ENDPROC

1200 REM save
1210 DEF PROCsave
1220 PROCtext(1)
1230 INPUT "FILENAME ",F$
1240 A$="*SAVE """+F$+""" 3000 7B00"
1249 REM use Command Line Interpreter to execute A$
1250 $32512=A$ : X%=0 : Y%=127 : CALL &FFF7
1260 PROCtext(0)
1270 ENDPROC

1300 REM load
1310 DEF PROCload
1320 PROCtext(1)
1330 INPUT "FILENAME ",F$
1340 A$="*LOAD """+F$+""" 3000"
1349 REM use Command Line Interpreter to execute A$
1350 $32512=A$ : X%=0 : Y%=127 : CALL &FFF7
1360 PROCtext(0)
1370 ENDPROC

1500 REM initdims
1510 DEF PROCinitdims
1520 ENDPROC

1600 REM initprompt
1610 DEF PROCinitprompt
1619 REM read prompts for keys for up to six levels of prompting
1620 DIM P$(5,3)
1630 FOR I%=0 TO 5 : FOR J%=0 TO 3
1640 READP$(I%,J%)
1650 NEXT J% : NEXT I%
1660 DATA"SAVE","LOAD","ERASE","ETC."
1670 DATA"","","",""
1680 DATA"","","",""
1690 DATA"","","",""
1700 DATA"","","",""
1710 DATA"","","",""
1720 ENDPROC

2000 REM key0
2010 DEF PROCkey0
2019 REM light key up when pressed & redisplay key
       as normal when finished
2020 PROClight(0,2,0)
2029 REM perform action appropriate to level when pressed.
       If OL is different to LEVEL either by LEVEL change or
       resetting OL to -1 prompts are refreshed.
2030 IF LEVEL=0 THEN PROCsave : OL=-1
2040 PROClight(0,1,3)
2050 ENDPROC
```

```
2200 REM key1
2210 DEF PROCkey1
2219 REM see key0
2220 PROClight(1,2,0)
2230 IF LEVEL=0 THEN PROCload : OL=-1
2240 PROClight(1,1,3)
2250 ENDPROC

2400 REM key2
2410 DEF PROCkey2
2419 REM see key0
2420 PROClight(2,2,0)
2430 IF LEVEL=0 THEN PROCtext(1) : INPUT "ARE YOU SURE ",A$
  : PROCtext(0) : OL=-1 : IF A$="Y" OR A$="y" THEN CLG
2440 PROClight(2,1,3)
2450 ENDPROC

2600 REM key3
2610 DEF PROCkey3
2619 REM see key0
2620 PROClight(3,2,0)
2630 PROClight(3,1,3)
2640 ENDPROC

2800 REM key4
2810 DEF PROCkey4
2819 REM see key0 but same action taken at any LEVEL
2820 PROClight(4,2,0)
2830 PROCtext(1) : INPUT"NEW POSITION   X,Y ",X,Y : PROCtext(0)
2840 OL=-1 : PROClight(4,1,3)
2850 ENDPROC
```

*Exercise 6.1*
Change the 'cursor' procedure so that the standard cursor keys may be used with the shift key held down. In this case the crosswires are to move in character block steps about the graphics area.

**The Four Diagram Construction Programs**

Having dealt with level 0 we now look at the four separate programs, each of which must be individually merged with listing 6.1 to produce the required DIAGRAM CONSTRUCTOR. Those who have a disc system will find that they do not have enough memory to hold and run each of these four programs. What they must do is create the program, strip the REMs, save it, and reload it after typing page =&1100. This will give them enough memory for loading and running. Now we shall look at each of the four programs in turn.

*Histograms*
Histograms (or bar-charts) can be constructed by our programs to any height and in any colour. Since we know how many addressable points are available on the screen we can formulate a method for calculating the spacing and

width of bars once we know their number. The first part of the 'histo'gram procedure (listing 6.2, which is used in conjunction with listing 6.1) is called by pressing f0 on level 1; f3 (ETC.) returns you to level 0. It immediately asks for the range of the vertical data (two integers in increasing order), creates the vertical scale, draws the horizontal and vertical axes, labels the vertical and then asks for the number of bars. Then the width of the bars and the size of the gaps between the neighbouring bars are calculated by a method similar to the scaling of the screen for two-dimensional graphics. For each bar the machine needs to know its height, and the inner and outer colours. On receiving these data the procedure uses the area-filling PLOT 85 option to colour in the bar. When the diagram is complete you must return to level 0 and SAVE the picture. Then load in the labelling program (listings 6.1 and 6.6), reLOAD the picture on level 0 and then on the lower levels add the necessary labels and headings.

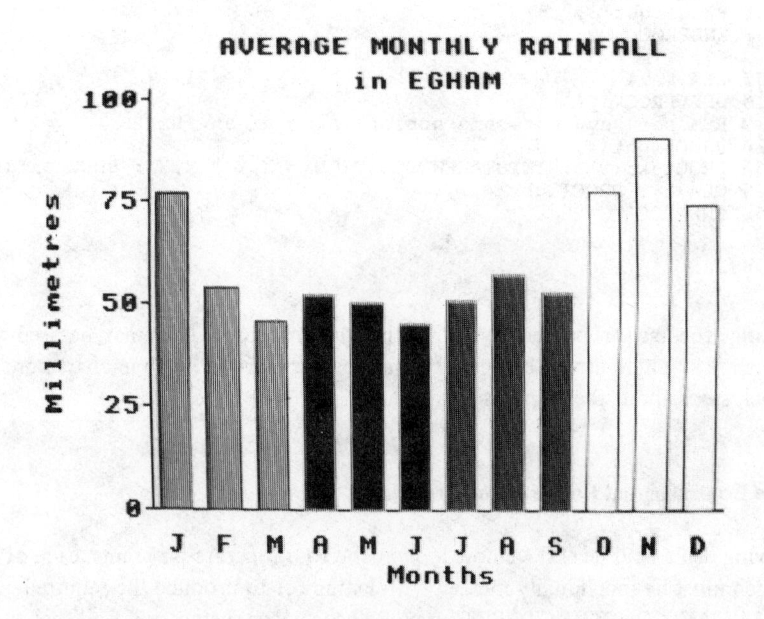


*Figure 6.1*

*Example 6.1*

Figure 6.1 for example, a diagram that presents the annual rainfall in Egham, was constructed (unlabelled) and saved, then reloaded with the general adjustment program (see later) and labels added until it was in the form above.

*Listing 6.2*

```
1500 REM initdims

1600 REM initprompt
1670 DATA"HISTOGRAM","","";"ETC."

2000 REM key0
2040 IF LEVEL=1 THEN PROChisto : OL=-1
2050 PROClight(0,1,3)
2060 ENDPROC

2200 REM key1

2400 REM key2

2600 REM key3
2630 LEVEL=(LEVEL+1) MOD 2
2640 PROClight(3,1,3)
2650 ENDPROC

2800 REM key4

3000 REM histo
3010 DEF PROChisto
3020 PROCtext(2) : INPUT"Range of vertical "YB," to "YT : PROCtext(0)
3030 IF YB>=YT THEN 3020
3040 YSCALE=640/(YT-YB)
3049 REM draw axes
3050 GCOL 0,3 : MOVE 208,864 : DRAW 208,208 : DRAW 1184,208
3060 YDIF=(YT-YB)/4 : TICK=YB
3069 REM put ticks & labels on y-axis
3070 FOR I%=1 TO 5 : TK=INT(TICK+0.5)
3080 Y=5*32*I%+48 : MOVE 208,Y : DRAW 196,Y : ROW=INT((1024-Y)/32)
3089 REM make sure label is sensible and correct length
3090 A$=STR$(TK) : IF LEN(A$)>3 THEN A$=LEFT$(A$,3)
     : IF TK>999 OR TK<-99 THEN A$="***"
3100 IF LEN(A$)<3 THEN REPEAT A$=" "+A$:UNTIL LEN(A$)=3
3110 PRINT TAB(3,ROW);A$ : TICK=TICK+YDIF
3120 NEXT I%
3130 PROCtext(2) : INPUT"NO OF BARS "NB : PROCtext(0)
3139 REM calculate width of bars and gaps to fit x-axis
3140 XSCALE=976/NB : GAP=XSCALE/3 : WID=XSCALE-GAP
3149 REM get details and display each of the bars
3150 FOR I%=1 TO NB
3160 PROCtext(2) : PRINT"DATA FOR BAR ";I%;
3170 INPUT":"D,"INNER COL "C,"OUTER COL "OC : PROCtext(0)
3179 REM calculate bottom-left and top-right corners of block
3180 GCOL 0,C : X1=208+GAP/2+(I%-1)*XSCALE : X2=X1+WID : Y1=208
3190 IF D<=YB THEN Y2=212 : GOTO 3210
3200 D=D-YB : Y2=Y1+INT(D*YSCALE+0.5)
3209 REM fill in bar in inner colour
3210 PROCfill(X1,Y1,X2,Y2,X1,Y2) : PROCfill(X1,Y1,X2,Y2,X2,Y1)
3219 REM outline bar in outer colour
3220 GCOL 0,OC : MOVE X1,Y1 : DRAW X1,Y2 : DRAW X2,Y2
     : DRAW X2,Y1 : DRAW X1,Y1
3230 NEXT I%
3240 ENDPROC
```

*Exercise 6.2*
Write variations on this standard 'histo' procedure that can be substituted into the complete package as and when required. For example write a procedure that draws the histogram as a set of pairs of bars. The space between any two bars that form a pair should be half the distance between neighbouring bars that do not form a pair. Use this to construct diagrams that are similar to figure 6.2.

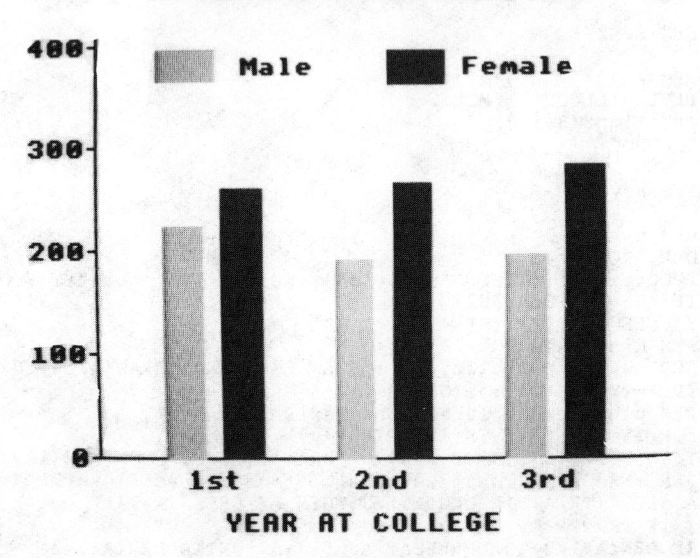


*Figure 6.2*

*Example 6.2*
In listing 6.3 we give an example of such a replacement 'histo' procedure. This version of 'histo' (using a variation on the fake-perspective cube procedure from chapter 1) produces an apparently three-dimensional graph. Two data values are requested for each bar, a MAXimum and a MINimum; the maximum bar is drawn behind the minimum bar. This program can be used to create charts similar to figure 6.3 which shows the monthly temperature variation in Egham.

*Exercise 6.3*
There are many, many more possible variations, for example drawing bars above and below a central line in order to display fluctuations in currency exchange rates. See the Money Programme on BBC2 for ideas. The fundamental notions we have introduced here should enable you to produce histograms to your own specifications.

*Listing 6.3*

```
15ØØ REM initdims

16ØØ REM initprompt
167Ø DATA"HISTOGRAM","","","ETC."

2ØØØ REM keyØ
2Ø4Ø IF LEVEL=1 THEN PROChisto : OL=-1
2Ø5Ø PROClight(Ø,1,3)
2Ø6Ø ENDPROC

22ØØ REM key1

24ØØ REM key2

26ØØ REM key3
263Ø LEVEL=(LEVEL+1) MOD 2
264Ø PROClight(3,1,3)
265Ø ENDPROC

28ØØ REM key4

3ØØØ REM histo
3Ø1Ø DEF PROChisto
3Ø2Ø PROCtext(2) : INPUT"Range of vertical "YB," to "YT : PROCtext(Ø)
3Ø3Ø IF YB>=YT THEN 3Ø2Ø
3Ø4Ø YSCALE=64Ø/(YT-YB)
3Ø49 REM draw axes
3Ø5Ø GCOL Ø,3 : MOVE 2Ø8,864 : DRAW 2Ø8,2Ø8 : DRAW 1184,2Ø8
3Ø6Ø YDIF=(YT-YB)/4 : TICK=YB
3Ø69 REM put ticks & labels on y-axis
3Ø7Ø FOR I%=1 TO 5 : TK=INT(TICK+Ø.5)
3Ø8Ø Y=5*32*I%+48 : MOVE 196,Y : DRAW 2Ø8,Y : MOVE 248,Y+4Ø
      : DRAW 168,Y-4Ø : ROW=INT((1Ø24-Y)/32)
3Ø89 REM make sure label is sensible and correct length
3Ø9Ø A$=STR$(TK) : IF LEN(A$)>3 THEN A$=LEFT$(A$,3)
      : IF TK>999 OR TK<-99 THEN A$="***"
31ØØ IF LEN(A$)<3 THEN REPEAT A$=" "+A$ : UNTIL LEN(A$)=3
311Ø PRINT TAB(3,ROW);A$ : TICK=TICK+YDIF
312Ø NEXT I%
313Ø PROCtext(2) : INPUT"NO OF BARS "NB : PROCtext(Ø)
3139 REM calculate width of bars and gaps to fit x-axis
314Ø XSCALE=976/NB : GAP=XSCALE/3 : WID=XSCALE-GAP
3149 REM get details and display each pair of bars
315Ø FOR I%=1 TO NB
316Ø PROCtext(2) : PRINT"DATA FOR BAR ";I%;
317Ø INPUT":"D,D1 : PROCtext(Ø)
318Ø C=1 : OC=3 : VDU 19,2,4,Ø,Ø,Ø
3189 REM calculate bottom-left and top-right corners of blocks
319Ø GCOL Ø,C : X1=2Ø8+GAP+(I%-1)*XSCALE : X2=X1+WID : Y1=2Ø8
32ØØ IF D<=YB THEN Y2=212 : GOTO 322Ø
321Ø D=D-YB : Y2=Y1+INT(D*YSCALE+Ø.5)
3219 REM draw back block in 3d then change colour and do front
         block over the top
322Ø PROCfake3d(X1,Y1,X2,Y2) : C=2
323Ø D1=D1-YB : Y2=Y1+INT(D1*YSCALE+Ø.5)
324Ø X2=X2-WID/3 : X1=X1-WID/3 : Y1=Y1-WID/3 : Y2=Y2-WID/3
325Ø PROCfake3d(X1,Y1,X2,Y2)
326Ø NEXT I%
327Ø ENDPROC
```

```
3400 REM fake3d
3410 DEF PROCfake3d(X1,Y1,X2,Y2)
3419 REM draw rectangle defined by coordinates of its diagonal
3420 PROCquad(X1,Y1,X1,Y2,X2,Y2,X2,Y1)
3429 REM add rhombus  to top and side to simulate a 3d box
3430 PROCquad(X2,Y1,X2,Y2,X2+WID/3,Y2+WID/3,X2+WID/3,Y1+WID/3)
3440 PROCquad(X1,Y2,X2,Y2,X2+WID/3,Y2+WID/3,X1+WID/3,Y2+WID/3)
3450 ENDPROC

3500 REM quad
3510 DEF PROCquad(XA,YA,XB,YB,XC,YC,XD,YD)
3519 REM fill in a quadrilateral in colour C
        and outline it in colour OC
3520 GCOL 0,C : MOVE XA,YA : MOVE XB,YB
3530 PLOT 85,XD,YD : PLOT 85,XC,YC
3540 GCOL 0,OC : DRAW XD,YD : DRAW XA,YA
3550 DRAW XB,YB : DRAW XC,YC
3560 ENDPROC
```

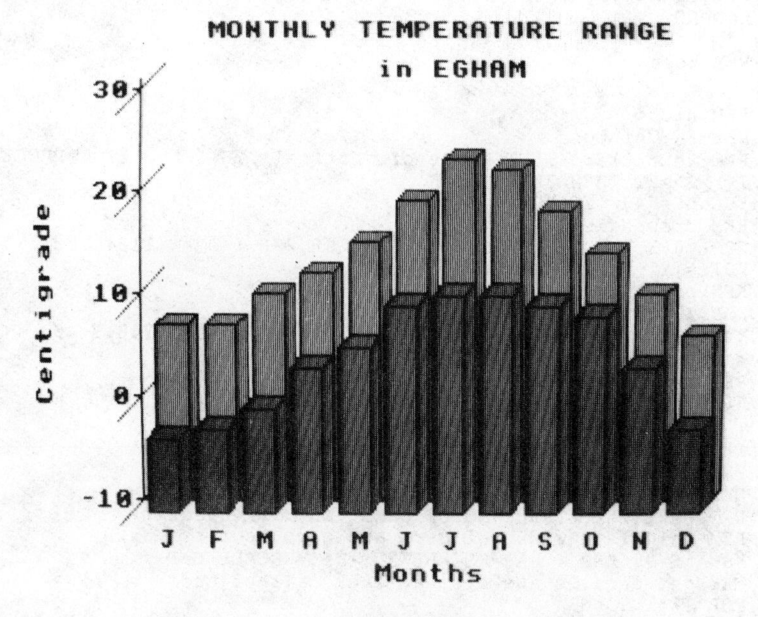


*Figure 6.3*

*Pie-charts*

The pie-chart is a favourite with economists and biologists who delight in telling us how big each slice of our capital expenditure cake is, or alternatively which fungi are growing on it. The usual requirements of a pie-chart program are that it should draw 'pies' of variable radii, it must be possible for some slices to be pulled out from the centre, and provision must be made for these slices to be filled-in or cross-hatched. A pie-chart and associated procedures are given in listing 6.4. It is entered by pressing f0 on level 1; pressing f3 (ETC.) returns you to level 0. The program first requires the number of pie-slices and the individual data values; the sum of values is used to establish an angular scale for the pie-chart. The 'pie' is centred by the crosswires, that is, by using the cursor keys to position it, and the coordinates are entered with f4 (showing white). The radius of the pie-chart (in addressable points) is then INPUT. Each slice is centred with the cursor; any displacement of the cursor from the centre of the 'pie' is treated as a distance along the bisector of the slice and not as an absolute position. With each new section the cursor re-appears at the original centre of the 'pie'. Then the program enquires if you wish to hatch the 'pie' (x, y, b, n?) in the $x$-direction, $y$-direction, both or neither (this is explained in a moment); should you wish to hatch a slice then the program asks for further information about the position of the hatching lines and the distance between them. It then requests the inner and outer colour of the pie-slice and finally draws it. Figure 6.4 was generated using this procedure, the 'hatch'ing procedure below and the labelling program. After the picture is complete you return to level 1.

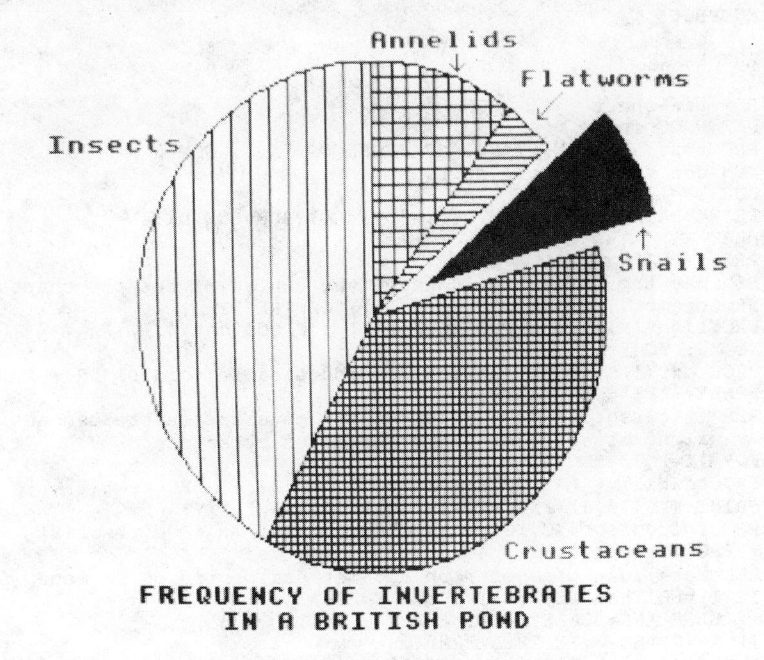


*Figure 6.4*

*Hatching*

Hatching the area of a pie-slice involves the intersection of a line with the boundaries of the slice. To make the calculations simpler we shall hatch only with lines in the horizontal or vertical directions, or both. Furthermore we only hatch 'pies' that subtend angles less than or equal to $\pi$ radians (180 degrees)

*Listing 6.4*

```
1500 REM initdims
1520 DIM D(20),Z(4)
1530 ENDPROC

1600 REM initprompt
1670 DATA"PIE-CHART","","","ETC."

2000 REM key0
2040 IF LEVEL=1 THEN PROCpie : OL=-1
2050 PROClight(0,1,3)
2060 ENDPROC

2200 REM key1

2400 REM key2

2600 REM key3
2630 LEVEL=(LEVEL+1) MOD 2
2640 PROClight(3,1,3)
2650 ENDPROC

2800 REM key4

3000 REM pie-chart
3010 DEF PROCpie
3020 PROCtext(2) : INPUT"No. OF SEGMENTS "NB : SUM=0
3029 REM get data for all sections
3030 FOR I%=1 TO NB
3040 PRINT"DATA ";I%; : INPUT": "D(I%) : SUM=SUM+D(I%)
3050 NEXT I%
3060 PROCtext(0)
3069 REM use the cursor to indicate the centre of the pie-chart
3070 PROCprompt(5) : PRINT TAB(0,31);"CENTRE PIE";
3080 PROClight(4,3,1) : PROCcursor(0) : PROClight(4,1,3)
3090 XC=X : YC=Y
3100 PROCtext(1) : INPUT"RADIUS (in addressable points) "R : PROCtext
3110 SCALE=2*PI/SUM : A1=PI/2
3119 REM if cursor is moved from centre movement is treated as
        along bisector of angle subtended by segment
3120 FOR I%=1 TO NB
3130 PROCtext(1) : PRINT"CENTRE SEGMENT ";I%; : PROCtext(0)
3140 PRINT TAB(30,31);X; : PRINT TAB(34,31);",";Y;
3150 PROCinitcursor(XC,YC) : PROClight(4,3,1) : PROCcursor(0)
     : PROClight(4,1,3)
3159 REM make sure pie joins up and get scale size of segment
3160 IF I%=NB THEN A2=-3*PI/2 : ANG=A1-A2
        ELSE ANG=SCALE*D(I%) : A2=A1-ANG
3170 IF X=XC AND Y=YC THEN 3200
3179 REM deal with displacement
3180 A3=A1-ANG/2 : DIST=SQR((X-XC)^2+(Y-YC)^2)
3190 X=INT(XC+DIST*COS(A3)+0.5) : Y=INT(YC+DIST*SIN(A3)+0.5)
3199 REM is hatching to be along the 'x' axis, 'y' axis, 'b'oth
        or 'n'ot at all
3200 PROCtext(1) : INPUT"HATCH (x,y,b,n) "H$
     : IF ASC(H$)<96 THEN H$=CHR$(ASC(H$)+32)
3209 REM what spacing between lines and what initial offset
3210 IF H$<>"n" THEN INPUT "JUMP"JUMP,"FROM "FROM
3220 INPUT"INNER COLOUR",IC,"OUTER COLOUR",OC
3229 REM fill in segment
```

```
3230 GCOL 0,IC : X1=X+INT(R*COS(A1)+0.5) : Y1=Y+INT(R*SIN(A1)+0.5)
3240 MOVE X1,Y1 : ADIF=-10/R
3250 FOR T=A1+ADIF TO A2 STEP ADIF
3260 MOVE X,Y : PLOT 81,COS(T)*R,SIN(T)*R
3270 NEXT T
3279 REM make sure filled in to end of segment
3280 MOVE X,Y : XS=INT(COS(A2)*R+0.5) : YS=INT(SIN(A2)*R+0.5)
     : PLOT 81,XS,YS
3289 REM draw outline round segment
3290 GCOL 0,OC : MOVE X,Y : DRAW X1,Y1
3300 FOR T=A1+ADIF TO A2 STEP ADIF
3310 DRAW X+COS(T)*R,Y+SIN(T)*R
3320 NEXT T
3329 REM make sure outline goes to edge of segment
3330 DRAW X+XS,Y+YS : DRAW X,Y
3340 IF H$="n" THEN 3370 ELSE A2S=A2
3349 REM deal with hatching if the segement is more than half circle
         treat as two parts
3350 IF ANG>PI THEN A2=A1-PI : X2=2*X-X1 : Y2=2*Y-Y1 : PROChatch(H$)
     : X1=X2 : Y1=Y2 : A1=A2 : A2=A2S
3360 PROCtext(0) : X2=X+XS : Y2=Y+YS : PROChatch(H$)
3370 A1=A2
3380 NEXT I%
3390 ENDPROC

3400 REM hatch
3410 DEF PROChatch(H$)
3419 REM if cross hatching is required then run routine twice.
3420 IF H$="b" THEN PROChatch("x") : PROChatch("y") : ENDPROC
3429 REM set hatching variables to control direction of lines.
3430 IF H$="y" THEN PZ=X : PT=Y : Z1=X1 : T1=Y1 : Z2=X2 : T2=Y2
3440 IF H$="x" THEN PZ=Y : PT=X : Z1=Y1 : T1=X1 : Z2=Y2 : T2=X2
3449 REM find max. and min. coordinates for lines which pass
         through segment
3450 T=PI/2 : MAX=0 : MIN=0
3460 IF H$="x" THEN V=COS(A1) ELSE V=SIN(A1)
3470 IF MAX < V THEN MAX=V ELSE IF MIN > V THEN MIN=V
3480 IF T>A1 THEN REPEAT : T=T-PI/2 : UNTIL T<=A1
3490 IF T<A2 THEN 3530
3500 IF H$="x" THEN V=COS(T) ELSE V=SIN(T)
3510 IF MAX < V THEN MAX=V ELSE IF MIN > V THEN MIN=V
3520 T=T-PI/2 : GOTO3490
3530 IF H$="x" THEN V=COS(A2) ELSE V=SIN(A2)
3540 IF MAX < V THEN MAX=V ELSE IF MIN > V THEN MIN=V
3550 NMIN=INT(INT(R*MIN+1)/JUMP)*JUMP+FROM
3559 REM for lines which cross segment find intersections
         with radii and arc
3560 FOR E=NMIN TO MAX*R STEP JUMP
3569 REM store intersection coordinate information in array z
3570 C=0 : DENOM=T1-PT : IF DENOM=0 THEN 3600
3580 MU=E/DENOM : IF MU<0 OR MU>1 THEN 3600
3590 C=C+1 : Z(C)=PZ+MU*(Z1-PZ)
3600 DENOM=T2-PT : IF DENOM=0 THEN 3640
3610 MU=E/DENOM : IF MU<0 OR MU>1 THEN 3640
3620 C=C+1 : Z(C)=PZ+MU*(Z2-PZ)
3629 REM if more than two points of intersection found,
         delete duplicates
3630 IF C=2 AND Z(1)=Z(2) THEN C=1
3640 IF C<>2 THEN 3670
3649 REM draw hatch lines.
3650 IF H$="y" THEN MOVE Z(1),E+PT : DRAW Z(2),E+PT : GOTO 3730
3660 IF H$="x" THEN MOVE E+PT,Z(1) : DRAW E+PT,Z(2) : GOTO 3730
```

```
3670 DISC=R*R-E*E : IF DISC<0 THEN 3730
3680 DISC=INT(SQR(DISC)+0.5)
3690 ZZ=PZ+DISC : AZ=DISC : PROCin : IF IN THEN C=C+1 : Z(C)=ZZ
3700 ZZ=PZ-DISC : AZ=-DISC : PROCin : IF IN THEN C=C+1 : Z(C)=ZZ
3710 IF C>2 AND Z(1)=Z(2) THEN Z(2)=Z(3)
3720 IF C>=2 THEN 3650
3730 NEXT E
3740 ENDPROC

3800 REM in
3810 DEF PROCin
3819 REM if angle lies between angles of ends of segment then point
         of intersection is on the arc of the segment
3820 IF H$="x" THEN BZ=E : EZ=AZ ELSE BZ=AZ : EZ=E
3829 REM find angle from centre to point of intersection
3830 IF BZ=0 THEN PHI=-PI/2 : IF EZ>0 THEN PHI=-PHI
3840 IF BZ<>0 THEN PHI=ATN(EZ/BZ) : IF BZ<0 THEN PHI=PHI-PI
3849 REM IN is true if PHI is between angles of edges
3850 IN=(PHI<=A1) AND (PHI>=A2)
3860 ENDPROC
```

at the centre. For obtuse angles the 'pie' is treated as two pieces, the first subtending $\pi$ radians at the centre. The 'pie' procedure enquires whether the hatching is to be horizontal (answer 'x'), vertical (answer 'y'), both ways (answer 'b') or neither (answer 'n').

The pie sections we are considering are each bounded by two line segments and a circular arc. We must find which part of a hatching line (if any) lies inside this segment. Because the 'pie' does not subtend an angle greater than $\pi$ radians at its centre there are only four possibilities:

(1) A line may miss the pie altogether.
(2) It may intersect the arc at two points.
(3) It may intersect the arc and one of the line segments.
(4) It may intersect both line segments.

The special cases where the line coincidently cuts the arc and a line segment at the same point may be included in one of the above four possibilities. The explanation of the hatching algorithm is given with reference to horizontal hatching; the vertical follows in an equivalent manner. We first find the MAXimum and MINimum $y$-values of points within the 'pie' section. Then we consider all horizontal hatching lines with equations of the form Y = k * JUMP + FROM between these limits ($0 \leqslant$ FROM $\leqslant$ JUMP $- 1$). For each hatching line we calculate the two points of intersection with the extended line segments and then check whether their MU values lie between 0 and 1, that is, whether the intersection is between the centre of the circle and the arc. Next we find the two points of intersection of the hatching line with the complete circle that contains the arc and then check whether they lie on the arc. From these we can find the two points of intersection of the pie section and the hatching line, and these are then joined. This whole process is programmed in listing 6.4 and an example of its use is given in figure 6.4 above. Note that if we set the JUMP to a number that is not the size of a whole number of pixels (in addressable points) we get unusual candy-stripe or dotted hatching.

*Graphs*

As our third example of graphical data presentation we must consider scientific graphs of functions and graphs of discrete points, called by f0 at level 1 (listings 6.1 and 6.5). Such diagrams require coordinate axes that need be neither of fixed size nor of fixed scale. The program requests the lower and upper $x$-value and $y$-value of the data. Then a standard method is used to decide on the placing of a particular axis: if zero should lie in the range of the graph then the axis passes through that point, otherwise it lies on the edge of the graphics area, closest to zero. Five marks are then placed along each axis and if automatic labelling is specified then the corresponding scale value is written close to each mark. The need for accuracy in scientific graphs necessitates the use of as many characters as possible across the screen. In mode 1 the BBC Model B has only 40 characters across the screen and 32 up it, so previously loaded 'thin' characters (character set 4 from chapter 5) are placed two per character block, enabling us to draw 80 characters on each line. When numbers are to be printed as 'thin' 'label's they need to be converted into strings and made consistent in length and/or decimal accuracy. This is achieved by the procedure 'number' (listing 6.5).

*Exercise 6.4*

Write an extended 'number' procedure that allows you to specify the format of the string to be printed. One way of doing this is to enter a string that contains a template for the number format, for example the string '##.###' could specify a number with two digits before the decimal point and three decimal places after it. Also see the @% option in the user manual.

The choice is now offered between entering a functional representation of points on a continuous curve, and entering a set of discrete data points to be joined in a saw-tooth type pattern by straight lines. In the functional section of the procedure the program asks for an algebraic expression for the function, which may include the standard in-built functions (like SIN or COS) as well as your own functions. The height of the point on the curve above each pixel point on the X-axis is calculated, and these points are joined by lines.

In the discrete section the number of data points is INPUT, followed by the individual X and Y coordinates which are sorted into ascending order of the X coordinate. Consecutive points are then joined by lines. One example of each type of diagram is given. Figure 6.5 shows a typical continuous cosine curve and figure 6.6 shows discrete scientific data that illustrate the pH levels of a river.

*Listing 6.5*

```
1500 REM initdims
1520 DIM X(100),Y(100)
1530 ENDPROC

1600 REM initprompt
1670 DATA"GRAPH","","","ETC."

2000 REM key0
2040 IF LEVEL=1 THEN PROCgraph : OL=-1
2050 PROClight(0,1,3)
2060 ENDPROC

2200 REM key1

2400 REM key2

2600 REM key3
2630 LEVEL=(LEVEL+1) MOD 2
2640 PROClight(3,1,3)
2650 ENDPROC

2800 REM key4

3000 REM graph
3010 DEF PROCgraph
3020 PROCtext(2)
3030 REPEAT : INPUT"X GOES FROM "XB,"TO "XT : UNTIL XT>XB
3040 REPEAT : INPUT"Y GOES FROM "YB,"TO "YT : UNTIL YT>YB
3050 INPUT"AUTOMATIC LABELLING (Y/N) ",L$ : PROCtext(0)
3060 XSCALE=1024/(XT-XB) : YSCALE=704/(YT-YB)
3069 REM draw axes through origin or on side closest to origin
3070 IF YT<0 THEN YO=896 ELSE IF YB>0 THEN YO=192
      ELSE YO=INT(-YB*YSCALE+192.5)
3080 IF XT<0 THEN XO=1152 ELSE IF XB>0 THEN XO=128
      ELSE XO=INT(-XB*XSCALE+128.5)
3090 MOVE XO,192 : DRAW XO,896 : MOVE 128,YO : DRAW 1152,YO
3100 XDIF=(XT-XB)/4 : YDIF=(YT-YB)/4
3109 REM put five ticks along each axis with 'thin' labels
3110 X=XB : Y=YB : FOR J=1 TO 5
3120 PX=INT((X-XB)*XSCALE+128.5) : PY=YO
3130 MOVE PX,PY-8 : DRAW PX,PY+8
3139 REM calculate text positions
3140 TX=PX DIV 32 -1 : TY=(1024-PY) DIV 32+1
3150 IF L$="Y" THEN PROCthin(1,TX,TY,STR$(X))
3160 PX=XO : PY=INT((Y-YB)*YSCALE+192.5)
3170 MOVE PX-8,PY : DRAW PX+8,PY
3180 TX=PX DIV 32 +1 : TY=(1024-PY) DIV 32-1
3190 IF L$="Y" THEN PROCthin(1,TX,TY,STR$(Y))
3200 X=X+XDIF : Y=Y+YDIF : NEXT J
3210 PROCtext(2)
3220 REPEAT : INPUT"CONTINUOUS OR DISCRETE ",D$ : UNTIL D$="C" OR D$="
3230 IF D$="D" THEN 3330
3239 REM section to plot graph of a function
3240 INPUT"F(X): Y="F$
3249 REM evaluate function for X to find point on curve
3250 X=XB : Y=EVAL(F$) : IY=INT((Y-YB)*YSCALE+192.5)
3260 MOVE 128,IY
3269 REM repeat for values of X one pixel apart
3270 FOR I%=128 TO 1152 STEP 4
```

```
3280 X=(I%-128)/XSCALE+XB
3290 Y=EVAL(F$) : IY=INT((Y-YB)*YSCALE+192.5)
3300 DRAW I%,IY
3310 NEXT I% : X=640 : Y=512
3320 ENDPROC
3329 REM come here if points to be joined are to be input
3330 INPUT"NO. OF POINTS "NP
3339 REM get all points
3340 FOR I%=1 TO NP
3350 PRINT"X(";I%;"),Y(";I%;") "; : INPUTX(I%),Y(I%)
3360 NEXT I%
3369 REM use simple bubble-sort to get points in ascending order
         of X-coordinate
3370 FOR I%=1 TO NP-1 : FOR J%=I%+1 TO NP
3380 IF X(J%)<X(I%) THEN T=X(J%) : X(J%)=X(I%) : X(I%)=T
     : T=Y(J%) : Y(J%)=Y(I%) : Y(I%)=T
3390 NEXT J% : NEXT I%
3399 REM find scale coordinates of first point and draw symbol
3400 X=INT((X(1)-XB)*XSCALE+128.5) : Y=INT((Y(1)-YB)*YSCALE+192.5)
3410 MOVE X,Y : PROCsymbol(X,Y)
3419 REM repeat for other points joining them up
3420 FOR I%=2 TO NP
3430 X=INT((X(I%)-XB)*XSCALE+128.5) : Y=INT((Y(I%)-YB)*YSCALE+192.5)
3440 DRAW X ,Y : PROCsymbol(X,Y)
3450 NEXT I%
3460 ENDPROC

3500 REM symbol
3510 DEF PROCsymbol(X,Y)
3519 REM draw a little square round X,Y to mark it
3520 MOVE X+8,Y+8 : DRAW X-8,Y+8 : DRAW X-8,Y-8
     : DRAW X+8,Y-8 : DRAW X+8,Y+8 : MOVE X,Y
3530 ENDPROC

4000 REM thin
4010 DEF PROCthin(M,X,Y,A$)
4019 REM output a numeric string using thin characters
4020 LOCAL I%,A%,P$
4030 A%=2^(4+M) : VDU 5
4040 MOVE X*A%,1023-Y*32
4050 FOR I%=1 TO LEN(A$) : P$=MID$(A$,I%,1)
4060 IF P$>="0" AND P$<="9" THEN VDU (80+ASC(P$)) : GOTO 4080
4070 IF P$="+" THEN VDU 144 ELSE IF P$="-" THEN VDU 145 ELSE VDU 146
4080 MOVE (X+I%/2)*A%,1023-Y*32
4090 NEXT I%
4100 VDU 4
4110 ENDPROC
```

### *Exercise 6.5*

It has been noted that the only requirement for such graphs is a set of coordinates in ascending order of X which are then joined up. This set can be created in any manner: by a series of READ statements or by a multi-line calculation in a user-defined function FNf, which can be drawn by simply typing Y = FNf(X) instead of just using functions provided by the system. DEFine a FN that allows the graph of SIN(X)/X to be drawn; avoid the calculation of SIN(0)/0!

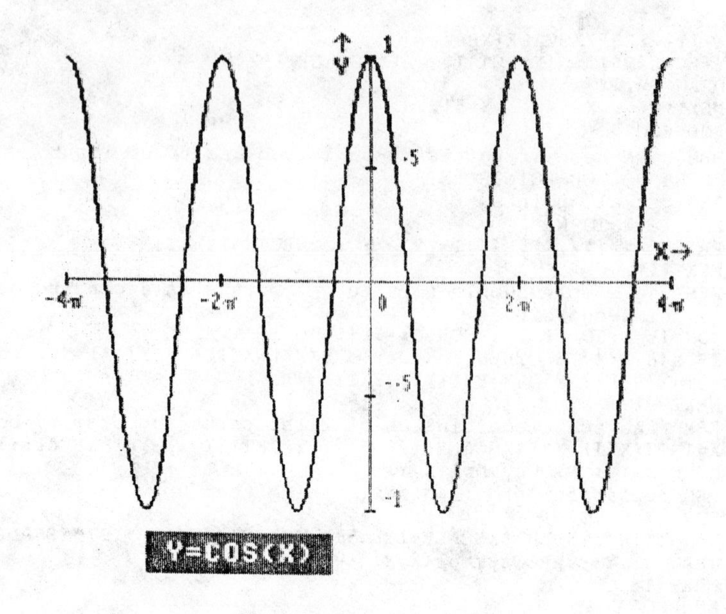


Figure 6.5

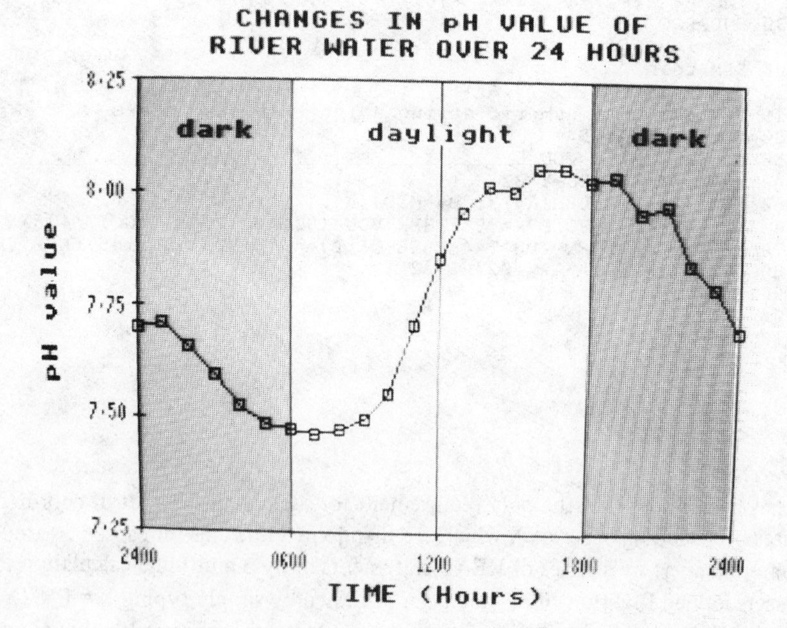


Figure 6.6

*Diagram adjustment and labelling*

Having drawn diagrams we now need simple control over the superimposition of labels and other graphics objects on them. This requires procedures for drawing lines and shapes, even perhaps for filling in the shapes (listing 6.6). On level 1 we have the options SKETCH (f0), LINE (f1), SHAPE (f2), ETC. (f3) and the Cursor adjustment (f4). SKETCH enables you to sketch in small details. The cursor keys move the crosswires around the screen, and if 'P' is pressed simultaneously then a trail is left behind (compare with listing 1.8). f0 returns you to level 1. It would be very tedious to sketch in every pixel for a large block of the screen. Instead we use a set of procedures that draw lines and draw and/or fill triangles, boxes, polygons and circles. The LINE option uses the 'line' procedure which specifies two points on the screen by using the cursor, and then draws a line between them. It also demonstrates some of the other procedures that are provided for this part of the diagram package, such as 'mark' which places a small cross on the screen to show previous positions of the cursor.

SHAPE takes us down to level 3 with options DRAW (f0), FILL (f1) or BOTH (f3) which specifies the mode of colouring: outline only (f0), solid area only (f1) or both (f2). This leads on directly to level 4 with options TRIANG (f0), BOX (f1), CIRCLE (f2) and POLY (f3). The first two options allow us to draw a triangle or a quadrilateral with corners entered via the cursor. CIRCLE draws a circle with centre and radius given by the cursor. POLY draws a regular polygon with centre and radius specified by the cursor and the angle that one of the vertices makes with the horizontal given as a multiple of PI, and then returns to level 1. ETC. (f3) leads directly to level 2 which defines labels and the colours in use. LABEL (f0) enters the 'label' procedure which asks for Normal, Thin or Graphics characters and the string to be printed. Note that references are regularly made to the level 0 procedures, and to the 'thin' procedure (taken from listing 5.4). Naturally we must first place the 'thin' characters in character set 4 position between &C00 and &D00. Obviously you can create other characters (such as a 'thin' $\pi$) and as long as you place them in set 4 they can be printed out by 'label'.

COLOUR (f1) changes the foreground and/or background colours of labels. GCOL (f2) changes the Graphics and outline colours. ETC. (f3) leads you back to level 0. In most of these levels if the pseudo-soft key f4 is coloured red then you can INPUT a new position for the cursor rather than use the cursor keys.

***Exercise 6.6***

Draw a picture of your BBC micro, or perhaps a scene like that given at the end of chapter 1. Adapt your program from exercise 1.3 for use as a procedure to draw an $n$-sided polygon by using the 'cursor' to enter the $n$ points.

If you have a graphics pad then you can copy rough sketches from the pad into the machine. You should then write programs to tidy up these pictures, that is to straighten lines and to smooth out curves.

*Listing 6.6*

```
1500 REM initdims

1600 REM initprompt
1670 DATA"SKETCH","LINE","SHAPE","ETC."
1680 DATA"LABEL","COLOUR","GCOL","ETC."
1690 DATA"DRAW","FILL","BOTH",""
1700 DATA"TRIANG","BOX","CIRCLE","POLY"

2000 REM key0
2040 IF LEVEL=1 THEN PROCsketch
2050 IF LEVEL=2 THEN PROClabel
2060 IF LEVEL=3 THEN OUTLINE=TRUE : FILL=FALSE : LEVEL=4 : GOTO 2080
2070 IF LEVEL=4 THEN PROCtriang : LEVEL =1
2080 PROClight(0,1,3)
2090 ENDPROC

2200 REM key1
2240 IF LEVEL=1 THEN PROCline : OL=-1
2250 IF LEVEL=2 THEN PROCtext(1) : INPUT "BACKGROUND ",BC,
     "TEXT COLOUR ",TC : PROCtext(0) : OL=-1
2260 IF LEVEL=3 THEN OUTLINE=FALSE : FILL=TRUE: LEVEL=4 : GOTO 2280
2270 IF LEVEL=4 THEN PROCbox : LEVEL=1
2280 PROClight(1,1,3)
2290 ENDPROC
2400 REM key2
2440 IF LEVEL=1 THEN LEVEL=3 : GOTO 2480
2450 IF LEVEL=2 THEN PROCtext(1) : INPUT "GCOL ",GC,
     "OUTLINE COLOUR ",OC : PROCtext(0) : OL=-1
2460 IF LEVEL=3 THEN OUTLINE=TRUE : FILL=TRUE : LEVEL=4 : GOTO 2480
2470 IF LEVEL=4 THEN PROCcircle : LEVEL=1
2480 PROClight(2,1,3)
2490 ENDPROC

2600 REM key3
2630 IF LEVEL<3 THEN LEVEL=(LEVEL+1) MOD 3
2640 IF LEVEL=4 THEN PROCtext(1) : INPUT "No. OF SIDES",N,"ANGLE PI*"
     : ANG=PI*A : PROCtext(0) : PROCpoly(N,ANG) :  LEVEL=1
2650 PROClight(3,1,3)
2660 ENDPROC

2800 REM key4

3000 REM sketch
3010 DEF PROCsketch
3020 REPEAT
3030 PROCcursor(1)
3040 IF INKEY(-56) THEN GCOL 3,GC : PLOT 69,X,Y : GCOL 3,3
3050 PROCcross : OX=-1 : OY=-1 : PROCcross
3060 UNTIL INKEY(K(0))
3070 ENDPROC

3100 REM label
3110 DEF PROClabel
3120 PROClight(4,3,1) : PROCcursor(0) : PROClight(4,1,3)
3130 PROCtext(1) : INPUT"LABEL TYPE (N,T,G) ",T$
     : INPUT"LABEL ",A$ : PROCtext(0)
3140 COLOUR 128+BC : COLOUR TC : GCOL 0,TC
3150 IF T$="T" THEN PROCthin(1,X/32,(1024-Y)/32,A$) : GOTO 3180
3160 IF T$="N" THEN PRINT TAB(X/32,(1024-Y)/32);A$
3170 IF T$="G" THEN MOVE X,Y : VDU 5 : PRINT A$ : VDU 4
```

```
3180 OL=-1
3190 ENDPROC

3200 REM point
3210 DEF PROCpoint(A$)
3220 PROClight(4,3,1) : PROCtext(1) : PRINTA$; : PROCtext(0)
3230 PROCcursor(0) : SOUND1,-15,200,1
3240 PROClight(4,1,3)
3250 ENDPROC

3300 REM mark
3310 DEF PROCmark(X,Y)
3320 GCOL3,3 : MOVE X-12,Y-12 : DRAW X+12,Y+12
3330 MOVE X+12,Y-12 : DRAW X-12,Y+12
3340 ENDPROC

3400 REM line
3410 DEF PROCline
3420 PROCpoint("START") : A=X : B=Y : PROCmark(A,B)
3430 PROCpoint("END") : PROCmark(A,B)
3440 MOVE A,B : GCOL 0,GC : DRAW X,Y
3450 ENDPROC

3500 REM triang
3510 DEF PROCtriang
3520 PROCpoint("FIRST") : A=X : B=Y : PROCmark(A,B)
3530 PROCpoint("SECOND") : C=X : D=Y : PROCmark(C,D)
3540 PROCpoint("FINAL") : PROCmark(A,B) : PROCmark(C,D)
3550 GCOL0,GC : IF FILL THEN PROCfill(X,Y,A,B,C,D) : GCOL 0,OC
3560 IF OUTLINE THEN MOVE X,Y : DRAW A,B : DRAW C,D : DRAW X,Y
3570 ENDPROC

3600 REM box
3610 DEF PROCbox
3620 PROCpoint("FIRST") : A=X : B=Y : PROCmark(A,B)
3630 PROCpoint("SECOND") : C=X : D=Y : PROCmark(C,D)
3640 PROCpoint("THIRD") : E=X : F=Y : PROCmark(E,F)
3650 PROCpoint("FINAL") : PROCmark(A,B) : PROCmark(C,D)
     : PROCmark(E,F)
3660 GCOL0,GC : IF FILL THEN PROCfill(X,Y,A,B,E,F)
     : PROCfill(A,B,E,F,C,D) : GCOL 0,OC
3670 IF OUTLINE THEN MOVE X,Y : DRAW A,B : DRAW C,D
     : DRAW E,F : DRAW X,Y
3680 ENDPROC

3700 REM poly
3710 DEF PROCpoly(N,PHI)
3720 PROCpoint("CENTRE") : A=X : B=Y : PROCmark(A,B)
3730 PROCpoint("RADIUS") : PROCmark(A,B)
3740 R=SQR((X-A)^2+(Y-B)^2)
3750 OX=A+COS(PHI)*R : OY=B+SIN(PHI)*R
3760 FOR I=PHI TO 2*PI+PHI+PI/N STEP 2*PI/N
3770 X=A+COS(I)*R : Y=B+SIN(I)*R
3780 IF FILL THEN GCOL 0,GC : PROCfill(A,B,X,Y,OX,OY)
3790 IF OUTLINE THEN GCOL 0,OC : MOVE OX,OY : DRAW X,Y
3800 OX=X : OY=Y
3810 NEXT I : PROCinitcursor(A,B)
3820 ENDPROC

3900 REM circle
3910 DEF PROCcircle
3920 PROCpoly(100,0)
3930 ENDPROC
```

```
4000 REM thin
4010 DEF PROCthin(M,X,Y,A$)
4020 LOCAL I%,A%,P$
4030 A%=2^(4+M) : VDU 5
4040 MOVE X*A%,1023-Y*32
4050 FORI%=1 TO LEN(A$) : P$=MID$(A$,I%,1)
4060 IF P$>="0" AND P$<="9" THEN VDU (80+ASC(P$)) : GOTO 4080
4070 IF P$="+" THEN VDU 144 ELSE IF P$="-" THEN VDU 145 ELSE VDU 146
4080 MOVE (X+I%/2)*A%,1023-Y*32
4090 NEXT I%
4100 VDU 4
4110 ENDPROC
```

---

## Complete Programs

To clarify the use of the programs given in this chapter we have underlined typical responses in the examples below. All the listings should be loaded with PAGE = &1100. Also use the REM stripper.

I Listings 6.1 and 6.2.

Type f3 (ETC.), f0 (histogram)
Range of vertical 0 to 100, number of bars 6
Data for bar 1: 75, inner colour 1, outer colour 3
Data for bar 2: 60, inner colour 0, outer colour 2
Data for bar 3: 88, inner colour 2, outer colour 1
Data for bar 4: 23, inner colour 3, outer colour 3
Data for bar 5: 17, inner colour 3, outer colour 1
Data for bar 6: 97, inner colour 1, outer colour 2
f3 (ETC.), f0 (SAVE), Filename? PIC1

II Listings 6.1 and 6.3.

Type f3 (ETC.), f0 (histogram/second type)
Range of vertical 0 to 200, number of bars 4
Data for bar 1: 166, 84
Data for bar 2: 100, 44
Data for bar 3: 80, 33
Data for bar 4: 40, 10
f3 (ETC.), f0 (SAVE), Filename? PIC2

III Listings 6.1 and 6.4.

Type f3 (ETC.), f0 (pie-chart), number of segments 4
Data 1: 4

Data 2: 3
Data 3: 2
Data 4: 3
Centre pie by using cursors, and enter with f4
Radius in addressable points 400
Centre segment 1 by using cursors and f4
Hatch? X, JUMP 8 FROM 1, inner colour 3, outer colour 1
Centre segment 2 using cursors and f4
Hatch? N, , inner colour 0, outer colour 3
Centre segment 3 by using cursors and f4
Hatch? B, JUMP 12 FROM 0, inner colour 1, outer colour 3
Centre segment 4 by using cursors and f4
Hatch? Y, JUMP 11 FROM 0, inner colour 0, outer colour 2
f3 (ETC.), f0 (SAVE), Filename? PIC3

IV Listings 6.1 and 6.5

Type f3 (ETC.), f0 (graph)
X goes from –10 to 10
Y goes from –1 to 1
Automatic labelling (Y/N) N
Continuous or Discrete, C
F(X): Y = COS(X)
f3 (ETC.), f0 (SAVE), Filename? PIC4

V Listings 6.1 and 6.6

Type f1 (LOAD), Filename? PIC1
f3 (ETC.), f3 (ETC.), note ETC. twice!
f1 (COLOUR), background 3, text colour 1, f3, f3
f2 (SHAPE), f2 (BOTH), f0 (TRIANG)
FIRST (use cursor and f4)
SECOND (use cursor and f4)
FINAL (use cursor and f4), f3
f0 (LABEL), cursor to position and f4
label type (N, T, G)? N
LABEL: HELLO FOLKS
f3 (ETC.), f0 (SAVE), Filename? PIC5

# 7 Three-Dimensional Coordinate Geometry

Before we lead on to a study of the graphical display of objects in three-dimensional space, we first have to come to terms with the three-dimensional Cartesian coordinate geometry. As in two-dimensional space, we arbitrarily fix a point in the space, named the *coordinate origin* (or *origin* for short). We then imagine three mutually perpendicular lines through this point, each line going off to infinity in both directions. These are the *x-axis*, the *y-axis* and the *z-axis*. Each axis is thought to have a positive and a negative half, both starting at the origin; that is, distances measured from the origin along the axis are positive on one side and negative on the other. We may think of the $x$-axis and $y$-axis in the same way as we did for two-dimensional space, both lying on the page of this book say, the positive $x$-axis 'horizontal' and to the right of the origin, and the positive $y$-axis 'vertical' and above the origin. This just leaves the position of the $z$-axis: it has to be perpendicular to the page (since it is perpendicular to both the $x$-axis and the $y$-axis). The positive $z$-axis can be into the page (the so-called *left-handed triad* of axes) or out of the page (the *right-handed triad*). *In this book we always use the left-handed triad notation*. What we say in the remainder of the book, using left-handed axes, has its equivalent in the right-handed system – it does not matter which notation you finally decide to use *as long as you are consistent.*

We specify a general point $\boldsymbol{p}$ in space by a coordinate triple or vector (X, Y, Z), where the individual coordinate values are the perpendicular projections of the point on to the respective $x$-axis, $y$-axis and $z$-axis. By projection we mean the unique point on the specified axis such that a line from that point to $\boldsymbol{p}$ is perpendicular to that axis.

Initially there are two operations we need to consider for three-dimensional vectors. Suppose we have two vectors $\boldsymbol{p}_1 \equiv (x_1, y_1, z_1)$ and $\boldsymbol{p}_2 \equiv (x_2, y_2, z_2)$ then

*scalar multiple*: we multiply the three individual coordinate values by a scalar number $k$

$$k\boldsymbol{p}_1 = (k \times x_1, k \times y_1, k \times z_1)$$

*vector addition*: we add the $x$-coordinates together, then the $y$-coordinates and finally the $z$-coordinates to form a new vector

$$\boldsymbol{p}_1 + \boldsymbol{p}_2 \equiv (x_1 + x_2, y_1 + y_2, z_1 + z_2)$$

**Definition of a Straight Line**

A *straight line* in three-dimensional space that passes through two points such as $\boldsymbol{p}_1 \equiv (x_1, y_1, z_1)$ and $\boldsymbol{p}_2 \equiv (x_2, y_2, z_2)$ is the next object to be defined. We may do this by describing the coordinates of a general point $\boldsymbol{p} \equiv (x, y, z)$ on the line by three equations

$$(x - x_1) \times (y_2 - y_1) = (y - y_1) \times (x_2 - x_1)$$

$$(y - y_1) \times (z_2 - z_1) = (z - z_1) \times (y_2 - y_1)$$

$$(z - z_1) \times (x_2 - x_1) = (x - x_1) \times (z_2 - z_1)$$

Although these are three equations in three unknowns, we shall see that they are inter-related (or so-called *linearly dependent*) and so there is no unique solution (this is natural since we are generating a general point on the line, not just one point). These equations enable us to calculate two of the coordinates in terms of a third (see example 7.1).

As with two dimensions, this is not the only way of representing a line, in fact the second way we introduce is possibly more useful. The general point on the line is represented as a vector that is dependent on only one real number $\mu$, and is given as the vector sum of two scalar multiples of vectors:

$$\boldsymbol{p}(\mu) \equiv (1 - \mu)\boldsymbol{p}_1 + \mu \boldsymbol{p}_2 \quad \text{where} \quad -\infty < \mu < \infty$$

That is

$$\boldsymbol{p}(\mu) \equiv ((1 - \mu) \times x_1 + \mu \times x_2, (1 - \mu) \times y_1 + \mu \times y_2, (1 - \mu) \times z_1 + \mu \times z_2)$$

This form is exactly equivalent to the two-dimensional parametric form of a line that we saw in chapter 3. Here we place $\mu$ in brackets after $\boldsymbol{p}$ to demonstrate the dependence of $\boldsymbol{p}$ on $\mu$; however, when this concept has been fully investigated, then $(\mu)$ will be ignored. Note that when $\mu = 0$ the equation returns point $\boldsymbol{p}_1$ and when $\mu = 1$ it gives point $\boldsymbol{p}_2$.

We may rewrite this vector expression as

$$\boldsymbol{p}(\mu) \equiv \boldsymbol{p}_1 + \mu(\boldsymbol{p}_2 - \boldsymbol{p}_1)$$

Like its counterpart in two dimensions, $\boldsymbol{p}_1$ is called a *base vector* and $(\boldsymbol{p}_2 - \boldsymbol{p}_1)$ a *directional vector*. Again we see the dual interpretation of a vector. A vector may be used to specify a point uniquely in three-dimensional space, or it may be considered as a general direction, namely any line parallel to the line that joins the origin to the vector (considered as a point). We can move along a line in one of two directions, so we say that the direction from the origin to the point has *positive sense*, and the direction from the point to the origin has *negative sense*. Hence vectors $\boldsymbol{d} \equiv (x, y, z)$ and $-\boldsymbol{d} \equiv (-x, -y, -z)$ represent the same line in space but their directions are of opposite senses. We define the length of a vector $\boldsymbol{d} \equiv (x, y, z)$ (sometimes called its modulus, or absolute value) as $|\boldsymbol{d}|$, and the distance of the point vector from the origin is

$$|\boldsymbol{d}| = \sqrt{(x^2 + y^2 + z^2)}$$

So any point on the line $\boldsymbol{p} + \mu \boldsymbol{d}$ is found by moving to the point $\boldsymbol{p}$ and then travelling along a line that is parallel to the direction $\boldsymbol{d}$, a distance of $\mu\,|\boldsymbol{d}|$ in the positive sense of $\boldsymbol{d}$ if $\mu$ is positive, and in the negative sense otherwise. Note that any point on the line can act as a base vector, and the directional vector may be replaced by any non-zero scalar multiple of itself.

If the directional vector $\boldsymbol{d} \equiv (x, y, z)$ makes angles of $\theta_x, \theta_y$ and $\theta_z$ with the respective positive $x$-direction, $y$-direction and $z$-direction, then

$$x : y : z = \cos\theta_x : \cos\theta_y : \cos\theta_z$$

which means that

$$\boldsymbol{d} \equiv (\lambda \times \cos\theta_x, \lambda \times \cos\theta_y, \lambda \times \cos\theta_z) \text{ for some } \lambda$$

We know from the properties of three-dimensional geometry that

$$\cos^2\theta_x + \cos^2\theta_y + \cos^2\theta_z = 1$$

Hence $\lambda = |\boldsymbol{d}|$, and if the directional vector has unit modulus (that is, modulus = $\lambda = 1$), then the coordinates of this vector must be $(\cos\theta_x, \cos\theta_y, \cos\theta_z)$. The coordinates of a directional vector given in this way are called the *direction cosines* of the set of lines that is generated by the vector. In general, if the direction vector is $\boldsymbol{d} \equiv (x, y, z)$ then the direction cosines are

$$\left(\frac{x}{|\boldsymbol{d}|}, \frac{y}{|\boldsymbol{d}|}, \frac{z}{|\boldsymbol{d}|}\right)$$

*Example 7.1*

Describe the line joining (1, 2, 3) to (−1, 0, 2), by using the three methods shown so far.

The general point $(x, y, z)$ on the line satisfies the equations

$$(x - 1) \times (0 - 2) = (y - 2) \times (-1 - 1)$$

$$(y - 2) \times (2 - 3) = (z - 3) \times (0 - 2)$$

$$(z - 3) \times (-1 - 1) = (x - 1) \times (2 - 3)$$

That is

$$-2x + 2y = 2 \qquad (7.1)$$

$$-y + 2z = 4 \qquad (7.2)$$

$$-2z + x = -5 \qquad (7.3)$$

Note that equation (7.1) is −2 times the sum of equations (7.2) and (7.3). Thus we need consider only these latter two equations, to get

$$x = 2z - 5$$

$$y = 2z - 4$$

Hence the general point on the line depends only on one variable, in this case $z$, and it is given by $(2z - 5, 2z - 4, z)$. This result can easily be checked by noting that when $z = 3$ we get $(1, 2, 3)$ and when $z = 2$ we get $(-1, 0, 2)$, the two original points that define the line.

In vector form the general point on the line (depending on $\mu$) is

$$\boldsymbol{p}(\mu) \equiv (1 - \mu)(1, 2, 3) + \mu(-1, 0, 2) \equiv (1 - 2\mu, 2 - 2\mu, 3 - \mu)$$

Again the coordinates depend on just one variable ($\mu$), and to check the validity of this representation of a line we note that $\boldsymbol{p}(0) \equiv (1, 2, 3)$ and $\boldsymbol{p}(1) \equiv (-1, 0, 2)$.

If we put the line into base/directional vector form we see that

$$\boldsymbol{p}(\mu) \equiv (1, 2, 3) + \mu(-2, -2, -1)$$

with $(1, 2, 3)$ as the base vector and $(-2, -2, -1)$ as the direction (which incidently has modulus $\sqrt{(4 + 4 + 1)} = \sqrt{9} = 3$). We also noted that any point on the line can act as a base vector, and so we can give another form for the general point on this line, $\boldsymbol{p}'$:

$$\boldsymbol{p}'(\mu) \equiv (-1, 0, 2) + \mu(-2, -2, -1)$$

We can change the directional vector into its direction cosine form $(-2/3, -2/3, -1/3)$ and represent the line in another version of the base/direction form:

$$\boldsymbol{p}''(\mu) \equiv (1, 2, 3) + \mu(-2/3, -2/3, -1/3)$$

Naturally the same $\mu$ value will give different points for different representations of the line; for example, $\boldsymbol{p}(3) \equiv (-5, -4, 0)$, $\boldsymbol{p}'(3) \equiv (-7, -6, -1)$ and $\boldsymbol{p}''(3) \equiv (-1, 0, 2)$. The direction of this line makes angles of 131.81 degrees ($= \cos^{-1}(-2/3)$), 131.81 degrees and 109.47 degrees ($= \cos^{-1}(-1/3)$) with the positive $x$-direction, $y$-direction and $z$-direction respectively.

## The Angle between Two Directional Vectors

In order to calculate such an angle we first introduce the operator $\cdot$, the *dot product* or *scalar product*. This operates on two vectors and returns a scalar (real) result thus:

$$\boldsymbol{p} \cdot \boldsymbol{q} = (x_1, y_1, z_1) \cdot (x_2, y_2, z_2) = x_1 \times x_2 + y_1 \times y_2 + z_1 \times z_2$$

If $\boldsymbol{p}$ and $\boldsymbol{q}$ are both unit vectors (that is, they are in direction cosine form), and $\theta$ is the angle between the lines, then $\cos\theta = \boldsymbol{p} \cdot \boldsymbol{q}$ (see chapter 3 for the equivalent two-dimensional relationship). In general, therefore, the angle between two directional vectors $\boldsymbol{p}$ and $\boldsymbol{q}$ (we can assume they meet at the origin) is

$$\cos^{-1}\left(\frac{\boldsymbol{p}}{|\boldsymbol{p}|} \cdot \frac{\boldsymbol{q}}{|\boldsymbol{q}|}\right)$$

Obviously $\boldsymbol{p}$ and $\boldsymbol{q}$ are mutually perpendicular directions if and only if $\boldsymbol{p} \cdot \boldsymbol{q} = 0$.

## Definition of a Plane

The plane is the next object we must consider in three-dimensional space. The general point $x \equiv (x, y, z)$ on the plane is given by the vector equation:

$$\boldsymbol{n} \cdot \boldsymbol{x} = k$$

where $k$ is a scalar, and $\boldsymbol{n}$ is the directional vector of the set of lines that are perpendicular to (or *normal* to) the plane (see example 7.2). If $\boldsymbol{a}$ is any point on the plane then naturally $\boldsymbol{n} \cdot \boldsymbol{a} = k$, and so by replacing $k$ in the above equation, we may rewrite it as

$$\boldsymbol{n} \cdot \boldsymbol{x} = \boldsymbol{n} \cdot \boldsymbol{a} \quad \text{or} \quad \boldsymbol{n} \cdot (\boldsymbol{x} - \boldsymbol{a}) = 0$$

This latter equation is self-evident from the property of the dot product – two mutually perpendicular lines have zero dot product. For any point $\boldsymbol{x} \equiv (x, y, z)$ in the plane that is not equal to $\boldsymbol{a}$, we know that $(\boldsymbol{x} - \boldsymbol{a})$ can be considered as the direction of a line in the plane. Since $\boldsymbol{n}$ is normal to the plane, and incidently perpendicular to every line in the plane, then $\boldsymbol{n} \cdot (\boldsymbol{x} - \boldsymbol{a}) = \cos(\pi/2) = 0$.

By expanding the original equation of the plane with normal $\boldsymbol{n} \equiv (n_1, n_2, n_3)$, we get the usual coordinate representation of a plane:

$$(n_1, n_2, n_3) \cdot (x, y, z) = n_1 \times x + n_2 \times y + n_3 \times z = k$$

Note that two planes with normals $\boldsymbol{n}$ and $\boldsymbol{m}$ (say) are parallel if and only if one normal is a scalar multiple of the other, that is if $\boldsymbol{n} = \lambda \boldsymbol{m}$ for some $\lambda \neq 0$.

## The Point of Intersection of a Line and a Plane

Suppose the line is given by $\boldsymbol{b} + \mu \boldsymbol{d}$ and the plane by $\boldsymbol{n} \cdot \boldsymbol{x} = k$. Since the point of intersection lies on both the line and the plane we have to find the unique value of $\mu$ (if one exists) for which

$$\boldsymbol{n} \cdot (\boldsymbol{b} + \mu \boldsymbol{d}) = k$$

that is

$$\mu = (k - \boldsymbol{n} \cdot \boldsymbol{b})/(\boldsymbol{n} \cdot \boldsymbol{d}) \text{ provided } \boldsymbol{n} \cdot \boldsymbol{d} \neq 0$$

$\boldsymbol{n} \cdot \boldsymbol{d} = 0$ if the line and plane are parallel and so either there is no point of intersection or the line is in the plane.

## The Distance of a Point from a Plane

The distance of a point $\boldsymbol{p}_1$ from a plane $\boldsymbol{n} \cdot \boldsymbol{x} = k$ is the distance of $\boldsymbol{p}_1$ from the nearest point $\boldsymbol{p}_2$ on the plane. Hence the normal from the plane at $\boldsymbol{p}_2$ must pass through $\boldsymbol{p}_1$. This line can be written $\boldsymbol{p}_1 + \mu\boldsymbol{n}$, and the $\mu$ value that defines $\boldsymbol{p}_2$ is such that

$$\mu = (k - \boldsymbol{n} \cdot \boldsymbol{p}_1)/(\boldsymbol{n} \cdot \boldsymbol{n})$$

from the equation above, and the distance of the point $\boldsymbol{p}_2 \equiv \boldsymbol{p}_1 + \mu\boldsymbol{n}$ from $\boldsymbol{p}_1$ is

$$\mu \times |\boldsymbol{n}| = |k - \boldsymbol{n} \cdot \boldsymbol{p}_1| / |\boldsymbol{n}|$$

In particular, if $\boldsymbol{p}_1$ is the origin $\boldsymbol{O}$ then the distance of the plane from the origin is $|k| / |\boldsymbol{n}|$. Furthermore, if $\boldsymbol{n}$ is a direction cosine vector we see that the distance of the origin from the plane is $|k|$, the absolute value of the real number $k$.

*Example 7.2*
Find the point of intersection of the line joining (1, 2, 3) to (−1, 0, 2) with the plane $(0, -2, 1) \cdot \boldsymbol{x} = 5$, and also find the distance of the plane from the origin.

$$\boldsymbol{n} \equiv (0, -2, 1)$$

$$\boldsymbol{b} \equiv (1, 2, 3)$$

$$\boldsymbol{d} \equiv (-1, 0, 2) - (1, 2, 3) \equiv (-2, -2, -1)$$

$$\boldsymbol{n} \cdot \boldsymbol{b} = (0 \times 1 + -2 \times 2 + 1 \times 3) = -1$$

$$\boldsymbol{n} \cdot \boldsymbol{d} = (0 \times -2 + -2 \times -2 + 1 \times -1) = 3$$

hence the $\mu$ value of the point of intersection is $(5 - (-1))/3 = 2$, and the point vector is

$$(1, 2, 3) + 2(-2, -2, -1) \equiv (-3, -2, 1)$$

and the distance from the origin is $5/|\boldsymbol{n}| = 5/\sqrt{5} = \sqrt{5}$.

The program given in listing 7.1 enables us to calculate the point of intersection (array P) of a line and a plane. The line has base vector B and direction D, and the plane has normal N and plane constant K. Note that, since we are working with decimal numbers, and thus are subject to rounding errors, we cannot check if a dot product is zero. We can find only if it is sufficiently small to be considered zero, and what is meant by sufficiently small is left to the programmer (on the BBC micro about six places after the decimal point is reasonable).

## The Point of Intersection of Two Lines

Suppose we have two lines $\boldsymbol{b}_1 + \mu\boldsymbol{d}_1$ and $\boldsymbol{b}_2 + \lambda\boldsymbol{d}_2$. Their point of intersection, if it exists (if the lines are not coplanar or are parallel then they will not intersect), is identified by finding unique values for $\mu$ and $\lambda$ that satisfy the vector equation (three separate coordinate equations):

$$\boldsymbol{b}_1 + \mu\boldsymbol{d}_1 = \boldsymbol{b}_2 + \lambda\boldsymbol{d}_2$$

*Listing 7.1*

```
100 REM Intersection of line and plane
110 DIM B(3),D(3),N(3),P(3)
119 REM input line and plane data
120 CLS : PRINT TAB(0,2)," Intersection of line and plane      "
130 INPUT" Base vector of line ",B(1),B(2),B(3)
140 INPUT" Direction vector of line ",D(1),D(2),D(3)
150 INPUT" Normal to plane ",N(1),N(2),N(3)
160 INPUT" Plane constant ",K
170 DOT=N(1)*D(1)+N(2)*D(2)+N(3)*D(3)
179 REM output line and plane data
180 CLS
190 PRINT TAB(0,5);"Base vector of line "
200 PRINT TAB(0,6);"(";B(1);",";B(2);",";B(3);")"
210 PRINT TAB(0,8);"Direction vector of line "
220 PRINT TAB(0,9);"(";D(1);",";D(2);",";D(3);")"
230 PRINT TAB(0,11);"Normal to plane "
240 PRINT TAB(0,12);"(";N(1);",";N(2);",";N(3);")"
250 PRINT TAB(0,14);"Plane constant  ";K
260 PRINT TAB(0,18);"Point of intersection"
269 REM find point of intersection
270 IF ABS(DOT)<0.000001 THEN PRINT TAB(22,18) "does not exist" : GOTO
280 MU=(K-N(1)*B(1)-N(2)*B(2)-N(3)*B(3))/DOT
290 FOR I%=1 TO 3
300 P(I%)=B(I%)+MU*D(I%)
310 NEXT I%
320 PRINT TAB(0,19);"(";P(1);",";P(2);",";P(3);")"
330 PRINT TAB(0,22); : STOP
```

Three equations in two unknowns means that for the equations to be meaningful there must be at least one pair of the equations that are independent, and the remaining equation must be a combination of these two. Two lines are parallel if one directional vector is a scalar multiple of the other. So we take two independent equations, find the values of $\mu$ and $\lambda$ (we have two equations in two unknowns), and put them in the third equation to see if they are consistent. Example 7.3 will demonstrate this method, and listing 7.2 is a way of implementing it on a computer. The first line has base and direction stored in arrays B and D, and the second line in C and E: the calculated point of intersection goes into array P.

Note that if the two independent equations are

$$a_{11} \times \mu + a_{12} \times \lambda = b_1$$

$$a_{21} \times \mu + a_{22} \times \lambda = b_2$$

then the *determinant* of this pair of equations, $\Delta = a_{11} \times a_{22} - a_{12} \times a_{21}$, will be non-zero (because the equations are not related), and we have the solutions:

$$\mu = (a_{22} \times b_1 - a_{12} \times b_2)/\Delta \quad \text{and} \quad \lambda = (a_{11} \times b_2 - a_{21} \times b_1)/\Delta$$

*Listing 7.2*

```
100 REM Intersection of two lines
110 DIM B(3),D(3),C(3),E(3),N(3),P(3)
120 CLS : PRINT TAB(1,2)"Intersection of two lines",SPC(9)
129 REM input data on two lines
130 INPUT" Base vector of first line ",B(1),B(2),B(3)
140 INPUT" Direction vector of first line ",D(1),D(2),D(3)
150 INPUT" Base vector of second line "C(1),C(2),C(3)
160 INPUT" Direction vector of second line ",E(1),E(2),E(3)
169 REM output data on two lines
170 CLS
180 PRINT TAB(0,5);"Base vector of first line "
190 PRINT TAB(0,6);"(";B(1);",";B(2);",";B(3);")"
200 PRINT TAB(0,8);"Direction vector of first line "
210 PRINT TAB(0,9);"(";D(1);",";D(2);",";D(3);")"
220 PRINT TAB(0,11);"Base vector of second line "
230 PRINT TAB(0,12);"(";C(1);",";C(2);",";C(3);")"
240 PRINT TAB(0,14);"Direction vector of second line "
250 PRINT TAB(0,15);"(";E(1);",";E(2);",";E(3);")"
260 PRINT TAB(0,18);"Point of intersection"
269 REM find independent equations
270 FOR I%=1 TO 3
280 J%=(I% MOD 3)+1
290 DELTA=E(I%)*D(J%)-E(J%)*D(I%)
300 IF ABS(DELTA)>0.000001 THEN GOTO 330
310 NEXT I%
319 REM find point of intersection
320 PRINT TAB(22,18) "does not exist" : GOTO 410
330 MU=(E(I%)*(C(J%)-B(J%))-E(J%)*(C(I%)-B(I%)))/DELTA
340 LAMBDA=(D(I%)*(C(J%)-B(J%))-D(J%)*(C(I%)-B(I%)))/DELTA
350 K%=(J% MOD 3)+1
360 IF ABS(B(K%)+MU*D(K%)-C(K%)-LAMBDA*E(K%)) > 0.000001 THEN GOTO 320
370 FOR I%=1 TO 3
380 P(I%)=B(I%)+MU*D(I%)
390 NEXT I%
400 PRINT TAB(0,19);"(";P(1);",";P(2);",";P(3);")"
410 PRINT TAB(0,22); : STOP
```

***Example 7.3***

Find the point of intersection (if any) of

(a) $(1, 1, 1) + \mu(2, 1, 3)$ with $(0, 0, 1) + \lambda(-1, 1, 1)$,

(b) $(2, 3, 4) + \mu(1, 1, 1)$ with $(-2, -3, -4) + \lambda(1, 2, 3)$.

In (a) the three equations are

$$1 + 2\mu = 0 - \lambda \tag{7.4}$$

$$1 + \mu = 0 + \lambda \tag{7.5}$$

$$1 + 3\mu = 1 + \lambda \tag{7.6}$$

From equations (7.4) and (7.5) we get $\mu = -2/3$ and $\lambda = 1/3$, which when substituted in equation (7.6) gives $1 + 3 \times (-2/3) = -1$ on the left-hand side and $1 + 1 \times (1/3) = 4/3$ on the right-hand side, which are obviously unequal so the lines do not intersect.

From (b) we get the equations

$$2 + \mu = -2 + \lambda \tag{7.7}$$

$$3 + \mu = -3 + 2\lambda \tag{7.8}$$

$$4 + \mu = -4 + 3\lambda \tag{7.9}$$

and from equations (7.7) and (7.8) we get $\mu = -2$ and $\lambda = 2$, and these values also satisfy equation (7.9) (left-hand side = right-hand side = 2). So the point of intersection is

$$(2, 3, 4) - 2(1, 1, 1) = (-2, -3, -4) + 2(1, 2, 3) = (0, 1, 2)$$

## The Plane through Three Non-collinear Points

In order to solve this problem we must introduce a new vector operator, $\times$ the *vector product*, which operates on two vectors $\boldsymbol{p}$ and $\boldsymbol{q}$ (say) giving the vector result

$$\boldsymbol{p} \times \boldsymbol{q} = (p_1, p_2, p_3) \times (q_1, q_2, q_3) = (p_2 \times q_3 - p_3 \times q_2, p_3 \times q_1 - p_1 \times q_3, p_1 \times q_2 - p_2 \times q_1)$$

If $\boldsymbol{p}$ and $\boldsymbol{q}$ are non-parallel directional vectors then $\boldsymbol{p} \times \boldsymbol{q}$ is the directional vector that is perpendicular to both $\boldsymbol{p}$ and $\boldsymbol{q}$. It should also be noted that this operation is *non-commutative*. That is, in general for given values of $\boldsymbol{p}$ and $\boldsymbol{q}$ we note that $\boldsymbol{p} \times \boldsymbol{q} \neq \boldsymbol{q} \times \boldsymbol{p}$; these two vector products will represent directions on the same line but with opposite sense. For example $(1, 0, 0) \times (0, 1, 0) = (0, 0, 1)$ but $(0, 1, 0) \times (1, 0, 0) = (0, 0, -1)$; $(0, 0, 1)$ and $(0, 0, -1)$ are both parallel to the $z$-axis (and so perpendicular to the directions $(1, 0, 0)$ and $(0, 1, 0)$), but they are of opposite sense. Listing 7.3 gives a main program that calls the procedures 'vecprod' (for the vector product of two vectors L and M returning vector N) and 'dotprod' (which calculates the dot product DOT of the vectors L and M).

Suppose we are given three non-collinear points $\boldsymbol{p}_1, \boldsymbol{p}_2$ and $\boldsymbol{p}_3$. Then the two vectors $\boldsymbol{p}_2 - \boldsymbol{p}_1$ and $\boldsymbol{p}_3 - \boldsymbol{p}_1$ represent the directions of two lines that are coincident at $\boldsymbol{p}_1$, both of which lie in the plane that contains the three points. We know that the normal to the plane is perpendicular to every line in the plane, in particular to the two lines mentioned above. Also, because the points are not collinear, $\boldsymbol{p}_2 - \boldsymbol{p}_1 \neq \boldsymbol{p}_3 - \boldsymbol{p}_1$, the normal to the plane is $(\boldsymbol{p}_2 - \boldsymbol{p}_1) \times (\boldsymbol{p}_3 - \boldsymbol{p}_1)$, and since $\boldsymbol{p}_1$ lies in the plane the equation is

$$((\boldsymbol{p}_2 - \boldsymbol{p}_1) \times (\boldsymbol{p}_3 - \boldsymbol{p}_1)) \cdot (\boldsymbol{x} - \boldsymbol{p}_1) = 0$$

*Example 7.4*
Give the coordinate equation of the plane through the points (0, 1, 1), (1, 2, 3) and (−2, 3, −1).

*Listing 7.3*

```
100 REM Example of dot/vector product
110 DIM L(3),M(3),N(3) : CLS
120 PRINT TAB(0,3)"Example of dot/vector product",SPC(10)
130 INPUT" Vector L ",L(1),L(2),L(3)
140 INPUT" Vector M ",M(1),M(2),M(3)
150 CLS : PROCvecprod
160 PRINT TAB(0,5);"Vector L "
170 PRINT TAB(0,6);"(";L(1);",";L(2);",";L(3);")"
180 PRINT TAB(0,8);"Vector M "
190 PRINT TAB(0,9);"(";M(1);",";M(2);",";M(3);")"
200 PRINT TAB(0,11);"Vector Product "
210 PRINT TAB(0,12);"(";N(1);",";N(2);",";N(3);")"
220 PRINT TAB(0,14);"Dot Product  "; FNdotprod
230 PRINT TAB(0,22) : STOP

300 REM vecprod
310 DEF PROCvecprod
320 LOCAL I%,J%,K%
330 FOR I%=1 TO 3
340 J%=(I% MOD 3)+1 : K%=(J% MOD 3)+1
350 N(I%)=L(J%)*M(K%)-L(K%)*M(J%)
360 NEXT I%
370 ENDPROC

400 REM dotprod
410 DEF FNdotprod=L(1)*M(1)+L(2)*M(2)+L(3)*M(3)
```

This is given by the general point $\boldsymbol{x} \equiv (x, y, z)$ where

$$(((1, 2, 3) - (0, 1, 1)) \times ((-2, 3, -1) - (0, 1, 1))) \cdot ((x, y, z) - (0, 1, 1)) = 0$$

that is

$$((1, 1, 2) \times (-2, 2, -2)) \cdot (x, y - 1, z - 1) = 0$$

or

$$(-6, -2, 4) \cdot (x, y - 1, z - 1) = 0$$

which in coordinate form is $-6x - 2y + 4z - 2 = 0$ or in the equivalent form $3x + y - 2z = -1$.

## The Point of Intersection of Three Planes

We assume that the three planes are defined by equations (7.10) to (7.12) below. The point of intersection of these three planes, $\boldsymbol{b} \equiv (x, y, z)$, must lie in all three planes and satisfy

$$n_1 \cdot x = k_1 \tag{7.10}$$

$$n_2 \cdot x = k_2 \tag{7.11}$$

$$n_3 \cdot x = k_3 \tag{7.12}$$

where $\boldsymbol{n}_1 \equiv (n_{11}, n_{12}, n_{13})$, $\boldsymbol{n}_2 \equiv (n_{21}, n_{22}, n_{23})$ and $\boldsymbol{n}_3 \equiv (n_{31}, n_{32}, n_{33})$. We can rewrite these three equations as one matrix equation

$$\begin{pmatrix} n_{11} & n_{12} & n_{13} \\ n_{21} & n_{22} & n_{23} \\ n_{31} & n_{32} & n_{33} \end{pmatrix} \times \begin{pmatrix} x \\ y \\ z \end{pmatrix} = \begin{pmatrix} k_1 \\ k_2 \\ k_3 \end{pmatrix}$$

and so the solution for $\boldsymbol{b}$ is given by the *column vector*

$$\begin{pmatrix} x \\ y \\ z \end{pmatrix} = \begin{pmatrix} n_{11} & n_{12} & n_{13} \\ n_{21} & n_{22} & n_{23} \\ n_{31} & n_{32} & n_{33} \end{pmatrix}^{-1} \times \begin{pmatrix} k_1 \\ k_2 \\ k_3 \end{pmatrix}$$

So any calculation that requires the intersection of three planes necessarily involves the inversion of a 3 x 3 matrix. Listing 7.4 gives the Adjoint method of finding NINV, the inverse of matrix N. It also returns variable SNG which equals 0 if N is non-singular and 1 otherwise.

*Listing 7.4*

```
500 REM Find NINV, the inverse of 3x3 matrix N
        using the Adjoint method
510 DEF PROCinv
520 LOCAL I%,J%,NI%,NNI%
529 REM find DET, determinant of N
530 DET=0 : NI%=2 : NNI%=3
540 FOR I%=1 TO 3
550 DET=DET+N(1,I%)*(N(2,NI%)*N(3,NNI%)-N(3,NI%)*N(2,NNI%))
560 NI%=NNI% : NNI%= (NNI% MOD 3)+1
570 NEXT I%
579 REM if DET zero then N singular
580 IF ABS(DET)<0.000001 THEN SNG=1 : ENDPROC ELSE SNG=0
589 REM calculate NINV
590 NI%=2 : NNI%=3
600 FOR I%=1 TO 3
610 NJ%=2 : NNJ%=3
620 FOR J%=1 TO 3
630 NINV(J%,I%)=(N(NI%,NJ%)*N(NNI%,NNJ%)-N(NI%,NNJ%)*N(NNI%,NJ%))/DET
640 NJ%=NNJ% : NNJ%= (NNJ% MOD 3)+1
650 NEXT J%
660 NI%=NNI% : NNI%= (NNI% MOD 3)+1
670 NEXT I%
680 ENDPROC
```

Again in the program to solve this problem (listing 7.5), vectors are represented as one-dimensional arrays, thus array B will contain the solution of the equations (***b***); array K will contain the plane constants. We are given the normals $\boldsymbol{n}_1, \boldsymbol{n}_2$ and $\boldsymbol{n}_3$ in the form of a 3 × 3 array N, so the values in B are found by the following code. Obviously if any two of the planes are parallel or the three meet in a line, then SNG equals 1 and there is no unique point of intersection.

*Listing 7.5*

```
100 REM Intersection of three planes
110 DIM N(3,3),NINV(3,3),K(3),B(3)
120 CLS :PRINT TAB(0,2),"Intersection of three planes",SPC(10)
129 REM input data on planes put in arrays N and K
130 FOR I%=1 TO 3
140 PRINT"Input normal and constant for plane ";I%
150 INPUT N(I%,1),N(I%,2),N(I%,3),K(I%)
160 NEXT I%
169 REM output data on planes
170 CLS
180 PRINT TAB(2,5);"PLANE No.    CONSTANT     NORMAL"
190 ROW=7
200 FOR I%=1 TO 3
210 PRINT TAB(0,ROW),I%,K(I%),"       (";
     N(I%,1);",";N(I%,2);",";N(I%,3);")"
220 ROW=ROW+2
230 NEXTI%
239 REM find NINV, the inverse of N and B, point of intersection
240 PRINT TAB(0,14);"Point of intersection"
250 PROCinv
260 IF SNG THEN PRINT TAB(22,14) "does not exist" : GOTO 340
270 FOR I%=1 TO 3
280 B(I%)=0
290 FOR J%=1 TO 3
300 B(I%)=B(I%)+NINV(I%,J%)*K(J%)
310 NEXT J%
320 NEXT I%
330 PRINT TAB(0,15);"(";B(1);",";B(2);",";B(3);")"
340 PRINT TAB(0,22); : STOP
```

*Example 7.5*

Find the point of intersection of the three planes $(0, 1, 1) \cdot \boldsymbol{x} = 2$, $(1, 2, 3) \cdot \boldsymbol{x} = 4$ and $(1, 1, 1) \cdot \boldsymbol{x} = 0$.

In the matrix form we have

$$\begin{pmatrix} 0 & 1 & 1 \\ 1 & 2 & 3 \\ 1 & 1 & 1 \end{pmatrix} \times \begin{pmatrix} x \\ y \\ z \end{pmatrix} = \begin{pmatrix} 2 \\ 4 \\ 0 \end{pmatrix}$$

The inverse of $\begin{pmatrix} 0 & 1 & 1 \\ 1 & 2 & 3 \\ 1 & 1 & 1 \end{pmatrix}$ is $\begin{pmatrix} -1 & 0 & 1 \\ 2 & -1 & 1 \\ -1 & 1 & -1 \end{pmatrix}$

and so

$$\begin{pmatrix} x \\ y \\ z \end{pmatrix} = \begin{pmatrix} -1 & 0 & 1 \\ 2 & -1 & 1 \\ -1 & 1 & -1 \end{pmatrix} \times \begin{pmatrix} 2 \\ 4 \\ 0 \end{pmatrix} = \begin{pmatrix} -2 \\ 0 \\ 2 \end{pmatrix}$$

This solution is easily checked: $(0, 1, 1) \cdot (-2, 0, 2) = 2$, $(1, 2, 3) \cdot (-2, 0, 2) = 4$ and $(1, 1, 1) \cdot (-2, 0, 2) = 0$, which means the point $(-2, 0, 2)$ lies on all three planes and so is their point of intersection.

## The Line of Intersection of Two Planes

Let the two planes be

$$\boldsymbol{p} \cdot \boldsymbol{x} = (p_1, p_2, p_3) \cdot \boldsymbol{x} = k_1$$

and

$$\boldsymbol{q} \cdot \boldsymbol{x} = (q_1, q_2, q_3) \cdot \boldsymbol{x} = k_2$$

We assume that the planes are not parallel, and so $\boldsymbol{p} \neq \lambda \boldsymbol{q}$ for all $\lambda$. The line common to the two planes naturally lies in each plane, and so it must be perpendicular to the normals of both planes ($\boldsymbol{p}$ and $\boldsymbol{q}$). Thus the direction of this line must be $\boldsymbol{d} \equiv \boldsymbol{p} \times \boldsymbol{q}$ and the line can be written in the form $\boldsymbol{b} + \mu \boldsymbol{d}$, where $\boldsymbol{b}$ can be any point on the line. In order completely to classify the line we have to find one such $\boldsymbol{b}$. We find a point that is the intersection of the two planes together with a third that is neither parallel to them nor cuts them in a common line. By choosing a plane with normal $\boldsymbol{p} \times \boldsymbol{q}$ we shall satisfy these conditions (and remember we have already calculated this vector product). We still need a value for $k_3$, but any value will do, so we take $k_3 = 0$ in order that this third plane goes through the origin. Thus $\boldsymbol{b}$ is given by the column vector

$$\boldsymbol{b} = \begin{pmatrix} p_1 & p_2 & p_3 \\ q_1 & q_2 & q_3 \\ p_2 \times q_3 - p_3 \times q_2 & p_3 \times q_1 - p_1 \times q_3 & p_1 \times q_2 - p_2 \times q_1 \end{pmatrix}^{-1} \times \begin{pmatrix} k_1 \\ k_2 \\ 0 \end{pmatrix}$$

*Example 7.6*

Find the line that is common to the planes $(0, 1, 1) \cdot \boldsymbol{x} = 2$ and $(1, 2, 3) \cdot \boldsymbol{x} = 2$.

$\boldsymbol{p} = (0, 1, 1)$ and $\boldsymbol{q} = (1, 2, 3)$, and so $\boldsymbol{p} \times \boldsymbol{q} = (1 \times 3 - 1 \times 2, 1 \times 1 - 0 \times 3, 0 \times 2 - 1 \times 1) = (1, 1, -1)$. We require the inverse of

$$\begin{pmatrix} 0 & 1 & 1 \\ 1 & 2 & 3 \\ 1 & 1 & -1 \end{pmatrix} = \frac{1}{3} \begin{pmatrix} -5 & 2 & 1 \\ 4 & -1 & 1 \\ -1 & 1 & -1 \end{pmatrix}$$

and hence the point of intersection of the three planes is

$$\frac{1}{3}\begin{pmatrix} -5 & 2 & 1 \\ 4 & -1 & 1 \\ -1 & 1 & -1 \end{pmatrix} \times \begin{pmatrix} 2 \\ 2 \\ 0 \end{pmatrix} = \frac{1}{3}\begin{pmatrix} -6 \\ 6 \\ 0 \end{pmatrix} = \begin{pmatrix} -2 \\ 2 \\ 0 \end{pmatrix}$$

and the line is $(-2, 2, 0) + \mu(1, 1, -1)$.

It is easy to check this result, because all the points on the line should lie in both planes:

$$(0, 1, 1) \cdot ((-2, 2, 0) + \mu(1, 1, -1))$$
$$= (0, 1, 1) \cdot (-2, 2, 0) + \mu(0, 1, 1) \cdot (1, 1, -1) = 2 \quad \text{for all } \mu$$

and

$$(1, 2, 3) \cdot ((-2, 2, 0) + \mu(1, 1, -1))$$
$$= (0, 1, 1) \cdot (-2, 2, 0) + \mu(1, 2, 3) \cdot (1, 1, -1) = 2 \quad \text{for all } \mu$$

The program to solve this problem is given as listing 7.6; note that it is very similar to the previous program. Also note that arrays are not explicitly used for $\boldsymbol{p}$ and $\boldsymbol{q}$ – these values are stored in the first two rows of array N. Array B holds the base vector of the line of intersection, but we do not place $\boldsymbol{d}$ in an array because the values are already in the third row of N.

## Functional Representation of a Surface

In our study of two-dimensional space in chapter 3 we noted that curves can be represented in a functional notation. This idea can be extended into three dimensions when we study surfaces. The simplest form of surface is an infinite plane with normal $\boldsymbol{n} \equiv (n_1, n_2, n_3)$, which we have seen can be given as a coordinate equation:

$$\boldsymbol{n} \cdot \boldsymbol{x} - k = n_1 \times x + n_2 \times y + n_3 \times z - k = 0$$

This can be rewritten in functional form for a general point $\boldsymbol{x} \equiv (x, y, z)$ on the surface:

$$f(\boldsymbol{x}) \equiv f(x, y, z) \equiv n_1 \times x + n_2 \times y + n_3 \times z - k \equiv \boldsymbol{n} \cdot \boldsymbol{x} - k$$

which is a simple expression in variables $x, y$ and $z$ ($\boldsymbol{x}$). This enables us to divide all the points in space into three sets, those with $f(\boldsymbol{x}) = 0$ (the zero set), those with $f(\boldsymbol{x}) < 0$ (the negative set) and those with $f(\boldsymbol{x}) > 0$ (the positive set). A point $\boldsymbol{x}$ lies on the surface if and only if it belongs to the zero set. If the surface divides space into two halves (each half being *connected*, that is any two points in a given half can be joined by a curve that does not cross the surface) then these two halves may be identified with the positive and negative sets. Again

*Listing 7.6*

```
100 REM Intersection of two planes
110 DIM N(3,3),NINV(3,3),K(3),B(3)
120 CLS : PRINT TAB(0,2),"Intersection of two planes",SPC(10)
129 REM input plane information
130 FOR I%=1 TO 2
140 PRINT"Input normal and constant for plane ";I%
150 INPUT N(I%,1),N(I%,2),N(I%,3),K(I%)
160 NEXT I%
169 REM find third rows of N and K directional vector of the
         line of intersection is (N(3,1),N(3,2),N(3,3))
170 N(3,1)=N(1,2)*N(2,3)-N(1,3)*N(2,2)
180 N(3,2)=N(1,3)*N(2,1)-N(1,1)*N(2,3)
190 N(3,3)=N(1,1)*N(2,2)-N(1,2)*N(2,1)
200 K(3)=0
209 REM output plane information
210 CLS
220 PRINT TAB(2,5);"PLANE No.   CONSTANT    NORMAL"
230 ROW=7
240 FOR I%=1 TO 2
250 PRINT TAB(0,ROW),I%,K(I%),"      (";
     N(I%,1);",";N(I%,2);",";N(I%,3);")"
260 ROW=ROW+2
270 NEXT I%
279 REM compare with listing 7.5
280 PRINT TAB(0,13);"Line of intersection"
290 PROCinv
300 IF SNG THEN PRINT TAB(22,13) "does not exist" : GOTO 410
310 FOR I%=1 TO 3
320 B(I%)=0
330 FOR J%=1 TO 3
340 B(I%)=B(I%)+NINV(I%,J%)*K(J%)
350 NEXT J%
360 NEXT I%
369 REM output line of intersection
370 PRINT TAB(0,15);"Base vector"
380 PRINT TAB(0,16);"(";B(1);",";B(2);",";B(3);")"
390 PRINT TAB(0,18);"Directional vector"
400 PRINT TAB(0,19);"(";N(3,1);",";N(3,2);",";N(3,3);")"
410 PRINT TAB(0,22); : STOP
```

beware, there are many surfaces that divide space into more than two connected volumes and then it is impossible to relate functional representation with connected sets; for example $f(x, y, z) \equiv \cos(y) - \sin(x^2 + z^2)$. There are, however, many useful well-behaved surfaces with this property, the sphere of radius $r$ for example:

$$f(\mathbf{x}) \equiv r^2 - |\mathbf{x}|^2$$

that is

$$f(x, y, z) \equiv r^2 - x^2 - y^2 - z^2$$

If $f(\mathbf{x}) = 0$ then $\mathbf{x}$ lies on the sphere, if $f(\mathbf{x}) < 0$ then $\mathbf{x}$ lies outside the sphere, and if $f(\mathbf{x}) > 0$ then $\mathbf{x}$ lies inside the sphere.

The functional representation of a surface is a very useful concept. It can be used to define sets of equations that are necessary in calculating the intersections of various objects. The major use, however, is to determine whether or not two points $\boldsymbol{p}$ and $\boldsymbol{q}$ (say) lie on the same side of a surface that divides space into two parts. All we need do is to compare the signs of $f(\boldsymbol{p})$ and $f(\boldsymbol{q})$. If they are of opposite signs then a line joining $\boldsymbol{p}$ and $\boldsymbol{q}$ must cut the surface. Some examples are now given.

*Is a point on the same side of a plane as the origin?*
Suppose the plane is defined (as earlier) by three non-collinear points $\boldsymbol{p}_1, \boldsymbol{p}_2$ and $\boldsymbol{p}_3$. Then the equation of the plane is

$$((\boldsymbol{p}_2 - \boldsymbol{p}_1) \times (\boldsymbol{p}_3 - \boldsymbol{p}_1)) \cdot (\boldsymbol{x} - \boldsymbol{p}_1) = 0$$

We may rewrite this in functional form

$$f(\boldsymbol{x}) \equiv ((\boldsymbol{p}_2 - \boldsymbol{p}_1) \times (\boldsymbol{p}_3 - \boldsymbol{p}_1)) \cdot (\boldsymbol{x} - \boldsymbol{p}_1)$$

So all we need do for a point $\boldsymbol{e}$ (say) is to compare $f(\boldsymbol{e})$ with $f(\boldsymbol{O})$, where $\boldsymbol{O}$ is the origin. We assume here that neither $\boldsymbol{O}$ nor $\boldsymbol{e}$ lie in the plane.

We shall see that this idea will be of great use in the study of hidden surface algorithms.

*Example 7.7*
Are the origin and point $(1, 1, 3)$ on the same side of the plane defined by points $(0, 1, 1)$, $(1, 2, 3)$ and $(-2, 3, -1)$?

From example 7.4 we see that the functional representation of the plane is

$$f(x) \equiv (-6, -2, 4) \cdot (x - (0, 1, 1))$$

Thus

$$f(0, 0, 0) = -(-6, -2, 4) \cdot (0, 1, 1) = -2$$

and

$$f(1, 1, 3) = (-6, -2, 4) \cdot ((1, 1, 3) - (0, 1, 1)) = 2$$

Hence $(1, 1, 3)$ lies on the opposite side of the plane to the origin and so a line segment that joins the two points will cut the plane at a point $(1 - \mu)(0, 0, 0) + \mu(1, 1, 3)$ where $0 < \mu < 1$.

*Is an oriented convex polygon of vertices in two-dimensional space clockwise or anticlockwise?*
We start by assuming that the polygon is a triangle that is defined by the three vertices $\boldsymbol{p}_1 \equiv (x_1, y_1)$, $\boldsymbol{p}_2 \equiv (x_2, y_2)$ and $\boldsymbol{p}_3 \equiv (x_3, y_3)$. Although these points are in two-dimensional space we can assume they lie in the $x/y$ plane through the origin of three-dimensional space by giving them all a $z$-coordinate value of zero. We systematically define the directions of the edges of the polygon to be

$(\mathbf{p}_2 - \mathbf{p}_1)$, $(\mathbf{p}_3 - \mathbf{p}_2)$ and $(\mathbf{p}_1 - \mathbf{p}_3)$. Since these lines all lie in the $x/y$ plane through the origin we know that for all $i = 1, 2$ or $3$ and for some real numbers $r_i$ that depend on $i$

$$(\mathbf{p}_{i+1} - \mathbf{p}_i) \times (\mathbf{p}_{i+2} - \mathbf{p}_{i+1}) = (0, 0, r_i)$$

This is because this vector product is perpendicular to the $x/y$ plane and so only $z$-coordinate values may be non-zero. The addition of subscripts is modulo 3. Because the vertices were taken systematically, note that the signs of these $r_i$ values are always the same; but what is more important, if the $\mathbf{p}_i$ values are clockwise then the $r_i$ values are all negative, and if the $\mathbf{p}_i$ values are anticlockwise the $r_i$ values are all positive.

Given an oriented convex polygon we need only consider the first three vertices to find if it is clockwise or anticlockwise. This technique will prove to be invaluable when we deal with hidden line/surface algorithms later in this book. Listing 7.7 allows us to find whether or not three ordered two-dimensional vertices form an anticlockwise triangle.

*Listing 7.7*

```
100 REM Orientation of 2-D triangle
110 DIM X(3),Y(3)
119 REM input data on triangle
120 CLS : PRINT TAB(0,3)"TRIANGLE DEFINED BY VERTICES"
130 ROW=2
140 FOR I%=1 TO 3
150 PRINT TAB(0,20) "Type in coordinates of vertex ";I%
160 INPUT X(I%),Y(I%)
170 PRINT TAB(0,21),SPC(32)
180 ROW=ROW+3
189 REM output data on triangle
190 PRINT TAB(0,ROW) "VERTEX ";I%
200 PRINT TAB(0,ROW+1);"(";X(I%);",";Y(I%);")"
210 NEXT I%
219 REM form two directional vectors (DX1,DY1,0) and (DX2,DY2,0)
220 DX1=X(2)-X(1) : DY1=Y(2)-Y(1)
230 DX2=X(3)-X(2) : DY2=Y(3)-Y(2)
240 PRINT TAB(0,15);"IS ";
249 REM check sign of z-coordinate of the vector product
250 IF DX1*DY2-DX2*DY1>0 THEN PRINT "ANTI-";
260 PRINT "CLOCKWISE"
270 PRINT TAB(0,20),SPC(32) : STOP
```

*Example 7.8*

Why is the polygon given in example 3.4 anticlockwise?

The vertices (considered in three dimensions) are $(1, 0, 0)$, $(5, 2, 0)$, $(4, 4, 0)$ and $(-2, 1, 0)$. The directions of the edges are $(4, 2, 0)$, $(-1, 2, 0)$, $(-6, -3, 0)$ and $(3, -1, 0)$.

$$(4, 2, 0) \times (-1, 2, 0) = (0, 0, 10)$$

$$(-1, 2, 0) \times (-6, -3, 0) = (0, 0, 15)$$

$(-6, -3, 0) \times (3, -1, 0) = (0, 0, 15)$

$(3, -1, 0) \times (4, 2, 0) = (0, 0, 10)$

Since these are all positive, the orientation of the polygon is anticlockwise. But be careful, if you lose this consistent order for calculating the vector product you can get the wrong answer. For example

$(-6, -3, 0) \times (4, 2, 0) = (0, 0, 0)$ – the lines are parallel!

or

$(-1, 2, 0) \times (3, -1, 0) = (0, 0, -5)$ – the edges have been taken out of sequence.

---

**Complete Programs**

I Listing 7.1 (intersection of line and plane). Data required: a base vector (B(1), B(2), B(3)) and direction vector (D(1), D(2), D(3)) for the line, a normal (N(1), N(2), N(3)) and constant K for the plane. Try (1, 2, 3), (0, 2, −1), (1, 0, 1) and 2 respectively.

II Listing 7.2 (intersection of two lines). Data required: a base and direction vectors for the two lines, (B(1), B(2), B(3)) and (D(1), D(2), D(3)), and (C(1), C(2), C(3)) and (E(1), E(2), E(3)). Try (1, 2, 3), (1, 1, −1), and (−1, 1, 3), (1, 0, 1).

III Listing 7.3 ('main program', 'vecprod' and 'dotprod'). Data required: two vectors (L(1), L(2), L(3)) and (M(1), M(2), M(3)). Try (1, 2, 3), (1, 1, −1).

IV Listings 7.4 ('inv') and 7.5 (intersection of three planes). Data required: normal (N(I, 1), N(I, 2), N(I, 3)) and constant K(I) for the three planes, $1 \leqslant I \leqslant 3$. Try (1, 2, 3), 0, (1, 1, −1), 1, (1, 0, 1), 2.

V Listings 7.4 ('inv') and 7.6 (intersection of two planes). Data required: normal (N(I, 1), N(I, 2), N(I, 3)) and constant K(I) for the two planes, $1 \leqslant I \leqslant 2$. Try (1, 2, 3), 0, (1, 1, −1), 1.

VI Listing 7.7 (orientation of two-dimensional triangle). Data required: the vertices (X(I), Y(I)), $1 \leqslant I \leqslant 3$. Try (1, 2), (2, 3) and (−1, 1).

# 8 Matrix Representation of Transformations on Three-Dimensional Space

In chapter 4 we saw the need for transforming objects in two-dimensional space. When we draw three-dimensional pictures there will be many times when we need to make the equivalent linear transformations on three-dimensional space. As in the lower dimension, there are three basic types of transformation: translation, scaling and rotation. We will represent transformations as square matrices (now they will be $4 \times 4$). A general point in space relative to a fixed coordinate triad, the row vector $(x, y, z)$, must be considered as a four-rowed column vector:

$$\begin{pmatrix} x \\ y \\ z \\ 1 \end{pmatrix}$$

All the operations on matrices (addition, scalar multiple, transpose, premultiplication of a column vector and matrix product) that we saw in chapter 4 are easily extended to cope with $4 \times 4$ matrices and column vectors by simply changing the upper bound of the index ranges from 3 to 4. In this way we can generate a procedure 'mult3' (see listing 8.1) for multiplying two $4 \times 4$ matrices together. It is exactly equivalent to procedure 'mult2' in the two-dimensional case, and for the very same reasons. The procedure multiplies matrix A by matrix R to give matrix B, which is then copied into R. We also need the procedure 'idR3' (see listing 8.1) which sets R to the identity matrix.

Consider the case of a general linear transformation on points in three-dimensional space. A point $(x, y, z)$ – 'before' – is transformed into $(x', y', z')$ – 'after' – according to three *linear equations*:

$$x' = A_{11} \times x + A_{12} \times y + A_{13} \times z + A_{14}$$

$$y' = A_{21} \times x + A_{22} \times y + A_{23} \times z + A_{24}$$

$$z' = A_{31} \times x + A_{32} \times y + A_{33} \times z + A_{34}$$

and as usual we add the extra equation:

$$1 = A_{41} \times x + A_{42} \times y + A_{43} \times z + A_{44}$$

which if it is to be true for all $x, y$ and $z$ means that $A_{41} = A_{42} = A_{43} = 0$ and that $A_{44} = 1$.

Then the equations may be written as a matrix equation where a column vector representing the 'after' point is the product of a matrix and the 'before' column vector:

$$\begin{pmatrix} x' \\ y' \\ z' \\ 1 \end{pmatrix} = \begin{pmatrix} A_{11} & A_{12} & A_{13} & A_{14} \\ A_{21} & A_{22} & A_{23} & A_{24} \\ A_{31} & A_{32} & A_{33} & A_{34} \\ A_{41} & A_{42} & A_{43} & A_{44} \end{pmatrix} \times \begin{pmatrix} x \\ y \\ z \\ 1 \end{pmatrix}$$

So if we store the transformation as a matrix, we can transform every required point by considering it as a column vector and *premultiplying* it by a transformation matrix. As before, transformations may be combined simply by obeying the sequence of transformations in order. If their equivalent matrices are A, B, C, . . . , L, M, N, then the matrix equivalent to the combination is $N \times M \times L \times \ldots \times C \times B \times A$. Remember the order. Since we are premultiplying a column vector, then the first transformation appears on the right of the matrix product and the last on the left.

As with the two-dimensional case, we note that the 'bottom row' of all transformation matrices is always (0, 0, 0, 1), and it is of no real use in calculations. It is added only to form square matrices which are necessary for the formal definition of matrix multiplication. We may adjust this definition, and that of the multiplication of a matrix and a column vector, so that instead we use only the top three rows of the $4 \times 4$ matrices (in chapter 4 we used the top two rows of $3 \times 3$ matrices in listings 4.2a, 4.3a, 4.4a and 4.5a).

*Listing 8.1*

```
9100 REM mult3
9110 DEF PROCmult3
9120 LOCAL I%,J%,K%
9130 FOR I%=1 TO 3
9140 FOR J%=1 TO 4
9150 B(I%,J%)=A(I%,1)*R(1,J%)+A(I%,2)*R(2,J%)+A(I%,3)*R(3,J%)
9160 NEXT J%
9170 B(I%,4)=B(I%,4)+A(I%,4)
9180 NEXT I%
9190 FOR I%=1 TO 3
9200 FOR J%=1 TO 4
9210 R(I%,J%)=B(I%,J%)
9220 NEXT J%
9230 NEXT I%
9240 ENDPROC

9300 REM idR3
9310 DEF PROCidR3
9320 R(1,1)=1 : R(1,2)=0 : R(1,3)=0 : R(1,4)=0
9330 R(2,1)=0 : R(2,2)=1 : R(2,3)=0 : R(2,4)=0
9340 R(3,1)=0 : R(3,2)=0 : R(3,3)=1 : R(3,4)=0
9350 ENDPROC
```

## Translation

Every point to be transformed is moved by a vector (TX, TY, TZ) say. This produces the following equations which relate the 'before' and 'after' coordinates:

$$x' = 1 \times x + 0 \times y + 0 \times z + \mathrm{TX}$$

$$y' = 0 \times x + 1 \times y + 0 \times z + \mathrm{TY}$$

$$z' = 0 \times x + 0 \times y + 1 \times z + \mathrm{TZ}$$

so that the matrix describing the translation is

$$\begin{pmatrix} 1 & 0 & 0 & \mathrm{TX} \\ 0 & 1 & 0 & \mathrm{TY} \\ 0 & 0 & 1 & \mathrm{TZ} \\ 0 & 0 & 0 & 1 \end{pmatrix}$$

The procedure 'tran3' for producing such a matrix A, given the parameters TX, TY and TZ, is given in listing 8.2.

*Listing 8.2*

```
9000 REM tran3
9010 DEF PROCtran3(TX,TY,TZ)
9020 A(1,1)=1 : A(1,2)=0 : A(1,3)=0 : A(1,4)=TX
9030 A(2,1)=0 : A(2,2)=1 : A(2,3)=0 : A(2,4)=TY
9040 A(3,1)=0 : A(3,2)=0 : A(3,3)=1 : A(3,4)=TZ
9050 ENDPROC
```

## Scaling

The $x$-coordinate of every point to be transformed is scaled by a factor SX, the $y$-coordinate by SY and the $z$-coordinate by SZ, thus

$$x' = \mathrm{SX} \times x + 0 \times y + 0 \times z + 0$$

$$y' = 0 \times x + \mathrm{SY} \times y + 0 \times z + 0$$

$$z' = 0 \times x + 0 \times y + \mathrm{SZ} \times z + 0$$

giving the matrix

$$\begin{pmatrix} \mathrm{SX} & 0 & 0 & 0 \\ 0 & \mathrm{SY} & 0 & 0 \\ 0 & 0 & \mathrm{SZ} & 0 \\ 0 & 0 & 0 & 1 \end{pmatrix}$$

Usually the scaling values are positive, but if any of the values are negative then this leads to a reflection as well as (possibly) scaling. For example, if SX = –1 and SY = SZ = 1 then points are reflected in the $y/z$ plane through the origin. A procedure 'scale3' to produce such a scaling matrix A given SX, SY and SZ is shown in listing 8.3.

*Listing 8.3*

```
8900 REM scale3
8910 DEF PROCscale3(SX,SY,SZ)
8920 A(1,1)=SX : A(1,2)=0  : A(1,3)=0  : A(1,4)=0
8930 A(2,1)=0  : A(2,2)=SY : A(2,3)=0  : A(2,4)=0
8940 A(3,1)=0  : A(3,2)=0  : A(3,3)=SZ : A(3,4)=0
8950 ENDPROC
```

**Rotation about a Coordinate Axis**

In order to consider the rotation about a general axis $\boldsymbol{p} + \mu\boldsymbol{q}$ by a given angle it is first necessary to simplify the problem by considering rotation about one of the coordinate axes.

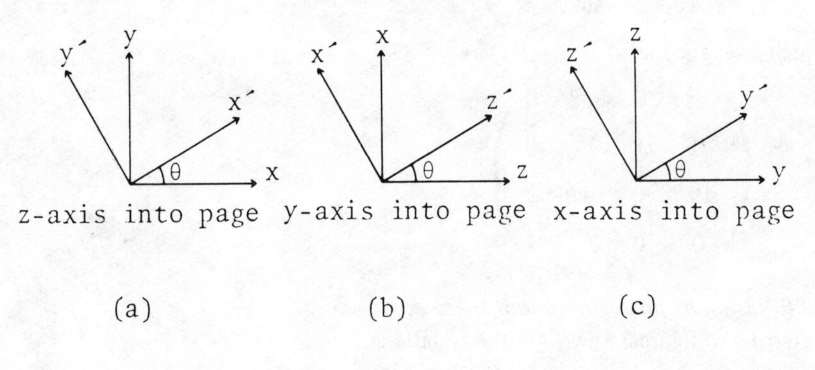


*Figure 8.1*

*(a) Rotation by an angle θ about the x-axis*

Referring to figure 8.1c, the axis of rotation is perpendicular to the page (the positive $x$-axis being into the page), and since we are using left-handed axes the figure shows the point $(x', y', z')$ that results from the transformation of an arbitrary point $(x, y, z)$. We see that the rotation actually reduces to a two-dimensional rotation in the $y/z$ plane that passes through the point; that is, after the rotation the $x$-coordinate remains unchanged. By using the ideas explained in chapter 4 we get the equations

$$x' = x$$

$$y' = \cos\theta \times y - \sin\theta \times z$$

$$z' = \sin\theta \times y + \cos\theta \times z$$

and thus the matrix is

$$\begin{pmatrix} 1 & 0 & 0 & 0 \\ 0 & \cos\theta & -\sin\theta & 0 \\ 0 & \sin\theta & \cos\theta & 0 \\ 0 & 0 & 0 & 1 \end{pmatrix}$$

*(b) Rotation by an angle θ about the y-axis*
Referring to figure 8.1b, we now have the positive $y$-axis into the page, and because of the left-handedness of the axes the positive $z$-axis is horizontal and to the right of the origin and the positive $x$-axis is above the origin. This leads us to the equations

$$x' = \sin\theta \times z + \cos\theta \times x$$

$$y' = y$$

$$z' = \cos\theta \times z - \sin\theta \times x$$

which gives the matrix

$$\begin{pmatrix} \cos\theta & 0 & \sin\theta & 0 \\ 0 & 1 & 0 & 0 \\ -\sin\theta & 0 & \cos\theta & 0 \\ 0 & 0 & 0 & 1 \end{pmatrix}$$

*(c) Rotation by an angle θ about the z-axis*
Referring to figure 8.1a we get the equations

$$x' = \cos\theta \times x - \sin\theta \times y$$

$$y' = \sin\theta \times x + \cos\theta \times y$$

$$z' = z$$

and the matrix

$$\begin{pmatrix} \cos\theta & -\sin\theta & 0 & 0 \\ \sin\theta & \cos\theta & 0 & 0 \\ 0 & 0 & 1 & 0 \\ 0 & 0 & 0 & 1 \end{pmatrix}$$

A subprogram 'rot3' to produce such a matrix A, given the angle THETA and the axis number AXIS (AXIS = 1 for the $x$-axis, AXIS = 2 for the $y$-axis and AXIS = 3 for the $z$-axis) is given in listing 8.4.

*Listing 8.4*

```
8600 REM rot3
8610 DEF PROCrot3(THETA,AXIS)
8620 LOCAL AX1,AX2,CT,ST
8630 AX1=(AXIS MOD 3)+1
8640 AX2=(AX1 MOD 3)+1
8650 CT=COS(THETA)    : ST=SIN(THETA)
8660 A(AXIS,AXIS)=1  : A(AXIS,AX1)=0  : A(AXIS,AX2)=0
8670 A(AX1,AXIS)=0   : A(AX1,AX1)=CT  : A(AX1,AX2)=-ST
8680 A(AX2,AXIS)=0   : A(AX2,AX1)=ST  : A(AX2,AX2)=CT
8690 A(1,4)=0 : A(2,4)=0 : A(3,4)=0
8700 ENDPROC
```

**Inverse Transformations**

Before we can consider the general rotation transformation, it is necessary to look at inverse transformations. An inverse transformation returns the points transformed by a given transformation back to their original position. If a transformation is represented by a matrix A, then the inverse transformation is given by matrix $A^{-1}$, the inverse of A. There is no need to explicitly calculate the inverse of a matrix by using such techniques as the Adjoint method (listing 7.4): we can use listings 8.2, 8.3 and 8.4 with parameters that are derived from the parameters of the original transformation:

(1) A translation by (TX, TY, TZ) is inverted with a translation by (–TX, –TY, –TZ).
(2) A scaling by SX, SY and SZ is inverted with a scaling by 1/SX, 1/SY and 1/SZ.
(3) A rotation by an angle $\theta$ about a given axis is inverted with a rotation by an angle $-\theta$ about the same axis.
(4) If the transformation matrix is the product of a number of translation, scaling and rotation matrices $A \times B \times C \times \ldots \times L \times M \times N$, then the inverse transformation is

$$N^{-1} \times M^{-1} \times L^{-1} \times \ldots \times C^{-1} \times B^{-1} \times A^{-1}$$

**Rotation of Points by an Angle $\gamma$ about a General Axis $p + \mu q$**

Assume $\boldsymbol{p} \equiv$ (PX, PY, PZ) and $\boldsymbol{q} \equiv$ (QX, QY, QZ). We break down the task into a number of subtasks:

(a) We translate all of space so that the axis of rotation goes through the origin. This is achieved by adding a vector $-\boldsymbol{p}$ to every point in space with a matrix F say, which is generated by a call to 'tran3' with parameters $-$PX, $-$PY and $-$PZ. The inverse matrix $F^{-1}$ will be needed later and is found by a call to 'tran3' with parameters PX, PY and PZ. After this transformation the axis of rotation is the line $\boldsymbol{O} + \mu\boldsymbol{q}$ that passes through the origin.

$$F = \begin{pmatrix} 1 & 0 & 0 & -PX \\ 0 & 1 & 0 & -PY \\ 0 & 0 & 1 & -PZ \\ 0 & 0 & 0 & 1 \end{pmatrix} \quad F^{-1} = \begin{pmatrix} 1 & 0 & 0 & PX \\ 0 & 1 & 0 & PY \\ 0 & 0 & 1 & PZ \\ 0 & 0 & 0 & 1 \end{pmatrix}$$

(b) We then rotate space about the $z$-axis by an angle $-\alpha$, where (ALPHA =) $\alpha = \tan^{-1}$ (QY/QX), given by the matrix G. The matrix may be generated by a call to 'rot3', with parameters angle $-$ALPHA and axis 3, and the inverse matrix $G^{-1}$ by a call to 'rot3' with ALPHA and 3. At this stage the axis of rotation is a line lying in the $x/z$ plane that passes through the point ($v$, 0, QZ).

$$G = \frac{1}{v}\begin{pmatrix} QX & QY & 0 & 0 \\ -QY & QX & 0 & 0 \\ 0 & 0 & v & 0 \\ 0 & 0 & 0 & v \end{pmatrix} \quad G^{-1} = \frac{1}{v}\begin{pmatrix} QX & -QY & 0 & 0 \\ QY & QX & 0 & 0 \\ 0 & 0 & v & 0 \\ 0 & 0 & 0 & v \end{pmatrix}$$

where $v$ is the positive number given by $v^2 = QX^2 + QY^2$.
(c) We now rotate space about the $y$-axis by an angle $-\beta$, where (BETA =) $\beta = \tan^{-1}$ ($v$/QZ), given by the matrix H which is obtained by the call 'rot3' with parameters angle $-$ BETA and axis 2, and the inverse matrix $H^{-1}$ by a 'rot3' call with parameters BETA and 2.

$$H = \frac{1}{w}\begin{pmatrix} QZ & 0 & -v & 0 \\ 0 & w & 0 & 0 \\ v & 0 & QZ & 0 \\ 0 & 0 & 0 & w \end{pmatrix} \quad H^{-1} = \frac{1}{w}\begin{pmatrix} QZ & 0 & v & 0 \\ 0 & w & 0 & 0 \\ -v & 0 & QZ & 0 \\ 0 & 0 & 0 & w \end{pmatrix}$$

where $w$ is the positive number given by $w^2 = v^2 + QZ^2 = QX^2 + QY^2 + QZ^2$. So the point ($v$, 0, QZ) is transformed to (0, 0, $w$), hence the axis of rotation is along the $z$-axis.
(d) We can now rotate space by an angle $\gamma$ (GAMMA) about the axis of rotation by using matrix W which is generated by 'rot3' (with angle GAMMA and axis 3):

$$W = \begin{pmatrix} \cos\gamma & -\sin\gamma & 0 & 0 \\ \sin\gamma & \cos\gamma & 0 & 0 \\ 0 & 0 & 1 & 0 \\ 0 & 0 & 0 & 1 \end{pmatrix}$$

(e) We need to return the axis of rotation to its original position so we multiply by $H^{-1}$, $G^{-1}$ and finally $F^{-1}$.

Thus the final matrix P that rotates space by the angle $\gamma$ about the axis $\boldsymbol{p} + \mu\boldsymbol{q}$ is $P = F^{-1} \times G^{-1} \times H^{-1} \times W \times H \times G \times F$. Naturally some of these matrices may reduce to the identity matrix in some special cases and can be ignored. For example if the axis of rotation goes through the origin then F and $F^{-1}$ are identical to the identity matrix I and can be ignored.

So it is possible to write a special procedure 'genrot' (listing 8.5) which achieves this rotation and returns the required matrix P given GAMMA, (PX, PY, PZ) and (QX, QY, QZ).

*Listing 8.5*

```
5000 REM genrot / rotate space about a general axis
5010 DEF PROCgenrot(PX,PY,PZ,QX,QY,QZ,GAMMA)
5020 LOCAL ALPHA,BETA
5030 PROCtran3(-PX,-PY,-PZ) : PROCmult3
5040 ALPHA=FNangle(QX,QY)
5050 PROCrot3(-ALPHA,3) : PROCmult3
5060 BETA=FNangle(QZ,SQR(QX*QX+QY*QY))
5070 PROCrot3(-BETA,2) : PROCmult3
5080 PROCrot3(GAMMA,3) : PROCmult3
5090 PROCrot3(BETA,2) : PROCmult3
5100 PROCrot3(ALPHA,3) : PROCmult3
5110 PROCtran3(PX,PY,PZ) : PROCmult3
5120 ENDPROC
```

***Example 8.1***

What happens to the points (0, 0, 0), (1, 0, 0), (0, 1, 0), (0, 0, 1) and (1, 1, 1) if space is rotated by $\pi/4$ radians about an axis $(1, 0, 1) + \mu(3, 4, 5)$.

Using the above theory we note that

$$F = \begin{pmatrix} 1 & 0 & 0 & -1 \\ 0 & 1 & 0 & 0 \\ 0 & 0 & 1 & -1 \\ 0 & 0 & 0 & 1 \end{pmatrix} \quad F^{-1} = \begin{pmatrix} 1 & 0 & 0 & 1 \\ 0 & 1 & 0 & 0 \\ 0 & 0 & 1 & 1 \\ 0 & 0 & 0 & 1 \end{pmatrix}$$

$$G = \frac{1}{5}\begin{pmatrix} 3 & 4 & 0 & 0 \\ -4 & 3 & 0 & 0 \\ 0 & 0 & 5 & 0 \\ 0 & 0 & 0 & 5 \end{pmatrix} \quad G^{-1} = \frac{1}{5}\begin{pmatrix} 3 & -4 & 0 & 0 \\ 4 & 3 & 0 & 0 \\ 0 & 0 & 5 & 0 \\ 0 & 0 & 0 & 5 \end{pmatrix}$$

$$H = \frac{1}{\sqrt{2}}\begin{pmatrix} 1 & 0 & -1 & 0 \\ 0 & \sqrt{2} & 0 & 0 \\ 1 & 0 & 1 & 0 \\ 0 & 0 & 0 & \sqrt{2} \end{pmatrix} \quad H^{-1} = \frac{1}{\sqrt{2}}\begin{pmatrix} 1 & 0 & 1 & 0 \\ 0 & \sqrt{2} & 0 & 0 \\ -1 & 0 & 0 & 0 \\ 0 & 0 & 0 & \sqrt{2} \end{pmatrix}$$

$$W = \frac{1}{\sqrt{2}}\begin{pmatrix} 1 & -1 & 0 & 0 \\ 1 & 1 & 0 & 0 \\ 0 & 0 & \sqrt{2} & 0 \\ 0 & 0 & 0 & \sqrt{2} \end{pmatrix} \text{ and}$$

$$P = \frac{1}{50\sqrt{2}}\begin{pmatrix} 41+9\sqrt{2} & -12-13\sqrt{2} & -15+35\sqrt{2} & -26+6\sqrt{2} \\ -12+37\sqrt{2} & 34+16\sqrt{2} & -20+5\sqrt{2} & 32-42\sqrt{2} \\ -15-5\sqrt{2} & -20+35\sqrt{2} & 25+25\sqrt{2} & -10+30\sqrt{2} \\ 0 & 0 & 0 & 50\sqrt{2} \end{pmatrix}$$

where $P = F^{-1} \times G^{-1} \times H^{-1} \times W \times H \times G \times F$ is the matrix representation of the required transformation. Premultiplying the column vectors equivalent to $(0, 0, 0), (1, 0, 0), (0, 1, 0), (0, 0, 1)$ and $(1, 1, 1)$ by P and changing the resulting column vectors back into row form and taking out a factor $1/50\sqrt{2}$ gives the coordinates $(-26 + 6\sqrt{2}, 32 - 42\sqrt{2}, -10 + 30\sqrt{2})$, $(15 + 15\sqrt{2}, 20 - 5\sqrt{2}, -25 + 25\sqrt{2})$, $(-38 - 7\sqrt{2}, 66 - 26\sqrt{2}, -30 + 65\sqrt{2})$, $(-41 + 41\sqrt{2}, 12 - 37\sqrt{2}, 15 + 55\sqrt{2})$ and $(-12 + 37\sqrt{2}, 34 + 16\sqrt{2}, -20 + 85\sqrt{2})$ respectively. Naturally, translating and rotating space should leave relative positions unchanged; in particular the angles between direction vectors should be unchanged (the same cannot be said about the scaling transformation which in general does alter relative positions). In the original system the three lines from $(0, 0, 0)$ to $(1, 0, 0)$, $(0, 1, 0)$ and $(0, 0, 1)$, respectively, are mutually perpendicular (that is, the dot product of pairs of these directions should be zero). The dot product of the directions in the transformed system should also be zero: the three directional vectors (with $1/50\sqrt{2}$ factored out) are $(41 + 9\sqrt{2}, -12 + 37\sqrt{2}, -15 - 5\sqrt{2})$, $(-12 - 13\sqrt{2}, 34 + 16\sqrt{2}, -20 + 35\sqrt{2})$ and $(-15 + 35\sqrt{2}, -20 + 5\sqrt{2}, 25 + 25\sqrt{2})$, and the dot product of any pair is zero.

Similarly the dot product of the direction vector from the origin to $(1, 1, 1)$

in the original system, taken with any of the original directions above, gives the same value (= 1). This is also true in the transformed system: the fourth direction is $(14 + 31\sqrt{2}, 2 + 58\sqrt{2}, -10 + 55\sqrt{2})$, and when we take the dot product with each of the three direction vectors above we get the value 5000, which when we take into account the factor $(1/50\sqrt{2})^2$ gives the value 1.

A program that reads in the axis of rotation (PX, PY, PZ) + $\mu$(QX, QY, QZ) and the angle GAMMA, and rotates any point (XX, YY, ZZ) about this axis by an angle GAMMA is given in listing 8.6.

*Listing 8.6*

```
100 REM Rotation about given axis
110 DIM A(4,4),B(4,4),R(4,4)
119 REM read in data on rotation
120 CLS : PRINT TAB(0,3),"Rotation about given axis",SPC(10)
130 INPUT"Base vector of axis ",PX,PY,PZ
140 INPUT"Direction vector of axis ",QX,QY,QZ
150 INPUT"Angle of rotation ",GAMMA
160 CLS
170 PRINT TAB(0,3);"Base vector of axis "
180 PRINT TAB(0,4);"(";PX;",";PY;",";PZ;")"
190 PRINT TAB(0,6);"Direction vector of axis "
200 PRINT TAB(0,7);"(";QX;",";QY;",";QZ;")"
210 PRINT TAB(0,9);"Angle of rotation "
220 PRINT TAB(0,10);GAMMA
229 REM calculate rotation matrix R
230 PROCidR3 : PROCgenrot(PX,PY,PZ,QX,QY,QZ,GAMMA)
239 REM input point (XX,YY,ZZ)
240 FOR I%=13 TO 21 : PRINT TAB(0,I%);SPC(40) : NEXT I%
250 PRINT TAB(0,12);"Coordinates of point"
260 INPUT XX,YY,ZZ
270 PRINT TAB(0,13);"(";XX;",";YY;",";ZZ;")"
279 REM (XX,YY,ZZ) becomes (RX,RY,RZ)
280 RX=R(1,1)*XX+R(1,2)*YY+R(1,3)*ZZ+R(1,4)
290 RY=R(2,1)*XX+R(2,2)*YY+R(2,3)*ZZ+R(2,4)
300 RZ=R(3,1)*XX+R(3,2)*YY+R(3,3)*ZZ+R(3,4)
310 PRINT TAB(0,15);"become"
320 PRINT TAB(0,17);"(";RX;",";RY;",";RZ;")"
330 PRINT TAB(0,21);"press any key to continue"
340 IF NOT INKEY(0) THEN PRINT TAB(0,20);SPC(40) : GOTO 240 ELSE 340
```

*Exercise 8.1*

Experiment with these ideas. You can always make a check on your final transformation matrix by considering simple values as above, and you can use the previous listings to check your answer. It is essential that you are confident in the use of matrices, and the best way to get this confidence is to experiment. You will make lots of arithmetic errors initially, but you will soon come to think of transformations in terms of their matrix representation, and this will greatly ease the study of drawing three-dimensional objects.

*Exercise 8.2*

You will have noticed that the procedure 'rot3' is usually called with THETA generated by 'angle' which uses values AX and AY as input parameters. 'rot3' calculates the cosine and sine of angle THETA – but we know these are $AX/\sqrt{(AX^2 + AY^2)}$ and $AY/\sqrt{(AX^2 + AY^2)}$ respectively. Write another rotation procedure 'rotxy' that calculates the rotation matrix direction from AX and AY without resorting to 'angle'.

*Exercise 8.3*

In chapter 4 we noted that some writers use row rather than column vectors, and postmultiply rather than premultiply. We decided against this interpretation so that the matrix of a transformation would correspond directly with the coefficients of the transformation equations. In this other interpretation it is the transpose of the matrix that is identical to the coefficients. It is useful to be aware of this other method, so use it to rewrite all the programs given in this chapter (and the remainder of this book). Remember though, it is not important which method you finally decide to use *as long as you are consistent*. We have used the column vector notation because we have found it causes less confusion in the early stages of learning the subject!

---

**Complete Programs**

I All the listings in this chapter, 8.1 ('mult3' and 'idR3'), 8.2 ('tran3'), 8.3 ('scale3'), 8.4 ('rot3'), 8.5 ('genrot'), 8.6 ('main program') and listing 3.3 ('angle'). Required data: base vector (PX, PY, PZ) and direction vector (QX, QY, QZ) of the axis of rotation and the angle GAMMA. Then any number of three-dimensional coordinates (XX, YY, ZZ). Try (0, 0, 0), (1, 1, 1) and $\pi/4$, and points (1, 0, 1), (1, 1, 1), (1, 2, 3).

# 9 Orthographic Projections

We may now address the problem of drawing views of three-dimensional objects on our (necessarily) two-dimensional graphics screen. The simple method we describe here is a direct generalisation of the method introduced in chapter 4 for two-dimensional objects. Again it involves the use of (up to) three *positions*. To illustrate these ideas we first give a brief outline, and then expand on this by using pictorial and numerical examples. We start by defining an arbitrary but fixed triad of axes in space which we call the ABSOLUTE system. Then, as in the two-dimensional case, we consider the three positions: (1) the SETUP position, (2) the ACTUAL position and (3) the OBSERVED position.

## (1) The SETUP Position

Most scenes will be composed of simple objects (such as cube(s) – see example 9.1) which are set at a particular position and orientation in space. It is very inefficient to calculate by hand the complicated coordinates of every vertex of these objects and input them into the program. Instead we look at each object in turn and initially define it in an elementary way relative to the ABSOLUTE triad, usually setting it about the origin. The information required will be that of vertices ($x$-coordinate, $y$-coordinate and $z$-coordinate), and perhaps lines (which join pairs of vertices) or (later when we consider hidden surface algorithms) facets, which are polygonal planar areas bounded by the above-mentioned lines. This elementary definition of the object is called its SETUP position. We could also have other information such as the colour of the object.

## (2) The ACTUAL Position

We may then use the matrix techniques of the last chapter to generate a matrix that will move the object from its SETUP position to its required ACTUAL position relative to the ABSOLUTE axes. We shall call this the SETUP to ACTUAL matrix P.

### (3) The OBSERVED Position

Viewing an object in three-dimensional space naturally involves an observer (the eye – and note only one eye!) placed at a position (EX, EY, EZ) relative to the ABSOLUTE axes looking in a fixed direction: this direction of view can be uniquely determined by any other point on the line of sight (DX, DY, DZ), say. The head can also be tilted, but more of this later. What the eye sees when it looks at a three-dimensional object is a projection of the vertices, lines and facets of the object on to a (two-dimensional) *view plane* which is normal to the line of sight. In order to calculate such projections we must standardise our approach. We use matrix methods to transform all the points in space so that the eye is placed at the origin, and the line of sight is along the positive $z$-axis. This is the OBSERVED position, and the matrix that transforms the ACTUAL to OBSERVED position is called Q throughout this book. The method for calculating Q will be dealt with in detail later, but for the time being we shall assume that the eye is already at the origin and is looking along the $z$-axis: so in this simple case Q is the identity matrix.

When all the points in space have been moved into this OBSERVED position we note that the view plane is now parallel to the $x/y$ plane through the origin. Having moved the eye into the correct position, we are now ready to project the object on to the view plane. But note, as yet we have neither defined the position of the view plane (we have only its normal), nor have we described the type of projection of three-dimensional space on to the plane. These two requirements are closely related. In this book we shall consider three possible projections – in a later chapter we shall deal with the *perspective and stereoscopic projections*, but first we introduce the simplest projection – the *orthographic*.

### The Orthographic Projection

Nothing could be simpler. In the orthographic projection we can set the view plane to be *any* plane with normal vector along the line of sight. When transformed into the OBSERVED position, the view plane will be any plane that is parallel to the $x/y$ plane given by the equation $z = 0$. For simplicity we take the $x/y$ plane through the origin. The vertices of the object are projected on to the view plane by the simple expedient of setting their $z$-coordinates to zero. Thus any two different points in the OBSERVED position, $(x, y, z)$ and $(x, y, z')$ say (where $z \neq z'$), are projected on to the same point $(x, y, 0)$ on the view plane. Then we identify the $x/y$ values on the plane with points in the graphics screen coordinate system (usually centred on the screen) by using the methods of chapter 2. Once the vertices have been projected on to the view plane and then on to the screen, we can construct the projection of lines and facets. These are related to the projected vertices in exactly the same way as the original lines and facets are related to the original vertices.

Before considering in detail the general case where the eye and direction of view are arbitrarily positioned, we shall consider an elementary example to demonstrate the orthographic projection.

***Example 9.1***

Use the above ideas to draw an orthographic projection of a cube. Figures such as those in figure 9.1 are called *wire diagrams* or *skeletons* (for obvious reasons).

In the SETUP position the cube may be thought to consist of eight vertices (1, 1, 1), (1, 1, –1), (1, –1, –1), (1, –1, 1), (–1, 1, 1), (–1, 1, –1), (–1, –1, –1) and (–1, –1, 1): vertices are labelled numerically 1 to 8. The twelve lines that form the wire cube join vertices 1 to 2, 2 to 3, 3 to 4, 4 to 1; 5 to 6, 6 to 7, 7 to 8, 8 to 1; 1 to 5, 2 to 6, 3 to 7 and 4 to 8.

Figure 9.1a shows the simplest possible example of an orthographic projection of the cube, where even the SETUP to ACTUAL matrix is the identity matrix, that is the cube stays in its SETUP position. We get a square: pairs of parallel lines from the front and back of the cube project into the same line on the screen. We put a '+' in these diagrams to show the position of the $z$-axis in the OBSERVED position (into the screen).

Figure 9.1b shows the same cube drawn after the following three transformations place it in its ACTUAL position:

(a) Rotate the cube by an angle $\alpha = -0.927295218$ radian about the $z$-axis – matrix A. This example is contrived so that $\cos \alpha = 3/5$ and $\sin \alpha = -4/5$, so ensuring that the rotation matrices consist of uncomplicated elements.
(b) Translate it by the vector (–1, 0, 0) – matrix B.
(c) Rotate it by an angle $-\alpha$ about the $y$-axis – matrix C.

The SETUP to ACTUAL matrix is thus P = C × B × A, where

$$A = \begin{pmatrix} 3/5 & 4/5 & 0 & 0 \\ -4/5 & 3/5 & 0 & 0 \\ 0 & 0 & 1 & 0 \\ 0 & 0 & 0 & 1 \end{pmatrix} \quad B = \begin{pmatrix} 1 & 0 & 0 & -1 \\ 0 & 1 & 0 & 0 \\ 0 & 0 & 1 & 0 \\ 0 & 0 & 0 & 1 \end{pmatrix} \quad C = \begin{pmatrix} 3/5 & 0 & 4/5 & 0 \\ 0 & 1 & 0 & 0 \\ -4/5 & 0 & 3/5 & 0 \\ 0 & 0 & 0 & 1 \end{pmatrix}$$

and P is given by the matrix

$$P = \frac{1}{25} \begin{pmatrix} 9 & 12 & 20 & -15 \\ -20 & 15 & 0 & 0 \\ -12 & -16 & 15 & 20 \\ 0 & 0 & 0 & 25 \end{pmatrix}$$

So the above eight vertex coordinate triples in the SETUP position are transformed into the following eight ACTUAL coordinate triples: (26/25, –5/25,

7/25), (–14/25, –5/25, –23/25), (–38/25, –35/25, 9/25), (2/25, –35/25, 39/25), (8/25, 35/25, 31/25), (–32/25, 35/25, 1/25), (–56/25, 5/25, 33/25), (–16/25, 5/25, 63/25).

For example (1, 1, 1) is transformed into (26/25, –5/25, 7/25) because

$$\frac{1}{25}\begin{pmatrix} 9 & 12 & 20 & -15 \\ -20 & 15 & 0 & 0 \\ -12 & -16 & 15 & 20 \\ 0 & 0 & 0 & 25 \end{pmatrix} \times \begin{pmatrix} 1 \\ 1 \\ 1 \\ 1 \end{pmatrix} = \frac{1}{25}\begin{pmatrix} 26 \\ -5 \\ 7 \\ 25 \end{pmatrix}$$

Since the ACTUAL to OBSERVED matrix Q is the identity matrix, the projected coordinates on the view plane are thus (26/25, –5/25), (–14/25, –5/25), (–38/25, –35/25), (2/25, –35/25), (8/25, 35/25), (–32/25, 35/25), (–56/25, 5/25), (–16/25, 5/25). We can place these points on the screen and join them with lines in the same order as they were defined in the SETUP cube.

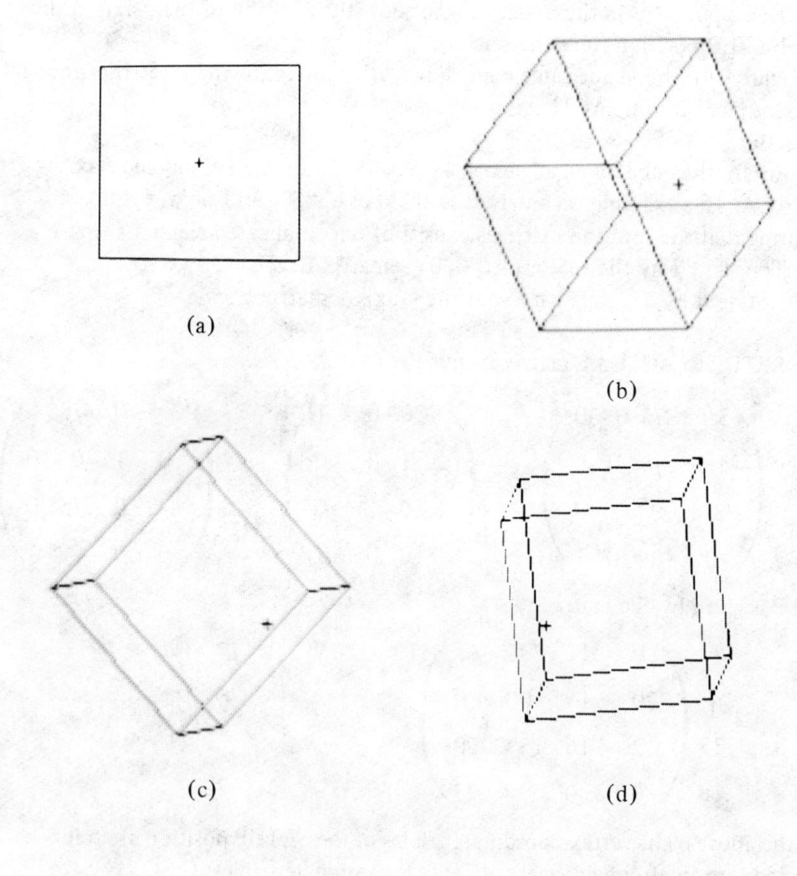


*Figure 9.1*

**Construction of the ACTUAL to OBSERVED Matrix Q**

We assume that the eye is at (EX, EY, EZ) relative to the ABSOLUTE axes, looking towards the point (DX, DY, DZ). The OBSERVED position is achieved in the following sequence of steps.

(1) A matrix D translates all the points in space by a vector (–DX, –DY, –DZ) so that now the eye is at (EX – DX, EY – DY, EZ – DZ) = (FX, FY, FZ) say, looking towards the origin:

$$D = \begin{pmatrix} 1 & 0 & 0 & -DX \\ 0 & 1 & 0 & -DY \\ 0 & 0 & 1 & -DZ \\ 0 & 0 & 0 & 1 \end{pmatrix}$$

(2) A matrix E changes (FX, FY, FZ) into $(r, 0\ FZ)$ by rotating space by an angle $-\alpha$, where $\alpha = \tan^{-1}$ (FY/FX), about the $z$-axis. Here $r^2 = FX^2 + FY^2$ and $r > 0$:

$$E = \frac{1}{r}\begin{pmatrix} FX & FY & 0 & 0 \\ -FY & FX & 0 & 0 \\ 0 & 0 & r & 0 \\ 0 & 0 & 0 & r \end{pmatrix}$$

(3) A matrix F transforms $(r, 0, FZ)$ into $(0, 0, -s)$ by rotating space by an angle $\pi - \theta$ about the $y$-axis – where $\theta = \tan^{-1}$ $(r/FZ)$. Here $s^2 = r^2 + FZ^2 = FX^2 + FY^2 + FZ^2$ and $s > 0$:

$$F = \frac{1}{s}\begin{pmatrix} -FZ & 0 & r & 0 \\ 0 & s & 0 & 0 \\ -r & 0 & -FZ & 0 \\ 0 & 0 & 0 & s \end{pmatrix}$$

(4) The transformation thus far places the eye at $(0, 0, -s)$ on the negative $z$-axis looking towards the origin and at the same distance from it $(s)$ as (EX, EY, EZ) was from (DX, DY, DZ). We now generate a matrix G which moves the eye to the origin:

$$G = \begin{pmatrix} 1 & 0 & 0 & 0 \\ 0 & 1 & 0 & 0 \\ 0 & 0 & 1 & s \\ 0 & 0 & 0 & 1 \end{pmatrix}$$

(5) If in example 9.1 we now premultiply P = C × B × A by our first approximation to the ACTUAL to OBSERVED matrix Q (= G × F × E × D) to find the SETUP to OBSERVED matrix R = Q × P = G × F × E × D × C × B × A, we draw figure 9.1c by orthographic projection. This view is not really satisfactory because the matrix Q places the cube at an arbitrary orientation within the view plane. It is much better to standardise our view, and one of the most popular ways is to *maintain the vertical*, that is a line that was vertical (that is, parallel to the $y$-axis) in its ACTUAL position remains vertical after transformation by Q into its OBSERVED position. Take the vertical line from (DX, DY, DZ) to (DX, DY + 1, DZ). Because of this peculiar construction, we note that intermediate matrix K (F × E × D) transforms this line into one that joins (0, 0, 0) to (K(1, 2), K (2, 2), K(3, 2)) = $(p, q, r)$, say. So if we further rotate about the $z$-axis by an angle $\beta = \tan^{-1}$ (K(1, 2)/K(2, 2)) = $\tan^{-1} (p/q) = \tan^{-1}$ (−FY × FZ/($s$ × FX)) using a matrix H, before multiplying by G, then the vertical is maintained:

$$H = \frac{1}{t}\begin{pmatrix} q & -p & 0 & 0 \\ p & q & 0 & 0 \\ 0 & 0 & t & 0 \\ 0 & 0 & 0 & t \end{pmatrix}$$

where $t^2 = p^2 + q^2$ and thus

$$H \times \begin{pmatrix} p \\ q \\ r \\ 1 \end{pmatrix} = \frac{1}{t}\begin{pmatrix} q & -p & 0 & 0 \\ p & q & 0 & 0 \\ 0 & 0 & t & 0 \\ 0 & 0 & 0 & t \end{pmatrix} \times \begin{pmatrix} p \\ q \\ r \\ 1 \end{pmatrix} \begin{pmatrix} 0 \\ t \\ r \\ 1 \end{pmatrix}$$

Thus the complete transformation (figure 9.1d) is achieved by the matrix R = Q × P = G × H × F × E × D × C × B × A, and the projection of the line joining points (DX, DY, DZ) to (DX, DY + 1, DZ) is the line joining (0, 0) to (0, $t$) on the screen; that is, the vertical – matrix G does not affect the $x/y$ values. Note that this technique works in all cases except where (EX, EY, EZ) is vertically above (DX, DY, DZ) to start with, and naturally in this case maintaining the vertical makes no sense. The procedure 'look3' (listing 9.1), given (EX, EY, EZ) and (DX, DY, DZ), generates the ACTUAL to OBSERVED matrix in the steps shown above, and at each step premultiplies the matrix R: so at the end of the process R will hold its original matrix value premultiplied by Q. If we wish to store Q explicitly then we need first to set R to the identity matrix (using 'idR3'), then call 'look3', and finally copy array R into array Q. Procedure 'look3' can be radically reduced if we assume that the eye always looks at the origin (that is, DX = DY = DZ = 0). Furthermore with the orthographic projection the OBSERVED position of the eye need not be at the origin, it merely needs to be on the $z$-axis: again the procedure can be cut down. We give the general case, which will be essential for later perspective projections.

*Listing 9.1*

```
8200 REM Look3 / maintain vertical
8210 DEF PROCLook3
8220 LOCAL FX,FY,FZ,THETA
8230 CLS : INPUT"(EX,EY,EZ)",EX,EY,EZ
8240 INPUT"(DX,DY,DZ)",DX,DY,DZ
8250 PROCtran3(-DX,-DY,-DZ) : PROCmult3
8260 FX=EX-DX : FY=EY-DY : FZ=EZ-DZ
8270 THETA=FNangle(FX,FY)
8280 PROCrot3(-THETA,3) : PROCmult3
8290 DIST=SQR(FX*FX+FY*FY)
8300 THETA=FNangle(FZ,DIST)
8310 PROCrot3(PI-THETA,2) : PROCmult3
8320 DIST=SQR(DIST*DIST+FZ*FZ)
8330 THETA=FNangle(DIST*FX,-FY*FZ)
8340 PROCrot3(THETA,3) : PROCmult3
8350 PROCtran3(0,0,DIST) : PROCmult3
8360 ENDPROC
```

If required, we can extend this program to deal with the situation where the head is tilted through an angle $\gamma$ from the vertical. This is achieved by further rotating space by $-\gamma$ about the $z$-axis. Thus matrix H should then rotate about the $z$-axis by an angle $\beta - \gamma$.

The construction of the ACTUAL to OBSERVED matrix is obviously independent of everything other than the position of the eye, line of sight and the tilt of the head. So if we wish to view a series of objects from the same position, we can store Q and use it repeatedly for placing each object.

## How to Define an Object

It is now time to deal with the problem of representing objects to the computer. There is no definite solution, it really depends on what is being drawn and how it is projected. In this section we describe various ways of setting up a data-base to hold the information that is necessary for drawing any given scene, but make no comment on their usefulness. This is considered in the remainder of the book where we give examples to illustrate the value of particular methods in different situations. We shall be using arrays to hold large sets of data, and so naturally the amount of space given to arrays will depend on the amount of information that is required for a scene: be sure that when you declare these arrays there is enough space for all the information – if in doubt, overestimate your store requirements.

*Vertices*

We will always need to define vertices and other special reference points in a scene, and these we store as *x*-coordinates, *y*-coordinates and *z*-coordinates in arrays X, Y and Z respectively, assuming that if the total number is not known explicitly then this value is calculated as NOV. So there must be space for not less than NOV values in each of the three arrays. These vertices may be in the SETUP, the ACTUAL or the OBSERVED position, it depends on the context of the problem. There will also be situations (perspective in particular) when we need to store the *x*/*y* coordinates of the projections of these NOV vertices – in arrays XD and YD. Naturally this is unnecessary in the case of an orthographic projection of points in the OBSERVED position since we can use the values already stored in the X and Y arrays. The choice of data-base really depends on the scene and type of projection.

*Lines*

We can store information on NOL (say) line segments in the two-dimensional integer array LIN. The $I^{th}$ line is defined by the integer indices (between 1 and NOV) of the two points at each end of the line – we store the indices in LIN(1, I) and LIN(2, I). The true coordinate values of the two points at each end of the line segment can be found from the X, Y and Z arrays. We normally assume that these lines are coloured implicitly by the program, usually black.

*Facets*

A facet is a convex polygonal area on the surface of a three-dimensional object, and can be defined in a number of ways. Most facets will be triangular or quadrilateral, rarely greater than six-sided, so we usually assume than no facet has greater than six sides in order to minimise waste of store. The NOF facets can be defined in terms of the indices of the vertices at their corners in array FACET: FACET(I, J) is the index of the $I^{th}$ vertex on the $J^{th}$ facet. Naturally if the facet is not hexagonal then some of the values are *garbage* so we need to store array SIZE, the number of vertices/edges on each facet. We can implicitly colour each facet or store it as an integer array COL, and we may implicitly colour the lines that form the edge of the facet. Another method is to store the facet in terms of the indices of the lines in the object in array FACET, which would thus refer to array LIN: FACET(I, J) would now be the index of the $I^{th}$ line on the edge of the $J^{th}$ facet. There are many other methods for representing these, and other elements of a three-dimensional object: you choose the one most suitable to your particular situation.

## Construction Procedures and the 'Building Block' Method

For any required object we define a *construction procedure* that needs as parameters a matrix R to move vertices into position and any other information about the size of the object (if the object is to be stored in the SETUP position then naturally no matrix is needed). The procedure can then define the vertices, lines, facets or any other elements of the object, and use the matrix R to move the vertices of the object into the required position. Depending on the context of the program the procedure can then either draw the object, or extend a database that contains this information. We shall give examples of both methods.

We can construct a scene that contains a number of similar objects (so the data will be in either the ACTUAL or the OBSERVED position). There is no need to produce a new construction procedure for each occurrence of the object, all we do each time is calculate a new SETUP to ACTUAL matrix P, and enter it (for the ACTUAL position) or Q × P (for the OBSERVED position) into the same procedure. Naturally we shall require one new procedure for each different type of object.

The complete scene is achieved by the execution of a main program (listing 9.2), which INPUTs the MODE of the picture (usually modes 1 or 4), prepares the graphics screen by using input values of HORIZ and VERT, and finally calls a procedure 'scene3' which organises the objects in space and then draws them. The main program below will be used in all the three-dimensional graphics programs that follow, so do not alter it without very good reason.

*Listing 9.2*

```
100 REM MAIN PROGRAM
110 INPUT"Which mode "MOWD : MODE MOWD
120 INPUT"HORIZ,VERT",HORIZ,VERT
130 PROCstart(3,0)
140 PROCsetorigin(HORIZ/2,VERT/2)
150 PROCscene3
160 STOP
```

'scene3' declares all the arrays that are required for storing information about a scene, together with matrices A, B, R and (perhaps) Q for moving objects into position. If required the values of NOV and NOL (or NOF) are initialised, and these will be updated in later construction procedures. For each individual object (a 'block'), 'scene3' must calculate a matrix P that moves this block into the ACTUAL position, and then call the construction procedure by using the correct matrix R (perhaps SETUP to ACTUAL or SETUP to OBSERVED). All the blocks finally construct the finished scene. Sometimes the drawing of the projection is done inside the construction procedure, or it can be elsewhere in other procedures that are specifically designed for special forms of drawing (as in hidden line and hidden surface pictures): it depends on what is being drawn and what is required of the view. As usual, because of the restriction of not passing array parameters into procedures, we do not normally explicitly generate P and Q: we usually rely on updating matrix R. If we require the ACTUAL to

OBSERVED matrix then this procedure calls 'look3'. Should we need to store Q then we must first call 'idR3' which sets matrix R to the identity – remember all matrix operations are done via matrices A and R, using matrix B to hold intermediate values.

Our first example of this method is listing 9.3, which is the 'scene3' procedure that is needed to construct a picture of a single cube as shown in figure 9.1d. The scene can be viewed from any position with the vertical maintained. We also have a construction procedure 'cube' (listing 9.4) which generates the data for a cube with sides of length 2. It places the vertices, eight sets of coordinate triples, in arrays X, Y and Z. There is no need to store the lines of the cube explicitly, we get the information from a DATA statement and draw the lines straight away. The data for figure 9.1d are HORIZ = 8, VERT = 6, (EX, EY, EZ) = (–2, 2, 2) and (DX, DY, DZ) = (–1, 0, 0).

*Listing 9.3*

```
6000 REM scene3 / cube (example 9.1)
6010 DEF PROCscene3
6020 DIM X(8),Y(8),Z(8)
6030 DIM A(4,4),B(4,4),R(4,4)
6040 PROCidR3
6050 PROCrot3(-0.92729522,3) : PROCmult3
6060 PROCtran3(-1,0,0) : PROCmult3
6070 PROCrot3(0.92729522,2) : PROCmult3
6080 PROClook3
6090 PROCcube
6100 ENDPROC
```

*Listing 9.4*

```
6500 REM cube / data not stored, lines drawn
6510 DEF PROCcube
6520 LOCALI%,XX,YY,ZZ,L1,L2
6530 DATA 1,1,1, 1,1,-1, 1,-1,-1, 1,-1,1,
          -1,1,1, -1,1,-1, -1,-1,-1, -1,-1,1
6540 DATA 1,2, 2,3, 3,4, 4,1, 5,6, 6,7, 7,8, 8,5,
          1,5, 2,6, 3,7, 4,8
6550 RESTORE
6559 REM READ vertex data, transform with matrix R
6560 FOR I%=1 TO 8
6570 READ XX,YY,ZZ
6580 X(I%)=R(1,1)*XX+R(1,2)*YY+R(1,3)*ZZ+R(1,4)
6590 Y(I%)=R(2,1)*XX+R(2,2)*YY+R(2,3)*ZZ+R(2,4)
6600 Z(I%)=R(3,1)*XX+R(3,2)*YY+R(3,3)*ZZ+R(3,4)
6610 NEXT I%
6619 REM draw lines
6620 FOR I%=1 TO 12
6630 READ L1,L2
6640 PROCmoveto(X(L1),Y(L1))
6650 PROClineto(X(L2),Y(L2))
6660 NEXT I%
6670 ENDPROC
```

We could have more than one cube in the scene. For example, should we rewrite 'scene3' as in listing 9.5, keeping all the other procedures the same, we would get figure 9.2. Note that the X, Y and Z values of the previous cube are overwritten in the second call to 'cube'. Also, because we have the same ACTUAL to OBSERVED matrix for both cubes (they have different SETUP to ACTUAL matrices) we need to store Q so that it can also be used for the second cube. Remember Q must premultiply the array P that moves the second cube into the ACTUAL position. The data for figure 9.2 are HORIZ = 8, VERT = 6, (EX, EY, EZ) = (3, 2, 1) and (DX, DY, DZ) = (0, 0, 0).

*Listing 9.5*

```
6000 REM scene3 / two cubes not stored
6010 DEF PROCscene3
6020 LOCAL I%,J%
6030 DIM X(8),Y(8),Z(8)
6040 DIM A(4,4),B(4,4),R(4,4),Q(4,4)
6049 REM calculate and store Q, draw first cube
6050 PROCidR3 : PROClook3 : PROCmult3 : PROCcube
6060 FOR I%=1 TO 4 : FOR J%=1 TO 4
6070 Q(I%,J%)=R(I%,J%)
6080 NEXT J% : NEXT I%
6089 REM put cube 2 in ACTUAL position
6090 PROCidR3
6100 PROCtran3(3,1.5,2) : PROCmult3
6109 REM then in OBSERVED position
6110 FOR I%=1 TO 4 : FOR J%=1 TO 4
6120 A(I%,J%)=Q(I%,J%)
6130 NEXT J% : NEXT I%
6139 REM draw second cube
6140 PROCmult3 : PROCcube
6150 ENDPROC
```

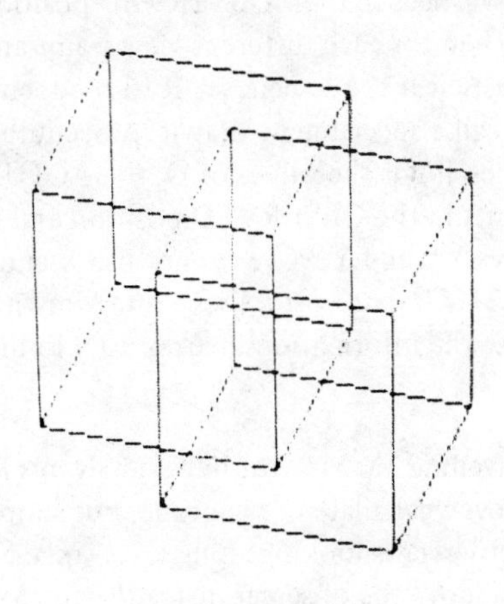

Figure 9.2

*Exercise 9.1*
Extend procedure 'cube' so that information about the size of a rectangular block is input, so enabling the procedure to construct a block of length LH, breadth BH and height HT: multiply the $x$-values of the SETUP cube by LH/2, the $y$-values by HT/2 and the $z$-values by BH/2.

Again it should be noted that the modular approach we have adopted may not be the most efficient method of drawing three-dimensional pictures. We chose this descriptive method in order to break down the complex situation into manageable pieces. Once the reader has mastered these concepts he should *cannibalise* our programs for the sake of efficiency. However, to show the value of this modular approach we give another example, which illustrates just how quickly programs can be altered to draw new scenes and situations. As the scenes get more complicated you may run out of store in modes 1 or 0. You should either run your programs in mode 4 (if you need only two-colour output) or load the complete program into store after having set PAGE = &1100, and it is also advisable to delete all REMarks and unused procedures (such as 'triangle' or 'scale').

*Example 9.2*
We wish to view a fixed scene (for example, the one shown in figure 9.2) from a variety of observation points.

In this case it is better to store the vertex coordinates of the scene in the ACTUAL position, rather than the OBSERVED position, and store the line information in array LIN. The 'scene3' procedure (listing 9.6) must first set NOV and NOL to zero and then place the objects in their ACTUAL position by using matrix R = P. The construction procedure 'cube' (listing 9.7) must therefore be altered to update the data-base (but note that the same procedure could be used to store vertices in their OBSERVED position: it needs only a different R = Q × P). Then for each different view point and direction the 'scene3' procedure must clear the screen, set R to the identity matrix and call 'look3', and then call a special new 'drawit' procedure (listing 9.8) which uses the matrix R (which holds the values of Q, the ACTUAL to OBSERVED matrix) to put the points in the OBSERVED position and orthographically project them into arrays XD and YD (we cannot use X and Y because this would corrupt our ACTUAL data-base). Procedure 'drawit' which was labelled in 'scene3' can then use the information in array LIN to draw the picture on the screen.

If the observer is travelling in a straight line and always looking in the same direction we need not even calculate Q each time, but simply initially manipulate space so that the observer is looking along the $z$-axis; then we can use the 'setorigin' procedure to move the observer instead! After you have gained expertise in drawing three-dimensional projections, you should choose your

*Listing 9.6*

```
6000 REM scene3 / 2 cubes stored.
6010 DEF PROCscene3
6020 DIM X(16),Y(16),Z(16),XD(16),YD(16)
6030 DIM LIN(2,24),A(4,4),B(4,4),R(4,4)
6039 REM put cubes in ACTUAL position
6040 NOV=0 : NOL=0
6050 PROCidR3 : PROCcube
6060 PROCtran3(3,1.5,2) : PROCmult3
6070 PROCcube
6079 REM draw in OBSERVED position
6080 PROCidR3 : PROClook3
6090 PROCdrawit
6100 GOTO 6080
6110 ENDPROC
```

*Listing 9.7*

```
6500 REM cube / add to data base
6510 DEF PROCcube
6520 LOCAL I%,XX,YY,ZZ,L1,L2
6530 DATA 1,2, 2,3, 3,4, 4,1, 5,6, 6,7, 7,8, 8,5,
          1,5, 2,6, 3,7, 4,8
6540 DATA 1,1,1, 1,1,-1, 1,-1,-1, 1,-1,1,
          -1,1,1, -1,1,-1, -1,-1,-1, -1,-1,1
6550 RESTORE
6559 REM store line information
6560 FOR I%=1 TO 12
6570 READ L1,L2 : NOL=NOL+1
6580 LIN(1.NOL)=L1+NOV : LIN(2,NOL)=L2+NOV
6590 NEXT I%
6599 REM store vertex information, put in position by matrix R
6600 FOR I%=1 TO 8
6610 READ XX,YY,ZZ : NOV=NOV+1
6620 X(NOV)=R(1.1)*XX+R(1,2)*YY+R(1,3)*ZZ+R(1,4)
6630 Y(NOV)=R(2,1)*XX+R(2,2)*YY+R(2,3)*ZZ+R(2,4)
6640 Z(NOV)=R(3.1)*XX+R(3.2)*YY+R(3,3)*ZZ+R(3,4)
6650 NEXT I%
6660 ENDPROC
```

*Listing 9.8*

```
7000 REM drawit
7010 DEF PROCdrawit
7020 LOCAL I%,L1,L2 : CLG
7029 REM put in OBSERVED position
7030 FOR I%=1 TO NOV
7040 XD(I%)=R(1,1)*X(I%)+R(1,2)*Y(I%)+R(1,3)*Z(I%)+R(1,4)
7050 YD(I%)=R(2,1)*X(I%)+R(2,2)*Y(I%)+R(2,3)*Z(I%)+R(2,4)
7060 NEXT I%
7069 REM draw lines of object
7070 FOR I%=1 TO NOL
7080 L1=LIN(1,I%) : L2=LIN(2,I%)
7090 PROCmoveto(XD(L1),YD(L1))
7100 PROClineto(XD(L2),YD(L2))
7110 NEXT I%
7120 ENDPROC
```

construction and viewing method with care. You will rarely need to go through the complete method given in this chapter, there will always be short-cuts.

*Exercise 9.2*

Produce construction procedures for a tetrahedron, pyramid etc. For example

(a) Tetrahedron: vertices (1, 1, 1), (1, –1, –1), (–1, 1, –1) and (–1, –1, 1); lines 1 to 2, 1 to 3, 1 to 4, 2 to 3, 2 to 4 and 3 to 4.
(b) Pyramid with square of side 1 and height HT: vertices (0, HT, 0), (1, 0, 1), (1, 0, –1), (–1, 0 –1) and (–1, 0, 1); lines 1 to 2, 1 to 3, 1 to 4, 1 to 5, 2 to 3, 3 to 4, 4 to 5 and 5 to 1.

*Exercise 9.3*

Set up a line drawing of any planar object in the $x/y$ plane (for example, the outline of an alphabetic character or string of characters) and view them in various orientations in three-dimensional space. You can place such planar objects on the side of a cube. All you need do is extend the 'cube' procedure above to include extra vertices and lines to define the symbols.

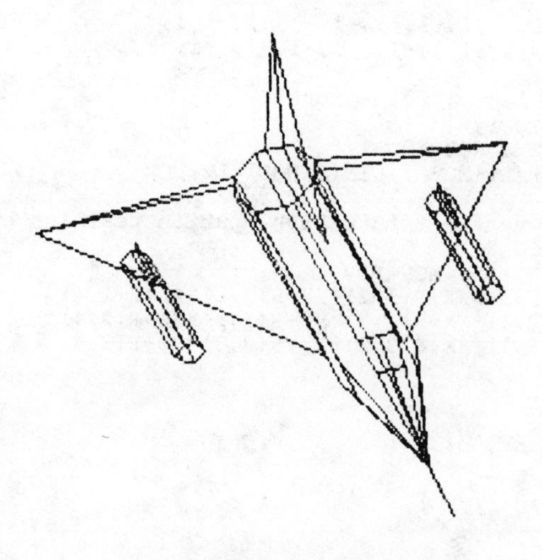

*Figure 9.3*

Thus far we have restricted our pictures to those of the simple cube. This is so that the methods we give are not obscured by the complexity of defining objects. Our programs will work for any object provided that it fits within the limitations of store (and time) that are available on the BBC micro. For complex objects we merely extend the size of our arrays, although some objects will have properties that enable us to minimise store requirements. Consider the *jet* shown in figure 9.3 – it possesses two-fold symmetry, which can be used to our advantage. We assume that the plane of symmetry is the $y/z$ plane, and so for every point $(x, y, z)$ on the jet there is also a corresponding point $(-x, y, z)$. To draw figure 9.3 we use all the graphics and $4 \times 4$ matrix routines, listings 9.1 and 9.2, together with listing 9.9, 'scene3' and construction procedure 'jet' which generates all the vertices of the aeroplane that have positive $x$-coordinates, and thus stores information only about one-half of the jet. To construct the complete aeroplane we also need a 'drawit' procedure (also in listing 9.9) which draws one side of the jet and then, by reversing the signs of all the $x$-values, draws the other.

It is simple to construct these figures, just plan your object in various sections on a piece of graph paper, number the important vertices and note which pairs of vertices are joined by lines. The coordinate values can be read directly from the grid on the paper. The data for figure 9.3 are HORIZ = 160, VERT = 120, (EX, EY, EZ) = (1, 2, 3) and (DX, DY, DZ) = (0, 0, 0).

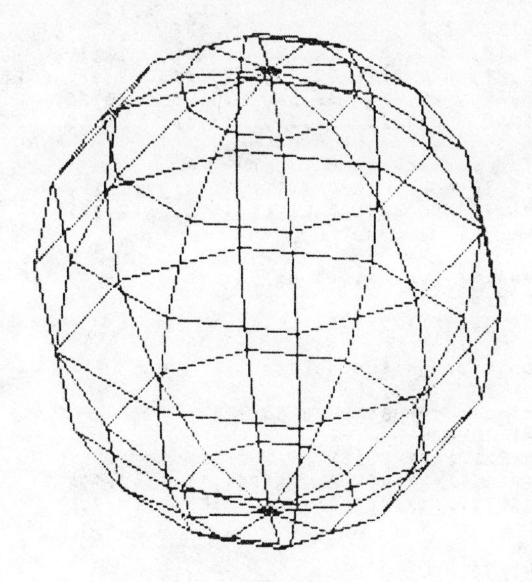

*Figure 9.4*

**Bodies of Revolution**

This far in our construction of objects we have relied on DATA to input all the information about lines and vertices. We now consider a type of object where only a small amount of information is required for a quite complex object – this is a body of revolution, an example of which is shown in figure 9.4.

The method is simply to create a defining sequence of NUMV lines in the $x/y$ plane through the origin; this is called the *definition set*. We then revolve

*Listing 9.9*

```
6000 REM scene3 / jet
6010 DEF PROCscene3
6020 DIM X(37),Y(37),Z(37),XD(37),YD(37)
6030 DIM LIN(2,46),A(4,4),B(4,4),R(4,4)
6040 PROCidR3 : PROClook3
6050 PROCjet : PROCdrawit
6060 ENDPROC

6500 REM jet
6510 DEF PROCjet
6520 LOCAL I%
6530 DATA 0,0,80,  0,0,64,  0,8,32,  4,8,32,  8,4,32,  8,0,32,
          4,-4,32,  0,8,-32, 4,8,-32, 8,4,-32, 8,0,-32,  4,-4,-32,
          0,-4,-32,  8,0,24,  48,0,-32,  8,2,-32,  0,8,0,  2,8,-32,
          0,32,-32,  28,-4,-24,  30,-2,-24,  32,-2,-24,  34,-4,-24
6540 DATA 32,-6,-24,  30,-6,-24,  28,-4,8,  30,-2,8,  32,-2,8,
          34,-4,8,  32,-6,8,  30,-6,8,  31,0,-24,  31,-2,-24,
          31,-2,-12,  31,0,-12,  0,6,40,  3,6,40
6550 DATA 1,2,  2,3,  2,4,  2,5,  2,6,  2,7,  3,4,  4,9,  5,10,
          6,11,  7,12,  8,9,  9,10,  10,11,  11,12,  12,13,  14,15,
          15,10,  15,16,  14,16,  17,18,  17,19,  18,19
6560 DATA 20,21,  21,22,  22,23,  23,24,  24,25,  25,20,  26,27,  27,
          28,29,  29,30,  30,31,  31,26,  20,26,  21,27,  22,28,  23,
          24,30,  25,31,  32,33,  33,34,  34,35,  35,32,  36,37
6570 RESTORE : NOV=37 : NOL=46
6579 REM SETUP vertices and lines
6580 FOR I%=1 TO NOV : READ X(I%),Y(I%),Z(I%) : NEXT I%
6590 FOR I%=1 TO NOL : READ LIN(1,I%),LIN(2,I%) : NEXT I%
6600 ENDPROC

7000 REM drawit / two halves of jet
7010 DEF PROCdrawit
7020 LOCAL I%,J%,S%,XX,YY,ZZ,L1,L2
7030 S%=1
7039 REM loop through two halves
7040 FOR J%=1 TO 2
7049 REM vertices in OBSERVED position
7050 FOR I%=1 TO NOV
7060 XX=S%*X(I%) : YY=Y(I%) : ZZ=Z(I%)
7070 XD(I%)=R(1,1)*XX+R(1,2)*YY+R(1,3)*ZZ+R(1,4)
7080 YD(I%)=R(2,1)*XX+R(2,2)*YY+R(2,3)*ZZ+R(2,4)
7090 NEXT I%
7099 REM draw lines
7100 FOR I%=1 TO NOL
7110 L1=LIN(1,I%) : L2=LIN(2,I%)
7120 PROCmoveto(XD(L1),YD(L1))
7130 PROClineto(XD(L2),YD(L2))
7140 NEXT I%
7150 S%=-1
7160 NEXT J%
7170 ENDPROC
```

this set about the vertical ($y$-axis) NUMH − 1 further times to create new vertical sets. The NUMV lines in the definition set are formed by joining the NUMV + 1 vertices (XD(I), YD(I), 0) (where $1 \leqslant I \leqslant$ NUMV + 1) in order. From this we generate NUMH different vertical sets: the $J^{th}$ vertical set is the definition set rotated through an angle PHI + $2\pi$(J – 1)/NUMH about the vertical $y$-axis, for some input value PHI ($\phi$). As well as the set of NUMH × NUMV vertical lines we also introduce horizontal lines. We consider a single point (XD(I), YD(I), 0) at the end of a line segment in the definition set: as we rotate about the vertical axis it moves into NUMH positions (provided that the point is not on the axis of rotation):

$$(\text{XD(I)} \times \cos(\theta + \phi), \text{YD(I)}, \text{XD(I)} \times \sin(\theta + \phi)) \quad \text{where}$$
$$\theta = 2\pi(\text{J} - 1)/\text{NUMH with } 1 \leqslant \text{J} \leqslant \text{NUMH}$$

These NUMH points are joined in order, and the NUMH$^{\text{th}}$ position is joined back to the first, to give the I$^{\text{th}}$ horizontal set. So there are (NUMH – $n$) × NUMV horizontal lines, where $n$ is the number of vertices on the axis of rotation. Listing 9.10 is a construction procedure 'revbod', which draws the body of revolution when given NUMV, NUMH, PHI, the original set of vertices in XD and YD and the positional matrix R. Listing 9.11 is the 'scene3' procedure which creates the scene of a spheroid in figure 9.4 by placing eight points from a semicircle into the definition set: HORIZ = 3.2, VERT = 2.4, PHI = $\pi$/25, NUMH = 10, NUMV = 8, viewed from (1, 2, 3) looking at (0, 0, 0).

*Listing 9.10*

```
6500 REM revbod / body of revolution
6510 DEF PROCrevbod
6520 LOCAL I%,J%,THETA,TD,N1,C,S,XX,YY,ZZ
6530 THETA=PHI : TD=PI*2/NUMH
6540 N1=NUMV+1 : C=COS(PHI) : S=SIN(PHI)
6549 REM find first vertical set
6550 FOR I%=1 TO N1
6560 XX=XD(I%)*C : YY=YD(I%) : ZZ=XD(I%)*S
6570 X(I%)=R(1,1)*XX+R(1,2)*YY+R(1,3)*ZZ+R(1,4)
6580 Y(I%)=R(2,1)*XX+R(2,2)*YY+R(2,3)*ZZ+R(2,4)
6590 NEXT I%
6599 REM loop thru second vertical set
6600 FOR J%=1 TO NUMH
6610 THETA=THETA+TD : C=COS(THETA) : S=SIN(THETA)
6620 FOR I%=1 TO N1
6630 XX=XD(I%)*C : YY=YD(I%) : ZZ=XD(I%)*S
6640 X(I%+N1)=R(1,1)*XX+R(1,2)*YY+R(1,3)*ZZ+R(1,4)
6650 Y(I%+N1)=R(2,1)*XX+R(2,2)*YY+R(2,3)*ZZ+R(2,4)
6660 NEXT I%
6669 REM join vertical lines
6670 PROCmoveto(X(1),Y(1))
6680 FOR I%=2 TO N1
6690 PROClineto(X(I%),Y(I%))
6700 NEXT I%
6709 REM join horizontal lines
6710 FOR I%=1 TO N1
6720 PROCmoveto(X(I%),Y(I%))
6730 PROClineto(X(I%+N1),Y(I%+N1))
6739 REM second set becomes first set
6740 X(I%)=X(I%+N1) : Y(I%)=Y(I%+N1)
6750 NEXT I% : NEXT J%
6760 ENDPROC
```

*Listing 9.11*

```
6000 REM scene3 / spheroid
6010 DEF PROCscene3
6020 LOCAL I%,THETA,TD
6030 DIM X(32),Y(32),XD(16),YD(16)
6040 DIM A(4,4),B(4,4),R(4,4)
6050 INPUT"NUMBER OF HORIZONTAL LINES",NUMH
6060 INPUT"NUMBER OF VERTICAL LINES",NUMV
6070 INPUT"INITIAL ROTATION",PHI
6080 THETA=PI/2 : TD=PI/NUMV
6089 REM definition set is semicircle
6090 FOR I%=1 TO NUMV+1
6100 XD(I%)=COS(THETA) : YD(I%)=SIN(THETA)
6110 THETA=THETA+TD
6120 NEXT I%
6130 PROCidR3 : PROClook3
6140 PROCrevbod
6150 ENDPROC
```

***Exercise 9.4***

Experiment with this technique – any line sequence will do. Try an ellipsoid: this is essentially the same as the spheroid except that the definition set is produced from a semi-ellipse rather than a semicircle. There is no need to produce only convex bodies: lines can cut one another or cross to and fro over the $y$-axis, and $x$-values can move up and down.

This idea can be extended into a *body of rotation*. Now as the set of lines moves around the central axis, the $y$-values of the points do not stay fixed. They can move in a regular manner, that is they can drop by the same amount with each rotation through $2\pi$/NUMH. Now, of course, the lines may make more than one complete rotation about the axis – see figure 9.5. Write a program to implement a body of rotation.

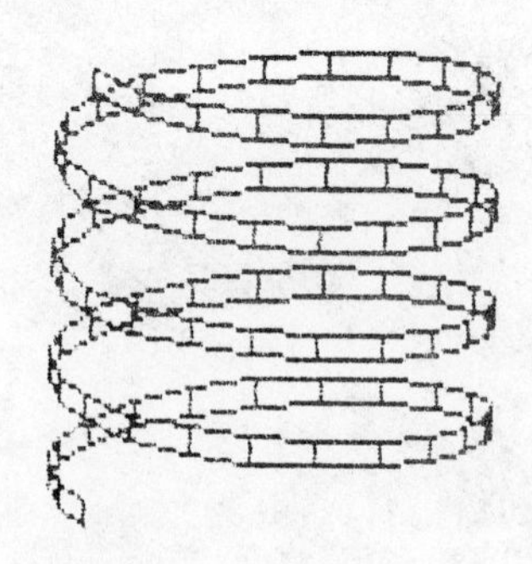

*Figure 9.5*

**Animation of Line Drawings**

We can animate simple line drawings like those created in this chapter by using the method of redefining the logical-actual colour relationships. The technique is to produce $n$ (for some even integer $n$) separate pictures of an object in different positions. We have a white background (logical colour binary 11) and a black foreground (logical 00). The object will be drawn in logical colours 01 or 10; at any time one logical colour will be set to actual white and the other to actual black. By ANDing a picture on to the screen in white an invisible picture will be drawn, which can be made visible later by redefining the logical colour to be actual black. ANDing a white line over a black pixel will leave the black pixel on the screen as required. ORing the same picture on to the screen in the opposite logical colour to which it was originally drawn will delete the picture from the screen memory (whether it be visible or invisible). This deletion will not leave holes in the visible lines from the other views still on the screen. This gives us a simple method:

(1) With the $(i - 1)^{th}$ picture visible draw the $i^{th}$ view so that it is invisible.
(2) Make the $i^{th}$ picture visible and the $(i - 1)^{th}$ invisible by redefining the logical-actual relationship.
(3) Delete the $(i - 1)^{th}$ view when it is invisible.

Here $i$ varies from 1 to $n$ (the number of views). If the views are such that the $(n + 1)^{th}$ view (if there was one) is the same as the first then we have an infinite movie.

***Example 9.3***
Listing 9.12 gives an implementation of this method for drawing a rotating cube. We change the 'look3' routine so that each time it is called the observer moves to a different position relative to the object. The 'scene3' routine sets up a SPOOL file called ROTCUB on backing store to hold all the graphics commands (the program is too slow to draw the figures in real-time animation). It also uses the 'drawit' routine which draws a 'cube' setup by the procedure from listing 9.7, and the 'lib1' and 'lib3' routines (excluding 'look3' naturally). By typing in the instructions below you load ROTCUB file back into store and then execute the commands in sequence over and over again to get a non-stop movie:

```
*OPT 1, 2: PAGE = &1900
*LOAD ROTCUB 1900
```

The size of the file will be displayed on the screen: in this case &C6C

```
MODE 1: GCOL 0, 131: CLG
REPEAT: FOR I% = 0 to &C6B: VDU I%?&1900: NEXT I%: UNTIL FALSE
```

*Listing 9.12*

```
6000 REM scene3
6010 DEF PROCscene3
6020 DIM X(8),Y(8),Z(8),XD(8),YD(8),LIN(2,12)
6030 DIM A(4,4),B(4,4),R(4,4)
6040 NOV=0 : NOL=0 : COLOR=2 : OTHER=1
6049 REM object in ACTUAL position
6050 PROCidR3 : PROCcube
6060 *SPOOL"ROTCUB"
6069 REM move around the origin in angular steps of PI/20
6070 FOR A=0.05 TO PI/2 STEP PI/20
6080 GCOL2,COLOR : AL=A
6089 REM make last view visible and present view invisible
6090 VDU19,COLOR,7,0,0,0,19,OTHER,0,0,0,0
6099 REM draw present view
6100 PROCidR3 : PROClook3 :PROCdrawit
6109 REM make last view invisible and present view visible
6110 VDU19,COLOR,0,0,0,0,19,OTHER,7,0,0,0
6120 AL=A-PI/20
6129 REM delete previous view
6130 PROCidR3 : PROClook3
6140 GCOL1,COLOR : PROCdrawit
6150 OTHER=COLOR : COLOR=3-COLOR
6160 NEXT
6170 *SPOOL
6180 ENDPROC

7000 REM drawit
7010 DEF PROCdrawit
7020 LOCAL I%
7030 FOR I%=1 TO NOV
7040 XD(I%)=R(1,1)*X(I%)+R(1,2)*Y(I%)+R(1,3)*Z(I%)+R(1,4)
7050 YD(I%)=R(2,1)*X(I%)+R(2,2)*Y(I%)+R(2,3)*Z(I%)+R(2,4)
7060 NEXT I%
7070 FOR I%=1 TO NOL
7080 L1=LIN(1,I%) : L2=LIN(2,I%)
7090 PROCmoveto(XD(L1),YD(L1))
7100 PROClineto(XD(L2),YD(L2))
7110 NEXT I%
7120 ENDPROC

8200 REM look3
8210 DEF PROClook3
8219 REM adjusted look3 routine. Observer moves in a circle
         around the origin making an angle AL with the +ve
         x-axis looking at the origin.
8220 EY=2 : EX=SQR(10)*COS(AL) : EZ=SQR(10)*SIN(AL)
8230 DX=0 : DY=0 : DZ=0
8240 PROCtran3(DX,DY,DZ) : PROCmult3
8250 FX=EX-DX : FY=EY-DY : FZ=EZ-DZ
8260 THETA=FNangle(FX,FY)
8270 PROCrot3(-THETA,3) : PROCmult3
8280 DIST=SQR(FX*FX+FY*FY)
8290 THETA=FNangle(FZ,DIST)
8300 PROCrot3(PI-THETA,2) : PROCmult3
8310 THETA=FNangle(R(2,2),R(1,2))
8320 PROCrot3(THETA,3) : PROCmult3
8330 DIST=SQR(DIST*DIST+FZ*FZ)
8340 PROCtran3(0,0,DIST) : PROCmult3
8350 ENDPROC
```

**Complete Programs**

From now on we shall refer to listings 3.3 ('angle'), 8.1 ('mult3' and 'idR3'), 8.2 ('tran3'), 8.3 ('scale3'), 8.4 ('rot3'), 9.1 ('look3') and 9.2 ('main program') as 'lib3'. Also from now on it is best to load programs with PAGE = &1100.

I 'lib1', 'lib3' and listings 9.3 ('scene3') and 9.4 ('cube'). Data required: mode, HORIZ, VERT, (EX, EY, EZ) and (DX, DY, DZ). Try 4, 6, 4, (1, 2, 3), (–1, 0, 1). Also use modes 0 and 1.

II 'lib1', 'lib3' and listings 9.5 ('scene3') and 9.4 ('cube'). Data required: mode, HORIZ, VERT, (EX, EY, EZ) and (DX, DY, DZ). Try 4, 8, 6, (1, 2, 3), (–1, 0, 1). Make systematic changes to one of these input values and keep all the other parameters fixed.

III 'lib1', 'lib3' and listings 9.6 ('scene3'), 9.7 ('cube') and 9.8 ('drawit'). Data required: mode, HORIZ, VERT, and then repeated input of (EX, EY, EZ) and (DX, DY, DZ). Try 4, 8, 6, then (1, 2, 3), (–1, 0, 1); (3, 2, 1), (0, 0, 1). Again make systematic changes to one of the input parameters.

IV 'lib1', 'lib3' and listing 9.9 ('scene3', 'jet' and 'drawit'). Data required: mode, HORIZ, VERT, and then (EX, EY, EZ) and (DX, DY, DZ). Try 4, 200, 150, then (1, 2, 31), (–1, 0, 30) or (3, 2, 20), (0, 0, 21). Again make systematic changes to one of the input parameters.

V 'lib1', 'lib3' and listings 9.10 ('scene3') and 9.11 ('revbod'). Data required: mode, HORIZ, VERT, NUMH, NUMV, PHI, (EX, EY, EZ) and (DX, DY, DZ). Try 1, 3.2, 2.4, 10, 10, 1, (1, 2, 3), (0, 0, 0); (3, 2, 1), (0, 0, 0).

VI 'lib1', 'lib3' (minus 'look3'), listings 9.7 ('cube') and 9.12 ('scene3', 'drawit' and 'look3'). Data required: mode, HORIZ, VERT. Try 1, 6, 4. This will create a file ROTCUB on backing store. Then type

```
*OPT 1, 2: PAGE = &1900
*LOAD ROTCUB 1900
MODE 1: GCOL 0, 131: CLG
REPEAT: FOR I% = 0 TO &C6B: VDU I%?&1900: NEXT I%: UNTIL FALSE
```

# *10 Simple Hidden Line and Hidden Surface Algorithms*

Having drawn a cube and other wire objects we soon become irritated by the lack of solidity in the figures. We would like to consider solid objects, in which case the facets at the front of the object will obviously restrict the view of the facets (and boundary lines) at the back. In order to draw pictures of such objects we have to introduce a hidden surface algorithm; or a hidden line algorithm if we wish to draw all, but only, the visible lines on the object. There are many, many such algorithms – some elementary for specially restricted situations, others very sophisticated for viewing general complicated scenes. The time and store limitations of microcomputers bar us from implementing the very complex algorithms. Nevertheless, by limiting the types and number of objects in the scenes it is possible to get most acceptable pictures. In chapter 12 we discuss a relatively complex algorithm, but here we consider two special types of scene – we use the properties implicit in these special configurations to minimise the work needed to discover which surfaces and lines are hidden. Later in this chapter we shall give a simple method for drawing mathematically defined three-dimensional surfaces, but to start we consider an algorithm for drawing a single solid convex body in three-dimensional space.

For our work on hidden line and surface algorithms we choose to define a scene by storing the NOV vertices of objects in the scene (in the OBSERVED position) in arrays X, Y and Z as usual. However we shall now use facet rather than line information. These data may be implicit in the program or the NOF facets are explicitly stored in an array FACET. The integer code for the colour of the facet will usually be implicit, but if necessary we can store it in an array COL. Should we store the facet data then we also need the array SIZE for the number of edges on each polygonal facet: and to save space we insist that no polygonal facet has more than six edges. Should we need more edges, then the facet must be broken down into a set of smaller polygons. In order to make the hidden surface algorithm easier we impose a restriction on the order of vertices within the array FACET. The vertices must be stored (or are understood to be) in the order in which they occur around the edge of the facet, and when viewed from the outside of an object they must be in an anticlockwise orientation. Naturally from the inside the vertices taken in this same order would appear clockwise. We shall also assume that all lines are the junction of two facets. Individual lines not related to facets must be added as trivial two-sided facets.

## The Orientation of a Three-dimensional Triangle

Once we have planned our object in terms of vertices and facets, how do we check that the facets are actually anticlockwise? Simply write a program! The orientation of any convex polygon can be calculated from any three of its vertices taken in order, and so we need consider only an ordered triangle of vertices from the facet. In chapter 7 we saw a method for calculating the orientation of a two-dimensional triangle. Our problem is solved if we can reduce the three-dimensional situation down into two dimensions.

For simplicity we shall assume that all objects are SETUP about and contain the origin. We also insist that the infinite planes that contain the facets on the surface of an object do not pass through the origin. Then we rotate space so that one of the vertices of the triangle in question lies on the negative $z$-axis (compare with procedure 'look3', listing 9.1). Since we assume that the origin is inside the object and the eye is outside, all we need do is project the transformed triangle back on to the $x/y$ plane (that is, ignore the $z$-coordinates) and treat it like a two-dimensional triangle (in fact one of the three vertices will be $(0, 0)$). Listing 10.1 is our solution of the problem.

*Exercise 10.1*
Rewrite the wire-figure procedures of the last chapter by assuming that the data are given as vertices and anticlockwise polygonal facets, and not as lines. Check your facet data with the above program. The line information is still there of course, implicit in the facet data – they are the edges of the facet considered as pairs of vertices. Within this information each line occurs twice, once on each of two neighbouring facets. We do not want to waste time drawing lines twice! Because of the anticlockwise manner of constructing the figures we note that if a line joins vertex I to vertex J on one facet then the equivalent line on the neighbouring facet joins vertex J to I. So for wire figures stored as facets we shall draw lines from vertex I to vertex J if and only if $I < J$.

## A Hidden Surface Algorithm for a Single Closed Convex Body

A finite *convex body* is one in which any line segment that joins two points inside the body lies totally within the body – a direct extension of the definition in two-dimensional space. It is automatically closed, and thus it is impossible to get inside the body without crossing through its surface. We orthographically project all the vertices of the object on to the view plane, while noting that a projection of a convex polygon with $n$ sides in three-dimensional space is an $n$-sided convex polygon (or degenerates to a line) in the view plane. By taking the projected vertices of any facet in the same order as the original, we find that either the new two-dimensional polygon is in anticlockwise orientation, in which case we are looking at the outside of the facet, or the new

*Listing 10.1*

```
100 REM Orientation of 3-D triangle
110 DIM X(3),Y(3),Z(3)
120 DIM A(4,4),B(4,4),R(4,4)
129 REM input and print vertex data
130 CLS : PRINT TAB(0,1) "Orientation of 3-D triangle"
140 PRINT TAB(0,3) "The triangle has vertices"
150 ROW=2
160 FOR I%=1 TO 3
170 ROW=ROW+3
180 PRINT TAB(0,17)"                                        "
190 PRINT TAB(0,16) "Type coordinates of vertex ";I%
200 INPUT X(I%),Y(I%),Z(I%)
210 PRINT TAB(0,ROW) "Vertex "; I%
220 PRINT TAB(0,ROW+1);"(";X(I%);",";Y(I%);",";Z(I%);")"
230 NEXT I%
240 PRINT TAB(0,14) "is ";
249 REM matrix R places first vertex on negative z-axis
250 PROCidR3 : THETA=-FNangle(X(1),Y(1))
260 PROCrot3(THETA,3) : PROCmult3
270 THETA=PI-FNangle(Z(1),SQR(X(1)*X(1)+Y(1)*Y(1)))
280 PROCrot3(THETA,2) : PROCmult3
289 REM position 3 vertices with R
290 FOR I%=1 TO 3
300 XX=X(I%) : YY=Y(I%) : ZZ=Z(I%)
310 X(I%)=R(1,1)*XX+R(1,2)*YY+R(1,3)*ZZ+R(1,4)
320 Y(I%)=R(2,1)*XX+R(2,2)*YY+R(2,3)*ZZ+R(2,4)
330 NEXT I%
339 REM (DX1,DY1,0) and (DX2,DY2,0) ordered directional vectors
340 DX1=X(2)-X(1) : DY1=Y(2)-Y(1)
350 DX2=X(3)-X(2) : DY2=Y(3)-Y(2)
359 REM find z-value of dot product negative = clockwise,
         positive = anticlockwise
360 IF DX1*DY2-DX2*DY1 >0 THEN PRINT"ANTI-";
370 PRINT "CLOCKWISE"
380 PRINT TAB(0,16)
    "if the eye and origin are on opposite sides of the facet"
390 PRINT TAB(0,21) : STOP
```

vertices are clockwise and we are looking at the underside. Since the object is closed we are able to see only the outside of facets, the view of their under-side being blocked by the bulk of the object. Therefore we need draw only the anticlockwise polygonal facets – a very simple algorithm, which can be implemented in either construction or 'drawit' procedures.

For example, an adjusted construction procedure 'cube' for eliminating the hidden surfaces from an orthographic picture of a cube is given as listing 10.2. Here we do not store the facets, but instead READ the information from DATA and draw the visible facets immediately. The facet data, including colour, are implied in the program listing. This program was used to produce figure 10.1, a hidden surface version of figure 9.1d. We take the procedures that were used in the last chapter to draw figure 9.1d, except of course for the construction procedure which sets up the data as vertices and facets, and draws the object (listing 10.2 replaces listing 9.4 in the program for drawing figure 9.1d). Naturally we use the same data that were used for figure 9.1d. Note that if we colour in the facets with the same logical colour as the background then we get a hidden line as well as a hidden surface algorithm.

*Listing 10.2*

```
6500 REM cube / not stored, no hidden surfaces
6510 DEF PROCcube
6520 LOCAL I%,XX,YY,ZZ,F1,F2,F3,F4,DX1,DY1,DX2,DY2
6530 DATA 1,1,1,  1,1,-1,  1,-1,-1,  1,-1,1,
         -1,1,1,  -1,1,-1,  -1,-1,-1,  -1,-1,1
6540 DATA 1,2,3,4,  5,8,7,6,  1,5,6,2,  2,6,7,3,  3,7,8,4,  4,8,5,1
6550 RESTORE
6559 REM READ and position vertices
6560 FOR I%=1 TO 8
6570 READ XX,YY,ZZ
6580 X(I%)=R(1,1)*XX+R(1,2)*YY+R(1,3)*ZZ+R(1,4)
6590 Y(I%)=R(2,1)*XX+R(2,2)*YY+R(2,3)*ZZ+R(2,4)
6600 Z(I%)=R(3,1)*XX+R(3,2)*YY+R(3,3)*ZZ+R(3,4)
6610 NEXT I%
6620 FOR I%=1 TO 6
6629 REM READ facet data
6630 READ F1,F2,F3,F4
6639 REM check orientation
6640 DX1=X(F2)-X(F1) : DY1=Y(F2)-Y(F1)
6650 DX2=X(F3)-X(F2) : DY2=Y(F3)-Y(F2)
6660 IF DX1*DY2-DX2*DY1 < 0 THEN 6750
6669 REM if anticlockwise draw facet
6670 PROCtriangle(X(F2),Y(F2),X(F1),Y(F1),X(F3),Y(F3),1,-2)
6680 PROCtriangle(X(F4),Y(F4),X(F1),Y(F1),X(F3),Y(F3),1,-2)
6690 GCOL 0,0
6699 REM draw edge lines of facet
6700 PROCmoveto(X(F1),Y(F1))
6710 PROClineto(X(F2),Y(F2))
6720 PROClineto(X(F3),Y(F3))
6730 PROClineto(X(F4),Y(F4))
6740 PROClineto(X(F1),Y(F1))
6750 NEXT I%
6760 ENDPROC
```

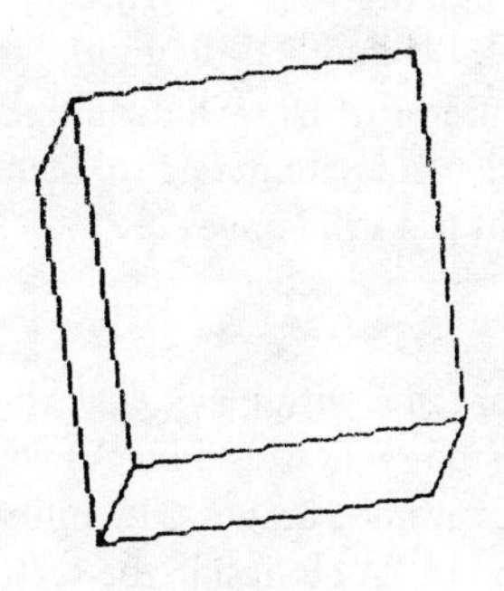

*Figure 10.1*

If we had stored the colours of the facets in the array COL then naturally we would call the 'triangle' procedure for the I%$^{th}$ facet with colour parameter COL(I%) or we can explicitly fill in the polygon in the program.

We now give a hidden surface construction procedure for an icosahedron (listing 10.3). Change line 6020 to hold 12 vertices.

*Listing 10.3*

```
6500 REM icosahedron
6510 DEF PROCicosahedron
6520 LOCAL I%,D,XX,YY,ZZ,F1,F2,F3,DX1,DY1,DX2,DY2
6530 D=(1+SQR(5))/2
6540 DATA 0,1,D, D,0,1, 1,D,0, 0,-1,D, D,0,-1, -1,D,0, 0,1,-D,
         -D,0,1, 1,-D,0, 0,-1,-D, -D,0,-1, -1,-D,0
6550 DATA 1,3,2, 1,2,4, 1,4,8, 1,8,6, 1,6,3, 2,3,5, 2,9,4, 4,12,8,
         8,11,6, 3,6,7, 2,5,9, 4,9,12, 8,12,11, 6,11,7, 3,7,5,
         5,10,9, 9,10,12, 12,10,11, 11,10,7, 7,10,5
6560 RESTORE
6570 FOR I%=1 TO 12
6580 READ XX,YY,ZZ
6590 X(I%)=R(1,1)*XX+R(1,2)*YY+R(1,3)*ZZ+R(1,4)
6600 Y(I%)=R(2,1)*XX+R(2,2)*YY+R(2,3)*ZZ+R(2,4)
6610 Z(I%)=R(3,1)*XX+R(3,2)*YY+R(3,3)*ZZ+R(3,4)
6620 NEXT I%
6630 FOR I%=1 TO 20
6640 READ F1,F2,F3
6650 DX1=X(F2)-X(F1) : DY1=Y(F2)-Y(F1)
6660 DX2=X(F3)-X(F2) : DY2=Y(F3)-Y(F2)
6670 IF DX1*DY2-DX2*DY1 < 0 THEN 6740
6680 PROCtriangle(X(F2),Y(F2),X(F1),Y(F1),X(F3),Y(F3),1,-2)
6690 GCOL 0,0
6700 PROCmoveto(X(F1),Y(F1))
6710 PROClineto(X(F2),Y(F2))
6720 PROClineto(X(F3),Y(F3))
6730 PROClineto(X(F1),Y(F1))
6740 NEXT I%
6750 ENDPROC
```

***Exercise 10.2***

Change listing 10.2 so that it can draw a rectangular block of length LH, breadth BH and height HT, where LH, BH and HT are input parameters to the procedure. Then draw a hidden line picture of it. Draw hidden line pictures of tetrahedra, pyramids, octahedra etc. Add extra parameters to distort these figures so that they are no longer regular, but are still convex.

***Exercise 10.3***

Rather than have a one-colour cube with black edges drawn in on a white background, give it three colours (red, yellow and black) where opposite faces have the same colour and the edges are not drawn. The information on the colour of a facet should be stored in DATA alongside the vertices, so the program would contain

READ F1, F2, F3, F4, COLOR

When it comes to colouring in a facet you must call the 'triangle' procedure with colour parameter COLOR.

Also draw an icosahedron in two colours (red and yellow) with edges in black.

Instead of drawing a hidden surface picture of a cube with facets drawn in one colour we can put patterns on the visible sides. Listing 10.4 can be used in conjunction with 'lib1' and 'lib3' to draw a flag, in a similar way to that of the two-dimensional example 4.1, on the side of a cube (see figure 10.2).

*Listing 10.4*

```
6000 REM scene3
6010 DEF PROCscene3
6020 DIM X(8),Y(8),Z(8)
6030 DIM FACE(4),XD(12),YD(12)
6040 DIM A(4,4),B(4,4),R(4,4)
6050 PROCidR3 : PROClook3
6060 PROCcube
6070 ENDPROC

6500 REM cube / with flags
6510 DEF PROCcube
6520 LOCAL I%,DX1,DY1,DX2,DY2
6530 DATA 1,1,1,  1,1,-1,  1,-1,-1,  1,-1,1,
         -1,1,1,  -1,1,-1,  -1,-1,-1,  -1,-1,1
6540 DATA 1,2,3,4,  5,8,7,6,  1,5,6,2,  2,6,7,3,  3,7,8,4,  4,8,5,1
6550 RESTORE
6559 REM vertices
6560 FOR I%=1 TO 8
6570 READ XX,YY,ZZ
6580 X(I%)=R(1,1)*XX+R(1,2)*YY+R(1,3)*ZZ+R(1,4)
6590 Y(I%)=R(2,1)*XX+R(2,2)*YY+R(2,3)*ZZ+R(2,4)
6600 Z(I%)=R(3,1)*XX+R(3,2)*YY+R(3,3)*ZZ+R(3,4)
6610 NEXT I%
6619 REM facets
6620 FOR I%=1 TO 6
6630 READ F1,F2,F3,F4
6640 DX1=X(F2)-X(F1) : DY1=Y(F2)-Y(F1)
6650 DX2=X(F3)-X(F2) : DY2=Y(F3)-Y(F2)
6660 IF DX1*DY2-DX2*DY1 < 0 THEN 6680
6669 REM draw flags on visible facets
6670 PROCflag
6680 NEXT I%
6690 ENDPROC

7000 REM flag / on face of cube
7010 DEF PROCflag
7020 LOCAL I%,J%,K% : K%=4
7030 FACE(1)=F1 : FACE(2)=F2 : FACE(3)=F3 : FACE(4)=F4
7039 REM place corners of cube face in (XD(i),YD(i)) where i=1,2,3,4
7040 FOR I%=1 TO 4
7050 XD(I%)=X(FACE(I%)) : YD(I%)=Y(FACE(I%))
7060 NEXT I%
7070 REM place vertices of diagonal stripes in (XD(i),YD(i))
         where i=5,6,7,8,9,10,11,12
7080 FOR I%=1 TO 4
7090 J%=(I% MOD 4)+1
7100 K%=K%+1
```

```
7110 XD(K%)=0.9*X(FACE(I%))+0.1*X(FACE(J%))
7120 YD(K%)=0.9*Y(FACE(I%))+0.1*Y(FACE(J%))
7130 K%=K%+1
7140 XD(K%)=0.1*X(FACE(I%))+0.9*X(FACE(J%))
7150 YD(K%)=0.1*Y(FACE(I%))+0.9*Y(FACE(J%))
7160 NEXT I%
7169 REM draw red background
7170 PROCquad(1,2,3,4)
7179 REM draw yellow diagonals
7180 PROChex(1,5,8,3,9,12)
7190 PROChex(2,7,10,4,11,6)
7199 REM draw edge of cube face
7200 GCOL 0,0
7210 MOVE FNX(X(F1)),FNY(Y(F1))
7220 DRAW FNX(X(F2)),FNY(Y(F2))
7230 DRAW FNX(X(F3)),FNY(Y(F3))
7240 DRAW FNX(X(F4)),FNY(Y(F4))
7250 DRAW FNX(X(F1)),FNY(Y(F1))
7260 ENDPROC

7300 REM quadrilateral
7310 DEF PROCquad(V1,V2,V3,V4)
7320 GCOL 0,1
7330 MOVE FNX(XD(V2)), FNY(YD(V2))
7340 MOVE FNX(XD(V1)), FNY(YD(V1))
7350 PLOT 85,FNX(XD(V3)), FNY(YD(V3))
7360 PLOT 85,FNX(XD(V4)), FNY(YD(V4))
7370 ENDPROC

7400 REM hexagon
7410 DEF PROChex(V1,V2,V3,V4,V5,V6)
7420 GCOL 0,2
7430 MOVE FNX(XD(V1)), FNY(YD(V1))
7440 MOVE FNX(XD(V2)), FNY(YD(V2))
7450 PLOT 85,FNX(XD(V6)), FNY(YD(V6))
7460 PLOT 85,FNX(XD(V3)), FNY(YD(V3))
7470 PLOT 85,FNX(XD(V5)), FNY(YD(V5))
7480 PLOT 85,FNX(XD(V4)), FNY(YD(V4))
7490 ENDPROC
```

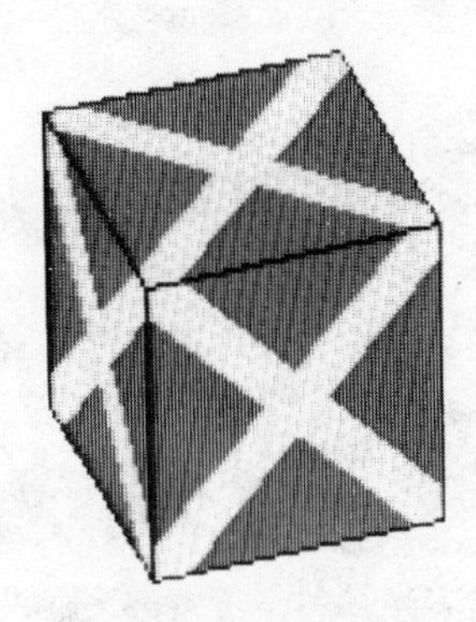

*Figure 10.2*

*Exercise 10.4*
Draw a hidden surface picture of a red die with black spots, and with edges drawn also in black. Remember that the values on opposite faces of a die sum to seven.

**Bodies of Revolution**

We can use this anticlockwise versus clockwise method to produce hidden surface pictures of the bodies of revolution that were defined in chapter 9. As we go through the NUMH revolutions we generate NUMV facets with each move. Provided that these quadrilateral (or perhaps degenerate triangular) facets are carefully constructed in an anticlockwise orientation then we may use the same algorithm. Listing 10.5 is such a 'revbod' procedure which produces figure 10.3, a hidden surface version of figure 9.4 (and uses the same input data). Again, because of the modular design of our programs, all the procedures needed to draw figure 10.3, except 'revbod', are the same as those given in chapter 9. Now, however, we must deal solely with convex bodies of revolution.

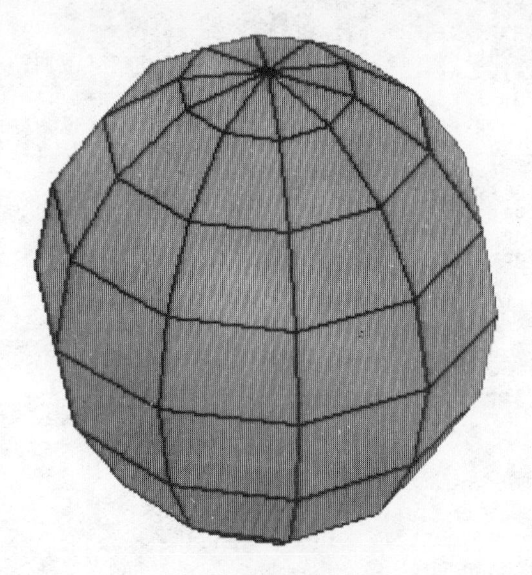

*Figure 10.3*

As the procedure rotates the definition set of lines about the vertical axis, it stores the vertices of two consecutive vertical sets of lines. These form the vertical edges of one *slice* of facets. The vertices on these facets are immediately transformed by R (the SETUP to OBSERVED matrix) and stored in arrays X and Y. In such a configuration of pairs of vertical lines the first set of vertices

*Listing 10.5*

```
6500 REM revbod / hidden surface
6510 DEF PROCrevbod
6520 LOCAL I%,J%,THETA,TD,N1,C,S,XX,YY,ZZ,F1,F2,F3,F4
6530 THETA=PHI : TD=PI*2/NUMH
6540 N1=NUMV+1 : C=COS(PHI) : S=SIN(PHI)
6549 REM first vertical set
6550 FOR I%=1 TO N1
6560 XX=XD(I%)*C : YY=YD(I%) : ZZ=XD(I%)*S
6570 X(I%)=R(1,1)*XX+R(1,2)*YY+R(1,3)*ZZ+R(1,4)
6580 Y(I%)=R(2,1)*XX+R(2,2)*YY+R(2,3)*ZZ+R(2,4)
6590 NEXT I%
6599 REM loop through second vertical set
6600 FOR J%=1 TO NUMH
6610 THETA=THETA+TD : C=COS(THETA) : S=SIN(THETA)
6620 FOR I%=1 TO N1
6630 XX=XD(I%)*C : YY=YD(I%) : ZZ=XD(I%)*S
6640 X(I%+N1)=R(1,1)*XX+R(1,2)*YY+R(1,3)*ZZ+R(1,4)
6650 Y(I%+N1)=R(2,1)*XX+R(2,2)*YY+R(2,3)*ZZ+R(2,4)
6660 NEXT I%
6669 REM facet formed by F1,F2,F3 and ( F4 )is SETUP anticlockwise
6670 FOR I%=1 TO NUMV
6680 F1=I% : F2=I%+1
6690 IF I%=NUMV THEN F3=F2+NUMV ELSE F3=F2+N1
6700 DX1=X(F2)-X(F1) : DY1=Y(F2)-Y(F1)
6710 DX2=X(F3)-X(F2) : DY2=Y(F3)-Y(F2)
6719 REM if OBSERVED anticlockwise then facet visible
6720 IF DX1*DY2-DX2*DY1 < 0 THEN 6810
6730 F3=F2+N1 : F4=F3-1
6740 PROCtriangle(X(F1),Y(F1),X(F2),Y(F2),X(F3),Y(F3),1,-1)
6750 PROCtriangle(X(F1),Y(F1),X(F4),Y(F4),X(F3),Y(F3),1,-1)
6760 GCOL0,0 : PROCmoveto(X(F1),Y(F1))
6770 PROClineto(X(F2),Y(F2))
6780 PROClineto(X(F3),Y(F3))
6790 PROClineto(X(F4),Y(F4))
6800 PROClineto(X(F1),Y(F1))
6810 NEXT I%
6820 FOR I%=1 TO N1
6830 X(I%)=X(I%+N1) : Y(I%)=Y(I%+N1)
6840 NEXT I% : NEXT J%
6850 ENDPROC
```

have indices from 1 to NUMV + 1 (= N1), and the second from N1 + 1 to 2 * N1. The $I^{th}$ facet is bounded by four lines, two vertical which join vertex I to I + 1, and I + N1 to I + N1 + 1, and two horizontal which join I to I + N1, and I + 1 to I + N1 + 1. Adjustments must be made if one of the original vertices is on the axis of rotation, in which case the quadrilateral degenerates to a triangle. The order of vertices in each facet is carefully chosen so that it is in anticlockwise orientation when viewed from outside the object. This allows us to use our simple algorithm to draw the object with the hidden surfaces suppressed. This technique was also used to draw figure I.1 in the introduction.

*Exercise 10.5*
Experiment with this technique. Any initial set of lines will do provided that it starts and ends on the vertical axis and the polygon thus formed in the $x/y$ plane is convex.

### The BACK to FRONT Method

The call for pictures of convex solids is limited, so we shall now look at another simple algorithm that can be used with non-convex figures. You will have noticed that when colouring a new area by using option GCOL 0, all the colours previously placed in that section of the screen are obliterated. This furnishes us with a very simple hidden surface algorithm, namely we draw the areas furthest from the eye first and the nearest last. Exactly what we mean by furthest/nearest is not that straightforward. It is not just a simple matter of comparing $z$-coordinates in a scene. Imagine a small book and a large table. There are some vertices on the table that have larger $z$-coordinates than those on the book, and some that are smaller. We do not know if the book is on the table or under it. However there are certain situations (for example, as described in the next section, and the stack of cubes of figure 11.5) where this phrase has a very simple meaning and the algorithm is easy to implement. See chapter 12 for a general solution.

### Drawing a Special Three-dimensional Surface

We consider the construction of a restricted type of three-dimensional surface in which the $y$-coordinate of each point on the surface is given by a single-valued function 'f' of the $x$-coordinate and $z$-coordinate of that point. 'f' will be included as a procedure in the program – one such example is given in listing 10.6, the function $y = 4 \times \text{SIN(XZ)/XZ}$ where $\text{XZ} = \sqrt{(x^2 + z^2)}$, which is shown in figure 10.4. The data required were mode = 1, HORIZ = 32, VERT = 24, NX = NZ = 16, XMIN = ZMIN = –10, XMAX = ZMAX = 10, (EX, EY, EZ) = (3, 2, 1), (DX, DY, DZ) = (0, 0, 0).

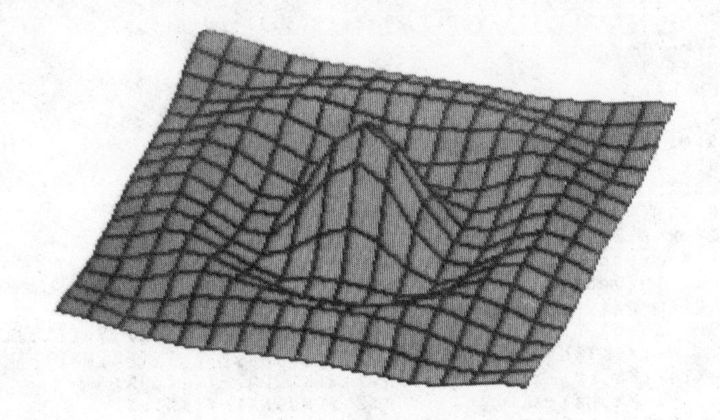

*Figure 10.4*

*Listing 10.6*

```
6000 REM scene3 / math. surface
6010 DEF PROCscene3
6020 DIM A(4,4),B(4,4),R(4,4)
6030 CLS
6039 REM INPUT grid data
6040 INPUT"NX,XMIN,XMAX ",NX,XMIN,XMAX
6050 INPUT"NZ,ZMIN,ZMAX ",NZ,ZMIN,ZMAX
6060 XD=(XMAX-XMIN)/NX : ZD=(ZMAX-ZMIN)/NZ : ZV=ZMIN : NX1=NX+1
6070 DIM X(2,NX1),Y(2,NX1),Z(2,NX1)
6079 REM view from (EX,EY,EZ) to (0,0,0) : EX and EZ > 0
6080 PROCidR3 : PROClook3
6089 REM draw the surface
6090 PROCsurface
6100 ENDPROC

6500 REM surface
6510 DEF PROCsurface
6520 LOCAL I%,J%,K%
6530 PROCsetpt(1)
6539 REM loop thru consecutive pairs of fixed-Z lines
6540 FOR I%=1 TO NZ
6550 ZV=ZV+ZD : PROCsetpt(2) : K%=1
6559 REM move along polygons formed between these two lines
6560 FOR J%=2 TO NX1
6570 PROCpoly(I%,J%,K%) : K%=J%
6580 NEXT J%
6590 FOR J%=1 TO NX1
6600 X(1,J%)=X(2,J%) : Y(1,J%)=Y(2,J%) : Z(1,J%)=Z(2,J%)
6610 NEXT J%
6620 NEXT I%
6630 ENDPROC

6700 REM setpt
6710 DEF PROCsetpt(M%)
6720 LOCAL I%,XV,YV
6729 REM points on fixed-Z = ZV line are put in OBSERVED position
6730 XV=XMIN
6740 FOR I%=1 TO NX1
6750 YV=FNf(XV,ZV)
6760 X(M%,I%)=R(1,1)*XV+R(1,2)*YV+R(1,3)*ZV+R(1,4)
6770 Y(M%,I%)=R(2,1)*XV+R(2,2)*YV+R(2,3)*ZV+R(2,4)
6780 Z(M%,I%)=R(3,1)*XV+R(3,2)*YV+R(3,3)*ZV+R(3,4)
6790 XV=XV+XD
6800 NEXT I%
6810 ENDPROC

6900 REM FNf / function to be drawn
6910 DEF FNf(XV,ZV)
6920 LOCAL R
6930 R=SQR(XV*XV+ZV*ZV)
6940 IF R<0.00001 THEN=4.0 ELSE =4*SIN(R)/R
7000 REM zvecprod / z-value of vector product
7010 DEF FNzvecprod(I%,J%,K%,L%,M%,N%)
7020 LOCAL DX1,DY1,DX2,DY2
7029 REM check orientation of triangle ((X(I%,J%),Y((I%,J%)) to
         ((X(K%,L%),Y((K%,L%)) to ((X(M%,M%),Y((M%,M%))
7030 DX1=X(K%,L%)-X(I%,J%) : DY1=Y(K%,L%)-Y(I%,J%)
7040 DX2=X(M%,N%)-X(K%,L%) : DY2=Y(M%,N%)-Y(K%,L%)
7050 =DX1*DY2-DX2*DY1
```

```
7100 REM poly
7110 DEF PROCpoly(I%,J%,K%)
7120 LOCAL L%,ZP1,ZP2,A1,B1,A2,B2,A3,B3,A4,B4,A5,B5,
          C11,C12,C21,C22,D1,D2,DET,RMU
7130 ZP1=FNzvecprod(1,K%,1,J%,2,J%)
7140 ZP2=FNzvecprod(2,J%,2,K%,1,K%)
7149 REM grid rectangle transforms to quadrilateral or 2 triangles
7150 IF SGN(ZP1) <> SGN(ZP2) THEN 7250
7159 REM draw quadrilateral
7160 PROCtriangle(X(1,K%),Y(1,K%),X(1,J%),Y(1,J%),X(2,J%),Y(2,J%),1,-1)
7170 PROCtriangle(X(2,J%),Y(2,J%),X(2,K%),Y(2,K%),X(1,K%),Y(1,K%),1,-1)
7180 GCOL 0,0
7189 REM draw outline
7190 PROCmoveto(X(2,J%),Y(2,J%))
7200 PROClineto(X(1,J%),Y(1,J%))
7210 PROClineto(X(1,K%),Y(1,K%))
7220 PROClineto(X(2,K%),Y(2,K%))
7230 PROClineto(X(2,J%),Y(2,J%))
7240 ENDPROC
7249 REM find intersection (A5,B5) of lines from (A1,B1) to (A2,B2)
        and from (A3,B3) to (A4,B4)
7250 A1=X(1,K%) : B1=Y(1,K%) : A2=X(1,J%) : B2=Y(1,J%)
7260 A3=X(2,J%) : B3=Y(2,J%) : A4=X(2,K%) : B4=Y(2,K%)
7270 FOR L%=1 TO 2
7280 C11=A2-A1 : C12=A3-A4 : C21=B2-B1 : C22=B3-B4
7290 D1=A3-A1 : D2=B3-B1 : DET=C11*C22-C21*C12
7300 IF ABS(DET)<0.0000001 THEN 7360
7310 RMU=(D1*C22-D2*C12)/DET : IF RMU<0 OR RMU>1 THEN 7360
7320 A5=A1+RMU*C11 : B5=B1+RMU*C21
7329 REM draw the two triangles (A1,B1) to (A4,B4) to (A5,B5)
        (A2,B2) to (A3,B3) to (A5,B5)
7330 PROCtriangle(A1,B1,A4,B4,A5,B5,1,-1)
7340 PROCtriangle(A2,B2,A3,B3,A5,B5,1,-1)
7350 GOTO 7180
7359 REM no intersection so swap (A2,B2) with (A4,B4)
7360 AA=A2 : A2=A4 : A4=AA
7370 AA=B2 : B2=B4 : B4=AA
7380 NEXT L%
7390 ENDPROC
```

Since it is impossible to draw every point on the surface we have to approximate by considering a subset of these surface points. We choose those points with $x/z$ coordinates on a grid, in other words, when orthographically viewed directly from above (thus ignoring the $y$-values), the points form a rectangular grid. This grid is composed of NX by NZ rectangles in the $x/z$ plane. The $x$-coordinates of the vertices are equi-spaced and vary between XMIN and XMAX (XMIN < XMAX) and the equi-spaced $z$-values vary between ZMIN and ZMAX (ZMIN < ZMAX). There are thus (NX + 1) × (NZ + 1) vertices (X, Z) in the grid which can be identified by the pair of integers $(i, j)$:

$$\mathrm{X} = \mathrm{XMIN} + i \times \mathrm{XV} \text{ where } 0 \leqslant i \leqslant \mathrm{NX} \text{ and } \mathrm{XV} = (\mathrm{XMAX} - \mathrm{XMIN})/\mathrm{NX}$$

$$\mathrm{Z} = \mathrm{ZMIN} + j \times \mathrm{ZV} \text{ where } 0 \leqslant j \leqslant \mathrm{NZ} \text{ and } \mathrm{ZV} = (\mathrm{ZMAX} - \mathrm{ZMIN})/\mathrm{NZ}$$

The equivalent point on the surface is (X, Y, Z) where Y = f(X, Z). Every one of the (NX + 1) × (NZ + 1) points generated in this way is joined to its four immediate neighbours along the grid (that is, those with equal $x$-values or equal $z$-values), unless it lies on the edge, in which case it is joined to three or, in the case of corners, to two neighbours.

The approximation to the surface that is formed in this way may undulate so not all the facets need be visible from a given view point – in fact some may even be partially visible. We devise a very simple method to eliminate the hidden surfaces by working from the back of the surface to the front. To simplify the algorithm we assume that the eye is always in the positive quadrant, that is, EX > 0 and EZ > 0, and that the eye is always looking at the origin (DX = DY = = DZ = 0). If the function is non-symmetrical and we wish to view it from another quadrant then we simply change the sign of $x$ and/or $z$ in the function. We can then transform the surface into the OBSERVED position.

We start by looping through the set of NX facets that are generated from the consecutive fixed-$x$ grid lines $x$ = XMIN + $i$ × XV and $x$ = XMIN + ($i$ + 1) × XV from the back ($i$ = 0) to the front ($i$ = NX – 1) (naturally the term back to front is used in the sense of the final OBSERVED position). Within each set we loop through the individual facets that are generated by the intersection of the fixed-$x$ lines with the fixed-$z$ grid lines starting at $z$ = ZMIN and $z$ = ZMIN + ZV, and working through to $z$ = ZMAX – ZV and $z$ = ZMAX. We may label the four grid points created in this way (1, K) and (1, K + 1) – on the fixed-$x$ line with smaller $x$-value – and (2, K) and (2, K + 1) – on the fixed-$x$ line with larger value (K + 1 is called J in the program, and in the explanation below). 'f' is used to form four points on the surface from these grid points, which when transformed on to the view plane form either a quadrilateral or two triangles. We distinguish between the two possibilities by finding the orientation of the two triangles that are formed by the grid points (1, K), (1, J) and (2, J), and (2, J), (2, K) and (1, K). If they have the same orientation (both clockwise or both anticlockwise) then we have a quadrilateral, otherwise two triangles. The extra vertex of the two triangles is found from either the intersection of the lines joining (1, K) to (1, J) and (2, J) to (2, K), or from (1, K) to (2, K) and (1, J) to (2, J): other combinations are topologically impossible. After having found the quadrilateral or two triangles they are coloured in and their edges also drawn (procedure 'poly'), and the back to front construction (because EX and EZ are positive) means that we get a correct hidden surface picture.

*Exercise 10.6*
Change the functions 'f' used by this program. For example use f = 4SIN($t$) where $t = \sqrt{(x^2 + z^2)}$.

*Exercise 10.7*
Extend the above program so that it draws the top-side of the surface in a different colour to the under-side.

**Complete Programs**

I 'lib3' and listing 10.1. Data required: the vertex coordinates of a triangle (X(I), Y(I), Z(I)), where $1 \leqslant I \leqslant 3$. Try (1, 0, 1), (1, 1, 0) and (0, 1, 1); also the same vertices in a different order (1, 1, 0), (1, 0, 1) and (0, 1, 1).

II 'lib1', 'lib3' and listings 9.3 ('scene3') and 10.2 ('cube'). Data required: mode, HORIZ, VERT, (EX, EY, EZ), (DX, DY, DZ). Try 1, 8, 6, (1, 2, 3), (0, 0, −1).

III 'lib1', 'lib3' and listing 10.3 ('icosa'hedron) and listing 9.3 ('scene3' but change 'cube' to 'icosa'). Data required: mode, HORIZ, VERT, (EX, EY, EZ) and (DX, DY, DZ). Try the same data as used in II. Change line 6020 to hold 12 vertices.

IV 'lib1', 'lib3' and listing 10.4 ('cube', 'flag' etc.). Data required: mode, HORIZ, VERT, (EX, EY, EZ) and (DX, DY, DZ). Try the same data as used in II.

V 'lib1', 'lib3' and listings 9.10 ('scene3') and 10.5 ('revbod'). Data required: mode, HORIZ, VERT, NUMH, NUMV, PHI, (EX, EY, EZ), (DX, DY, DZ). Try 1, 3.2, 2.4, 10, 10, 1, (1, 2, 3), (0, 0, 0).

VI 'lib1', 'lib3' and listing 10.6 ('scene3', 'surface', 'setpt', 'f', 'zvecprod' and 'poly'). Data required: mode, HORIZ, VERT, NX, XMIN, XMAX, NZ, ZMIN, ZMAX, (EX, EY, EZ), (DX, DY, DZ). Try 1, 28, 21, 16, −8, 8, 16, −8, 8, (1, 2, 3) and (0, 0, 0). Use the VDU 19 command to change the colour of the surface; for example VDU 19, 1, 3, 0, 0, 0. If you find that there is not enough store even after changing PAGE, then you can run the program in mode 4, or strip off all the REMs from the program and rerun in mode 1. Just type AUTO 9, 10 and hold the RETURN key down and this will do the trick.

# 11 Perspective and Stereoscopic Projections

## Perspective

We have seen that the orthographic projection has the property that parallel lines in three-dimensional space are projected into parallel lines on the view plane. Although very useful, such views do look odd! Our brains are used to the perspective phenomenon of three-dimensional space, and so they attempt to interpret orthographic figures as if they were perspective views. For example, the cubes of figures 9.1 and 10.1 look distorted.

So it is essential to produce a projection that displays perspective phenomena, that is, parallel lines should meet on the horizon – an object should appear smaller as it moves away from the observer. The *drawing-board* methods devised by artists over the centuries are of no value to us. Three-dimensional coordinate geometry and the concept of ACTUAL to OBSERVED positions, however, furnish us with a relatively straightforward technique.

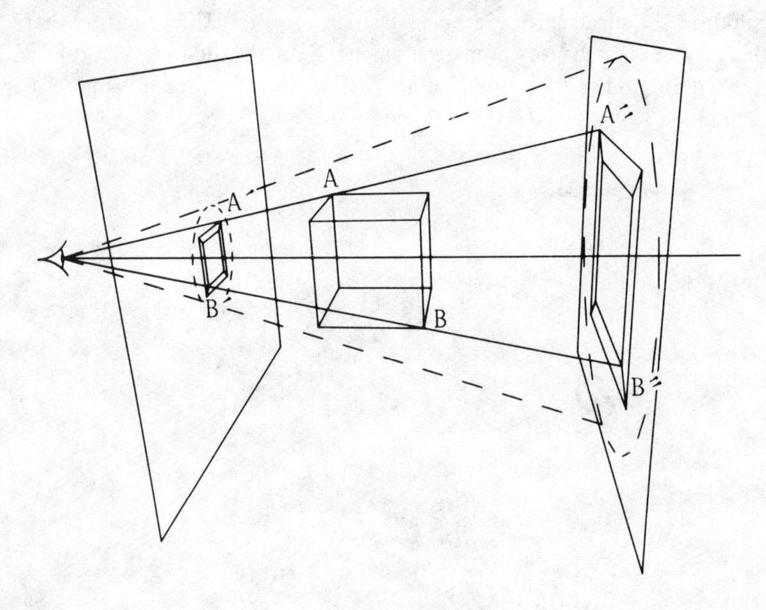


*Figure 11.1*

*What is perspective vision?*

To produce a perspective view we introduce a very simple definition of what we mean by vision. We imagine that every visible point in space is sending out a ray which enters the eye. Naturally the eye cannot see all of space, it is limited to the cone of rays that fall on the retina, the so-called *cone of vision*, which is outlined by the dashed lines of figure 11.1. The axis of this cone is called the *straight-ahead ray*. We imagine that space has been transformed into the OBSERVED position with the eye at the origin and the straight-ahead ray identified with the positive $z$-axis.

We place the view plane (which we call the *perspective plane* in this special case) perpendicular to the axis of the cone of vision at a distance $d$ from the eye. In order to form the perspective projection we mark the points of intersection of each ray with this plane. Since there are an infinity of such rays this appears to be an impossible task. Actually the problem is not that great because we need consider only the rays that emanate from the important points in the scene, that is the vertices at the ends of line segments or the corners of polygonal facets. The final view is formed by relating the projected points on the perspective plane in exactly the same way as they are related in three-dimensional space, and then by identifying the view plane with the graphics screen.

Figure 11.1 shows a cube that is observed by an eye and projected on to two planes: the whole scene is also drawn in perspective! Two example rays are shown: the first from the eye to A, one of the near corners of the cube (relative to the eye), and the second to B, one of the far corners of the cube. The perspective projections of these points on to the near plane are A′ and B′, and on to the far plane A″ and B″. Note that the projections will have the same shape and orientation, but they will be of different sizes.

*Calculation of the perspective projection of a point*

We let the perspective plane be a distance $d$ from the eye (variable PPD in later programs). Consider a point $P = (x, y, z)$ in space that sends a ray into the eye. We must calculate the point where this line cuts the view plane (the $z = d$ plane) – suppose it is the point $P' \equiv (x', y', d)$. Let us first consider the value of $y'$ by referring to figure 11.2. By similar triangles we see that $y'/d = y/z$, that is $y' = y \times d/z$. Similarly $x' = x \times d/z$. Hence $P' \equiv (x \times d/z, y \times d/z, d)$. Since the view plane is identified with the $x/y$ coordinate system of the graphics screen we can ignore the $z = d$ coordinate.

***Example 11.1***

Calculate the perspective projection of a cube that has eight vertices $(0, 0, 4) + (\pm 1, \pm 1, \pm 1)$ on the perspective plane $z = 4$, where the eye is origin and the straight-ahead ray is the positive $z$-axis.

The space is defined so that the scene is in the OBSERVED position. We can calculate the projections of the eight vertices by using the above method. For example $(1, 1, 3)$ is projected to $(1 \times 4/3, 1 \times 4/3, 4) = (4/3, 4/3, 4) \rightarrow (4/3, 4/3)$ on the screen. So we get the eight projections:

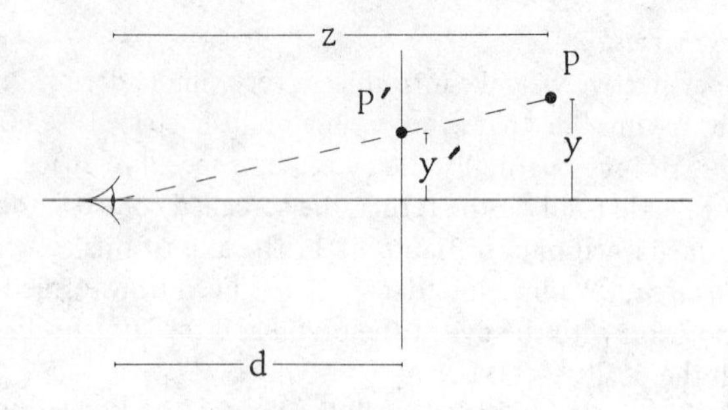


*Figure 11.2*

$$(1, 1, 3) \rightarrow (4/3, 4/3) \qquad (1, -1, 3) \rightarrow (4/3, -4/3)$$

$$(-1, 1, 3) \rightarrow (-4/3, 4/3) \qquad (-1, -1, 3) \rightarrow (-4/3, -4/3)$$

$$(1, 1, 5) \rightarrow (4/5, 4/5) \qquad (1, -1, 5) \rightarrow (4/5, -4/5)$$

$$(-1, 1, 5) \rightarrow (-4/5, 4/5) \qquad (-1, -1, 5) \rightarrow (-4/5, -4/5)$$

and the resulting diagram is shown in figure 11.3a.

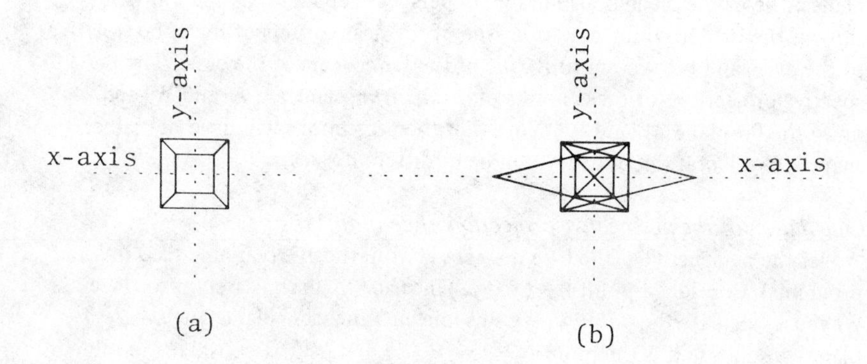


*Figure 11.3*

*Properties of the perspective transformation*

(1) The perspective transformation of a straight line ($\Gamma_3$ say) is a straight line ($\Gamma_2$ say). This is obvious because the origin (the eye) and the line $\Gamma_3$ form a plane ($\Omega$ say) in three-dimensional space and all the rays emanating from points on $\Gamma_3$ lie in this plane. (If the line enters the eye, $\Omega$ degenerates into a line.) Naturally $\Omega$ cuts the perspective plane in a line $\Gamma_2$ (or degenerates to a point) and so the perspective projection of a point on the original line $\Gamma_3$ now lies on the new line $\Gamma_2$. It is important to realise that a line does not become curved on perspective projection.

(2) The perspective transformation of a facet (a closed sequence of coplanar line segments) is a facet in the perspective plane. If the facet is an area bounded by $n$ coplanar line segments then the transform of this facet is naturally an area in the $z = d$ plane that is bounded by the transforms of the $n$ line segments. Again note that no curves are introduced in this projection: if they were, then the task of producing perspective pictures would be far more complicated.
(3) The projection of a convex facet is also convex. Suppose that facet $F_3$ is projected on to facet $F_2$. Since the projection of a closed facet is also closed and lines go into lines, then points inside $F_3$ are projected into points inside $F_2$. Suppose $F_2$ is not convex. Then there exist two points $\boldsymbol{p}_1$ and $\boldsymbol{p}_2$ inside $F_2$ such that the line joining them goes outside this facet. Hence there is at least one point $\boldsymbol{p}$ on the line outside $F_2$. If $\boldsymbol{p}_1$ and $\boldsymbol{p}_2$ are projections of points $\boldsymbol{q}_1$ and $\boldsymbol{q}_2$ from $F_3$, then $\boldsymbol{p}$ is the projection of some point $\boldsymbol{q}$ on the line joining $\boldsymbol{q}_1$ and $\boldsymbol{q}_2$. Since $F_3$ is convex then $\boldsymbol{q}$ must be inside $F_3$ and thus $\boldsymbol{p}$ must be inside $F_2$ – a contradiction and our proposition is thus proved.
(4) All infinitely long parallel lines appear to meet at one point, their so-called *vanishing point*. If we take a general line (with base vector $\boldsymbol{p}$) from a set of parallel lines with direction vector $\boldsymbol{h}$

$$\boldsymbol{p} + \mu\boldsymbol{h} \equiv (x_p, y_p, z_p) + \mu(x_h, y_h, z_h)$$

where $z_h > 0$, then the perspective transform of a general point on this line is

$$\left(\frac{(x_p + \mu x_h) \times d}{(z_p + \mu z_h)}, \frac{(y_p + \mu y_h) \times d}{(z_p + \mu z_h)}\right)$$

which can be rewritten as

$$\left(\frac{(x_h + x_p/\mu) \times d}{(z_h + z_p/\mu)}, \frac{(y_h + y_p/\mu) \times d}{(z_h + z_p/\mu)}\right)$$

As we move along the line towards large $z$-coordinates, that is as $\mu \to \infty$, then the line moves towards its vanishing point, which is therefore given by $(d \times x_h/z_h, d \times y_h/z_h)$. This vanishing point is independent of $\boldsymbol{p}$, the base point of the line, and hence all lines parallel to the direction $\boldsymbol{h}$ have the same vanishing point. Of course the case $z_h < 0$ is ignored because the line would disappear outside the cone of vision as $\mu \to \infty$.
(5) The vanishing points of all lines in parallel planes are collinear. Suppose that the set of parallel planes has a common normal direction $\boldsymbol{n} \equiv (x_n, y_n, z_n)$. If a general line in one of these planes has direction $\boldsymbol{h} \equiv (x_h, y_h, z_h)$, then $\boldsymbol{h}$ is perpendicular to $\boldsymbol{n}$ (all lines in these planes are perpendicular to the normal to the plane $\boldsymbol{n}$). Thus $\boldsymbol{n} \cdot \boldsymbol{h} = 0$, which in coordinate form is

$$x_n \times x_h + y_n \times y_h + z_n \times z_h = 0$$

Dividing by $z_h$ gives

$$x_n \times x_h/z_h + y_n \times y_h/z_h + z_n = 0$$

and so the vanishing point $(d \times x_h/z_h, d \times y_h/z_h)$ lies on the straight line

$$x_n \times x + y_n \times y + d \times z_n = 0$$

and the statement is proved.

*Example 11.2*

Find the vanishing points of the edges of the cube in example 11.1, and of the diagonals of its top and bottom planes.

We divide the twelve edges of the cube into three sets of four edges; each set is parallel to the $x$-axis, $y$-axis and $z$-axis respectively and so has directional vectors $(1, 0, 0)$, $(0, 1, 0)$ and $(0, 0, 1)$. The first two sets have zero $z$-values, and so their extended edges disappear outside the cone of vision and are ignored, whereas the third direction has the vanishing point $(4 \times 0/1, 4 \times 0/1) \equiv (0, 0)$ on the view plane. On the top and bottom faces the diagonals have directions $(1, 0, 1)$, the major diagonal, and $(-1, 0, 1)$, the minor diagonal. The major diagonal on the top plane is $(-1, 1, 3) + \mu(1, 0, 1)$, and so the vanishing point is $(4 \times 1/1, 4 \times 0/1) \equiv (4, 0)$. The minor diagonal on the top plane is $(1, 1, 3) + \mu(-1, 0, 1)$ and has the vanishing point $(4 \times -1/1, 4 \times 0/1) \equiv (-4, 0)$. By similar calculations we find that the vanishing points of the major and minor diagonals on the lower face are also $(4, 0)$ and $(-4, 0)$ respectively. The relevant edges are extended to their vanishing points in figure 11.3b. Note that all the lines mentioned lie in the two parallel planes (the top and bottom faces of the cube) and so the vanishing points should be collinear: they are because $(4, 0)$, $(0, 0)$ and $(-4, 0)$ all lie on the $x$-axis. By a similar calculation we would find that the vanishing points of the diagonals of the side faces lie on a vertical line through the origin.

*Exercise 11.1*

Draw a perspective view of a tetrahedron with vertices $(1, 1, 5)$, $(1, -1, 3)$, $(-1, 1, 3)$ and $(-1, -1, 5)$. Find the vanishing points (inside the cone of vision) of lines that join pairs of mid-points of the edges of the tetrahedron.

*Programming the perspective transformation*

The main program for drawing a perspective view of any scene is the same as that for the orthographic view, namely listing 9.2. Again the overall scene is created by a call to a procedure 'scene3', which is similar to those discussed in chapter 9. We shall often need to calculate explicitly the ACTUAL to OBSERVED matrix, so that the eye is in the OBSERVED position at the origin and looking along the positive $z$-axis. This is achieved by procedure 'look3' given in chapter 9 (listing 9.1). Calls are made to construction procedures, each having a matrix R as parameter. Finally the figure must be drawn, inside the construction procedures or in a 'drawit' procedure.

Note that the only difference between the program that draws a perspective view and that of the orthographic view of chapter 9 is in the calculation of the coordinates of the projected image on the view plane. Unlike the orthographic, in the perspective projection the coordinates on the view plane cannot be identified with the $x$-value and the $y$-value of the point in the OBSERVED position. We need to store the perspective transformation of the vertices in the arrays XD and YD: the $I^{th}$ vertex (X (I), Y (I), Z (I)) in the OBSERVED position is projected to (XD (I), YD (I)). The values in arrays XD and YD are given by

XD(I) = X(I)*PPD/Z(I) and YD(I) = Y(I)*PPD/Z(I) for I = 1, 2, . . . , NOV

The value of PPD is set to 3*VERT in 'scene3' – the reason for this is given in the next section. The calculation of XD and YD can be made in the construction procedure, or in the 'scene3' or 'drawit' procedures: it simply depends on the scene that is being considered.

*Example 11.3*

We draw a fixed scene (the two cubes that are described in example 9.2) in perspective from a variety of observation points, setting HORIZ = 4 and VERT = 3. Rerun the program with HORIZ = 8 and VERT = 6 (is there any difference?). The necessary 'scene3' procedure will be almost the same as listing 9.6 except that it calculates PPD. It has the one addition:

```
6040 NOV = 0:  NOL = 0:  PPD = 3*VERT
```

It places the group of cubes in their ACTUAL position by using the 'cube' procedure of listing 9.7, and then loops through a number of different OBSERVED positions. For each time through the loop we call 'look3' which requires (EX, EY, EZ) and (DX, DY, DZ) to calculate the ACTUAL to OBSERVED matrix. Then the perspective 'drawit' procedure (listing 11.1) is called. This uses the matrix to transform the vertices from their (stored) ACTUAL position to the OBSERVED position, and places the projected vertex coordinates in arrays XD and YD, according to the above equations. The procedure can then finally draw the edges of the cubes in perspective.

Figure 11.4 was drawn by using (EX, EY, EZ) ≡ (15, 10, 5) and (DX, DY, DZ) ≡ (0, 0, 0). Compare this with the orthographic view of the same scene given in figure 9.2.

*Exercise 11.2*

Draw various perspective views of a wire tetrahedron and a pyramid.

*The choice of perspective plane*

The only value required for the perspective transformation that we have not yet discussed is that of PPD, the distance of the perspective plane from the eye. We can see from figure 11.1 that different values of PPD produce pictures of different sizes. Which one do we choose? Is there a correct value?

If we consider the practical situation, we note that the observer is sitting

*Listing 11.1*

```
7000 REM drawit / perspective cube not stored
7010 DEF PROCdrawit
7020 LOCAL I%,XX,YY,ZZ,L1,L2 : CLG
7030 FOR I%=1 TO NOV
7039 REM move ACTUAL points to their OBSERVED position (XX,YY,ZZ)
7040 XX=R(1,1)*X(I%)+R(1,2)*Y(I%)+R(1,3)*Z(I%)+R(1,4)
7050 YY=R(2,1)*X(I%)+R(2,2)*Y(I%)+R(2,3)*Z(I%)+R(2,4)
7060 ZZ=R(3,1)*X(I%)+R(3,2)*Y(I%)+R(3,3)*Z(I%)+R(3,4)
7069 REM store perspective projections in arrays XD and YD
7070 XD(I%)=XX*PPD/ZZ
7080 YD(I%)=YY*PPD/ZZ
7090 NEXT I%
7099 REM draw the lines
7100 FOR I%=1 TO NOL
7110 L1=LIN(1,I%) : L2=LIN(2,I%)
7120 PROCmoveto(XD(L1),YD(L1))
7130 PROClineto(XD(L2),YD(L2))
7140 NEXT I%
7150 ENDPROC
```

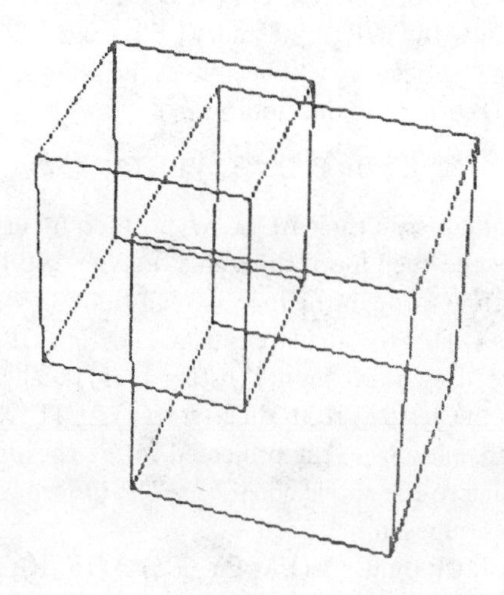

*Figure 11.4*

in front of a television screen and that the perspective view plane is identified with the plane of the television screen. Normally the observer is sitting at a distance that is about three times the height of the screen from the terminal. In the scale of our mapping from the real-world to the graphics area of pixels, this is a distance 3*VERT (the value we used above). If we choose PPD to be greater than this value it is as though we are creating a *close up*, and if PPD is less than 3*VERT we get the smaller image of a *long shot*. You will have noticed that perspective pictures are independent of the screen size, that is the absolute values of HORIZ and VERT are irrelevant, only their relative values matter, therefore in perspective pictures we shall always take HORIZ = 4 and VERT = 3: you can change the main program accordingly.

***Example 11.4***

We now draw a perspective hidden surface view of a stack of cubes (listing 11.2). Note how the vertical edges appear jagged. This is always the case in true perspective views because of the concept of vanishing points: compare this with the cubes drawn by listing 1.15, where we cheat! Figure 11.5 was drawn with mode 1, HORIZ = 4, VERT = 3, (EX, EY, EZ) = (20, 10, 40) and (DX, DY, DZ) = (4, 1, 0). To demonstrate that the picture is independent of the screen size try the same picture with HORIZ = 40 and VERT = 30. Then try HORIZ = VERT = 1: now there is a difference.

*Figure 11.5*

*Clipping*

Theoretically, objects may be positioned throughout space, even behind the eye, although we consider only points with positive $z$-coordinates in the OBSERVED position. Even so, some of these points go outside the cone of vision and become invisible. In fact, part of the cone of vision is outside the screen area (we can after all see the outside of the graphics area). We are left with a subset of the

*Listing 11.2*

```
6000 REM scene3 / stacking 27 cubes, hidden surfaces
6010 DEF PROCscene3
6020 LOCAL I%,J%,XV%,YV%,ZV%
6030 DIM X(8),Y(8),Z(8),XD(8),YD(8)
6040 DIM A(4,4),B(4,4),R(4,4),Q(4,4)
6050 CLS : CLG : PPD=3*VERT
6059 REM Q : ACTUAL to OBSERVED matrix
6060 PROCidR3 : PROClook3
6070 FOR I%=1 TO 4 : FOR J%=1 TO 4
6080 Q(I%,J%)=R(I%,J%)
6090 NEXT J% : NEXT I%
6099 REM loop thru different placings of the cubes
6100 FOR ZV%=-16 TO -4 STEP 6
6110 FOR YV%=-6 TO 6 STEP 6
6120 FOR XV%=-6 TO 6 STEP 6
6129 REM move cube to ACTUAL position
6130 PROCidR3 : PROCtran3(XV%,YV%,ZV%) : PROCmult3
6139 REM then to OBSERVED position
6140 FOR I%=1 TO 4 : FOR J%=1 TO 4
6150 A(I%,J%)=Q(I%,J%)
6160 NEXT J% : NEXT I%
6169 REM draw visible faces of cube
6170 PROCmult3 : PROCcube
6180 NEXT XV% : NEXT YV% : NEXT ZV%
6190 ENDPROC

6500 REM cube / perspective hidden surfaces
6510 DEF PROCcube
6520 LOCAL I%,XX,YY,ZZ,F1,F2,F3,F4,DX1,DY1,DX2,DY2
6530 DATA 1,1,1,  1,1,-1,  1,-1,-1,  1,-1,1,
          -1,1,1,  -1,1,-1,  -1,-1,-1,  -1,-1,1
6540 DATA 1,2,3,4, 5,8,7,6, 1,5,6,2, 2,6,7,3, 3,7,8,4, 4,8,5,1
6550 RESTORE
6559 REM position vertices
6560 FOR I%=1 TO 8
6570 READ XX,YY,ZZ
6580 X(I%)=R(1,1)*XX+R(1,2)*YY+R(1,3)*ZZ+R(1,4)
6590 Y(I%)=R(2,1)*XX+R(2,2)*YY+R(2,3)*ZZ+R(2,4)
6600 Z(I%)=R(3,1)*XX+R(3,2)*YY+R(3,3)*ZZ+R(3,4)
6609 REM put perspective projection of Vertices in arrays XD and YD
6610 XD(I%)=X(I%)*PPD/Z(I%)
6620 YD(I%)=Y(I%)*PPD/Z(I%)
6630 NEXT I%
6639 REM loop thru facets
6640 FOR I%=1 TO 6
6650 READ F1,F2,F3,F4
6660 DX1=XD(F2)-XD(F1) : DY1=YD(F2)-YD(F1)
6670 DX2=XD(F3)-XD(F2) : DY2=YD(F3)-YD(F2)
6679 REM if visible draw facets
6680 IF DX1*DY2-DX2*DY1 < 0 THEN 6770
6690 PROCtriangle(XD(F2),YD(F2),XD(F1),YD(F1),XD(F3),YD(F3),1,-2)
6700 PROCtriangle(XD(F4),YD(F4),XD(F1),YD(F1),XD(F3),YD(F3),1,-2)
6710 GCOL 0,0
6720 PROCmoveto(XD(F1),YD(F1))
6730 PROClineto(XD(F2),YD(F2))
6740 PROClineto(XD(F3),YD(F3))
6750 PROClineto(XD(F4),YD(F4))
6760 PROClineto(XD(F1),YD(F1))
6770 NEXT I%
6780 ENDPROC
```

cone of vision – the *pyramid of vision*. Thus all points outside this pyramid, that is those whose perspective transformation take them off the screen, must be ignored. This is conveniently done for us on the BBC Model B; however you should note that this is not necessarily true on other computers. In fact we further limit scenes so that all vertices in the OBSERVED position will have positive $z$-values, that is all objects must lie in front of the eye (although not necessarily inside the cone of vision). This will avoid a peculiar property of our perspective projection, namely points that lie behind the eye appear on the screen. If you run the above program (the stack of cubes) and vary the values of (EX, EY, EZ), for example (0.9. 0, 0), while all the other values stay the same, then the eye may be in among the cubes and the picture will go haywire or even fail. Also see project XVII in chapter 16.

*Exercise 11.3*
Experiment with perspective views of all types of wire figures, such as bodies of revolution or regular solids. Consider cases where an object is drawn inside the construction routine, that is the values of XD and YD must now be calculated here and not in the 'drawit' routine. Change the program that drew the jet of figure 9.3 so that you get a perspective view, and note that the further the eye gets from the plane the smaller it appears – a phenomenon that does not occur with the orthographic projection.

*Exercise 11.4*
Write a hidden line algorithm for a single convex body by using the ideas of listing 11.2.

*Exercise 11.5*
Write a program that draws a perspective view of a mathematical surface that is similar to the one given in chapter 10. The method will be exactly equivalent to listing 10.6, with the exception that you must work with the XD/YD values rather than the X/Y arrays.

These hidden surface and line algorithms are perfectly adequate for specially defined single objects. We extend these ideas in chapter 12 where we consider the more general case of a number of objects that are scattered arbitrarily about space. But first we look at stereoscopic projections which enable us to get true three-dimensional images from the BBC micro.

**Stereoscopic Views**

Perspective views are all very well but unfortunately (or fortunately!) we have two eyes. Each eye should have its own perspective view, which will differ slightly from that of the other eye. This is the means by which we appreciate the three-dimensional quality of our world. We use this concept to produce a stereoscopic view of space, namely we produce a perspective view for each eye. This leads to a problem. We cannot simply draw two such projections because the left eye will see not only the view created for it, but also that made for the right eye, and vice versa. To stop this confusion we must ensure that each eye sees its own view, but only its view. This is achieved by using a pair of stereoscopic spectacles: a pair of transparent plastic sheets, one red (left eye) and one cyan or light blue (right eye). In this way the left eye cannot see red lines because they appear to be the same colour as the white background (that is, both are tinted red) but cyan lines appear black. Similarly for the right eye which cannot see cyan lines, but red lines look black. So the computer must make two line drawings of a scene: one in cyan for the left eye, and one in red for the right eye. The brain will merge the two black images into one and the cyan and red background into white, to give a three-dimensional effect.

So we wish to devise a method of producing the stereoscopic projection of a general point $P \equiv (x, y, z)$, that is two points $PL \equiv (x_l, y_l)$ for the left eye and $PR \equiv (x_r, y_r)$ for the right eye, in the coordinate system of the perspective view plane (see figure 11.6). We sensibly choose the same view plane for both eyes. We shall assume that the origin is between the eyes, that space is in the OBSERVED position, and that the direction of view for each eye (the straight-ahead ray) is parallel to the $z$-axis. The eyes have coordinates $(-e, 0, 0)$, left, and $(e, 0, 0)$, right: in the program that follows, $e$ is given by variable ED, which is normally about 0.2*VERT. Again the perspective view plane is a distance $d$ (variable PPD) from the origin. In order to find PL we move space by $(e, 0, 0)$ so that P becomes $(x + e, y, z)$ and the perspective transform of this point for the left eye is $((x + e) \times d/z, y \times d/z)$, which when we return space to its original position becomes $((x + e) \times d/z - e, y \times d/z)$. Similarly, the right-eye transformation produces $PR \equiv ((x - e) \times d/z + e, y \times d/z)$. Listing 11.3 is a 'drawit' routine which draws a stereoscopic view of a wire object with NOV vertices and NOL lines stored in the usual way. Figure 11.7 shows a grey-scale picture of such a stereoscopic view of the two cubes of figure 9.2 by using 'lib1', 'lib3' and listings 9.6 (line 6040 adjusted for PPD) and 9.7. It has mode 1, HORIZ = 16, VERT = 12, (EX, EY, EZ) = (10, 20, 30) and (DX, DY, DZ) = (0, 0, 0).

For the best stereoscopic views it is best to make the view plane cut the object being viewed, that is make $\sqrt{(EX^2 + EY^2 + EZ^2)}$ = PPD (= 3*VERT). Therefore in the case of stereoscopic views we cannot keep HORIZ and VERT fixed, since for the best projections VERT (and hence HORIZ) depends on (EX, EY, EZ).

### *Exercise 11.6*

Draw stereoscopic views of all the objects drawn previously, including the jet and bodies of revolution.

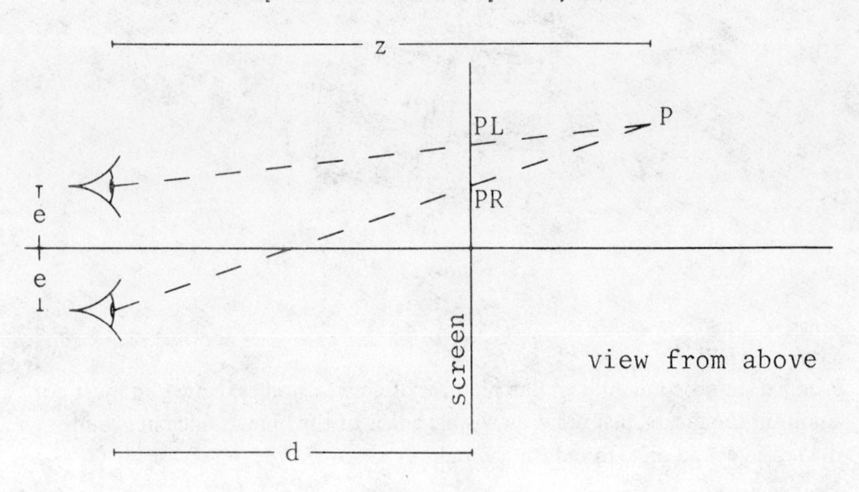


*Figure 11.6*

*Listing 11.3*

```
7000 REM drawit / stereoscopic
7010 DEF PROCdrawit
7020 LOCAL I%,L1,L2 : CLG
7028 REM use stereoscopic glasses with red over left eye
         and cyan over right eye
7029 REM our background is white so the image for right eye must
          be drawn in colour 1( red ) and for left eye in colour 2
          redefined to be cyan, in order that lines are seen as black
7030 VDU19,2,6,0,0,0
7039 REM first left eye then right
7040 ED=VERT*0.2 : GCOL 2,2
7050 FOR J%=1 TO 2
7060 FOR I%=1 TO NOV
7069 REM vertices in OBSERVED position
7070 XX=R(1,1)*X(I%)+R(1,2)*Y(I%)+R(1,3)*Z(I%)+R(1,4)
7080 YY=R(2,1)*X(I%)+R(2,2)*Y(I%)+R(2,3)*Z(I%)+R(2,4)
7090 ZZ=R(3,1)*X(I%)+R(3,2)*Y(I%)+R(3,3)*Z(I%)+R(3,4)
7099 REM stereoscopic projection
7100 XD(I%)=PPD*(XX+ED)/ZZ-ED
7110 YD(I%)=PPD*YY/ZZ
7120 NEXT I%
7129 REM draw object
7130 FOR I%=1 TO NOL
7140 L1=LIN(1,I%) : L2=LIN(2,I%)
7150 PROCmoveto(XD(L1),YD(L1))
7160 PROClineto(XD(L2),YD(L2))
7170 NEXT I%
7179 REM now use right eye
7180 ED=-ED : GCOL 2,1
7190 NEXT J%
7200 ENDPROC
```

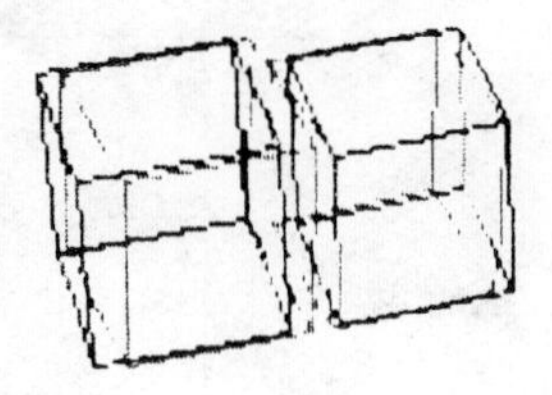

*Figure 11.7*

*Exercise 11.7*
Produce stereoscopic hidden line pictures of convex bodies. Now you must not colour in the facets, just draw the visible edges of the object, once in cyan for the left eye, and once in red for the right eye.

---

**Complete Programs**

I 'lib1', 'lib3' and listings 9.6 ('scene3'), 9.7 ('cube') and 11.1 ('drawit'). The 'scene3' routine must be adjusted for perspective thus:

    6040 NOV = 0: NOL = 0: PPD = 3*VERT

Data required: mode, HORIZ, VERT, and repeated values for (EX, EY, EZ) and (DX, DY, DZ). Try 1, 4, 3 (5, 15, 10) and (0, 0, 0); (1, 2, 20) and (0, 0, 1).

II 'lib1', 'lib3' and listings 11.2 ('scene3' etc. for the stack of cubes). Data required: mode, HORIZ, VERT, (EX, EY, EZ) and (DX, DY, DZ). Try 1, 4, 3, (20, 30, 40) and (0, 0, −6).

III 'lib1', 'lib3' and listings 9.6 ('scene3'), 9.7 ('cube') and 11.3 ('drawit': stereoscopic). Adjust line 6040 as in I above. Data required: mode, HORIZ, VERT, (EX, EY, EZ) and (DX, DY, DZ). Try 1, 16, 12, (10, 20, 30) and (0, 0, 0).

# *12 A General-Purpose Hidden Surface and Hidden Line Algorithm*

There are many different types of hidden line and/or surface algorithm. One variety has a rectangular array that represents the totality of pixels on the screen. We imagine rays of light that leave the eye through each of the pixels on the screen. These rays naturally pass through objects in our scene and we can note the coordinates of these points of intersection. The array will hold the '*z*-coordinate' (initially infinity) of the nearest point of intersection. So we build up a picture by adding new objects, finding where the rays cut the object, and changing the array values (and the pixel colour on the screen) whenever the latest point of intersection is nearer the eye than the corresponding value stored in the array. This technique (*ray tracing*) is very useful if we wish to shade-in areas in subtly differing tones of a given colour. It does, however, have enormous storage requirements and needs a very powerful computer, well beyond the capacity of microcomputers. Because we must work with only four colours and have limited storage we give another general algorithm which works on the 'back to front' principle mentioned earlier.

As in previous chapters, we assume that objects are set up by the 'scene3' procedure; however we now insist that the NOV vertices in the scene are stored in the X, Y, and Z arrays. Their perspective projections on to the view plane are stored in arrays XD and YD. The NOF convex facets are stored as a list of vertex indices (a maximum of six) in array FACET, and the number of edges on any facet is placed in array SIZE. Non-convex facets can be constructed out of convex facets.

We assume that all objects are closed. They need not be convex but each must be closed and its surface must be composed of convex facets which are stored in anticlockwise orientation. Thus it is impossible to see the under-side of any facet; that is, when projected on to the view plane we see only facets that maintain their anticlockwise orientation. Strictly speaking, this means that we cannot draw planar objects. If these are required for a particular scene then we avoid the problem by storing each facet of a planar object twice – once clockwise and once anticlockwise – so whatever the position of the eye, on perspective projection we shall see one and only one occurrence of the facet. This restriction was imposed to speed up the hidden surface algorithm. This is very necessary because we are now approaching the limits of the processing power of the BBC micro.

Nevertheless, we think it is important to study general hidden line/surface algorithms for educational reasons. It is essential for anyone with more than a passing interest in computer graphics to understand the problems implicit in drawing views of three-dimensional objects with the hidden lines/surfaces suppressed. The procedure given in listings 12.1 and 12.2 is such a hidden surface algorithm, which can be transferred to larger machines where it will run with ease. If you get the opportunity to use more powerful computers it will be very instructive to run our programs on them.

In order to produce a hidden surface picture of a scene that is stored in the OBSERVED position, each facet on the objects in the scene must be compared with every other facet in order to discover whether their projections overlap on the view plane. Because of the above restrictions we need compare only the visible facets, that is those that when projected keep their anticlockwise orientation. If they do overlap we then need to find which facet lies in front and which behind. Once this information is compiled we can work from the back of the scene to the front to get a correct hidden surface picture. We do have another limitation: we assume that it is impossible for a facet to be simultaneously in front of and behind another facet (that is facets do not intersect one another except at their edges) and we cannot have situations where facet A is in front of (>) facet B > facet C etc. > facet A.

Our algorithm for discovering whether two facets (I% and J% from our database) do overlap when projected on to the view plane is given in procedure 'overlap' in listing 12.1. The method depends on the concept of *inside* and *outside* developed in chapter 3. We place the $x$-coordinate and $y$-coordinate of the vertices of facet I% in arrays XF(1, . .) and YF(1, . .) respectively. We then take one line from facet J% and cut off all parts of the facet that lie on the negative side of the line: the resulting polygon is placed in arrays XF(2, . . ) and YF(2, . .). We then take the next line and compare it with these values and store the resulting polygon in XF(1, . . ) and YF(1, . . ) etc. After all the lines from facet J% have been used then we are left with the polygon that is common to both projected facets. If at any time this polygon becomes empty we know that the projected facets do not overlap and so we leave the procedure setting OVER = 0.

If the facets do overlap then OVER = 1 and we draw a line from the eye to intersect a point inside the common polygon on the view plane and find the intersections with facets I% and J%: the point we choose is the median of the first three points on the polygon. Comparing the $z$-coordinates of the respective intersections enables us to discover which of I% and J% is in FRONT and which is at the BACK.

*Listing 12.1*

```
7300 REM overlap
7310 DEF PROCoverlap(I%,J%)
7319 REM check if views of facets I% and J% overlap
7320 P1=1 : SI=SIZE(I%) : SJ=SIZE(J%)
```

```
7329 REM place projected vertices of facet I%
        in arrays XF(1,..) and YF(1,..)
7330 FOR K%=1 TO SI
7340 FI=FACET(K%,I%)
7350 XF(P1,K%)=XD(FI) : YF(P1,K%)=YD(FI)
7360 NEXT K%
7369 REM use each line of the J%th facet to slice off part of
        polygon stored in XF,YF. Line joins (X1,Y1) to (X2,Y2)
7370 VJ1=FACET(SJ,J%) : X1=XD(VJ1) : Y1=YD(VJ1)
7380 FOR K%=1 TO SJ
7390 VJ2=FACET(K%,J%) : X2=XD(VJ2) : Y2=YD(VJ2)
7399 REM line is CA.y+CB.x+CC=0
7400 CA=X2-X1 : CB=Y1-Y2 : CC=-X1*CB-Y1*CA
7409 REM go round SI vertices in XF, YF. If positive relative to
        line, then add to new XF,YF. If negative ignore. If an
        intersection then add this to new XF,YF arrays.
7410 P2=3-P1 : XI1=XF(P1,SI) : YI1=YF(P1,SI)
7420 V1=CA*YI1+CB*XI1+CC : A1=ABS(V1) : PCN=0
     : IF A1<EPS THEN S1=0 ELSE S1=SGN(V1)
7430 FOR M%=1 TO SI
7440 XI2=XF(P1,M%) : YI2=YF(P1,M%)
7450 V2=CA*YI2+CB*XI2+CC : A2=ABS(V2)
     : IF A2<EPS THEN S2=0 ELSE S2=SGN(V2)
7460 IF S1>=0 THEN PCN=PCN+1 : XF(P2,PCN)=XI1 : YF(P2,PCN)=YI1
     : IF S1=0 THEN 7500
7470 IF S1=S2 OR S2=0 THEN 7500
7479 REM calculate intersection
7480 MU=A1 : UM=A2 : DENOM=A1+A2
7490 PCN=PCN+1 : XF(P2,PCN)=(UM*XI1+MU*XI2)/DENOM
     : YF(P2,PCN)=(UM*YI1+MU*YI2)/DENOM
7500 V1=V2 : S1=S2 : A1=A2 : XI1=XI2 : YI1=YI2
7510 NEXT M%
7519 REM facets do not overlap: OVER=0
7520 IF PCN<3 THEN OVER=0 : ENDPROC
7530 SI=PCN : P1=P2 : X1=X2 : Y1=Y2
7540 NEXT K%
7549 REM find (XMID,YMID) common to both projected facets
7550 XMID=(XF(P1,1)+XF(P1,2)+XF(P1,3))/3
     : YMID=(YF(P1,1)+YF(P1,2)+YF(P1,3))/3
7559 REM MU1 is the distance from the eye of equivalent point
     on the 3D plane containing facet I%
7560 V1=FACET(1,I%) : V2=FACET(2,I%) : V3=FACET(3,I%)
7570 DX1=X(V1)-X(V2) : DX3=X(V3)-X(V2)
7580 DY1=Y(V1)-Y(V2) : DY3=Y(V3)-Y(V2)
7590 DZ1=Z(V1)-Z(V2) : DZ3=Z(V3)-Z(V2)
7600 A=DY1*DZ3-DY3*DZ1 : B=DZ1*DX3-DZ3*DX1 : C=DX1*DY3-DX3*DY1
7610 D=A*X(V1)+B*Y(V1)+C*Z(V1)
7620 MU1=D/(A*XMID+B*YMID+C*PPD)
7629 REM MU2 is the distance from the eye of equivalent point
     on the 3D plane containing facet J%
7630 V1=FACET(1,J%) : V2=FACET(2,J%) : V3=FACET(3,J%)
7640 DX1=X(V1)-X(V2) : DX3=X(V3)-X(V2)
7650 DY1=Y(V1)-Y(V2) : DY3=Y(V3)-Y(V2)
7660 DZ1=Z(V1)-Z(V2) : DZ3=Z(V3)-Z(V2)
7670 A=DY1*DZ3-DY3*DZ1 : B=DZ1*DX3-DZ3*DX1 : C=DX1*DY3-DX3*DY1
7680 D=A*X(V1)+B*Y(V1)+C*Z(V1)
7690 MU2=D/(A*XMID+B*YMID+C*PPD)
7699 REM if MU1>MU2 then FRONT=J% else FRONT=I% : OVER set to 1
7700 OVER=1 : IF MU1 > MU2 THEN FRONT=J% : BACK=I%
                            ELSE FRONT=I% : BACK=J%
7710 ENDPROC
```

The next step is to work out how to use this information to produce the final picture. This is achieved in listing 12.2, which contains the routines 'hidden', 'topsort', 'push' and 'pop'. The method is to compare each visible facet with every other and to produce a *network* of information about the relative positions of the facets (in front or behind). For each visible facet (I% say) the idea is to set up a *linked list* (LIS(I%)) that contains the indices of all facets that lie in front of it, and the array G(I%) will contain the number of facets that facet I% obscures. Array G is also used initially to denote if the facet is clockwise and invisible (G(I%) = −1), or anticlockwise and visible (G(I%) = 0).

We then create a *stack* on to which we initially 'push' any facet that does not obscure any other (that is, whose G value is zero). Then one at a time we 'pop' a facet off the stack and draw it on the screen. Once the facet is drawn, we go down the linked list for that facet and decrement the G counts for each facet in the list. If the G count for any facet becomes zero then the number of that facet is pushed on to the stack. Eventually this method, called *topological sorting* (the 'topsort' procedure), gives the correct order in which facets may be drawn to give the true back to front hidden surface view.

The linked lists and the stack are implemented by using a method known as a *HEAP*. HEAP% is an array of integers whose values are divided into two parts, the *information* section and a *pointer*. Because we are using relatively small integers, both information and pointer can be stored in one array location: multiply the information by 10 000 and add in the pointer. Initially the heap contains zero information and each location points to the next in the array. There is a variable called FREE which denotes the next available location in the heap. Whenever store is required for a linked list or a stack (which is itself a linked list) the FREE location in HEAP is made available, and the value of FREE changed. A *garbage collector* is built into this system so that whenever a location is no longer needed it is reallocated to the FREE list. The stack can only become empty when all the facets have been drawn because of our restriction that facets cannot be simultaneously in front of and behind one another. See Knuth (1973), or Horowitz and Sahni (1976) for a formal description of linked lists, stacks and topological sorting.

Because we cannot be sure of the size of the HEAP and of the XF and YF arrays, these must be input into the program. As a rough guide the lists rarely exceed 20, and the heap size is best set at about twice the number of facets. If you underestimate these array requirements then the program will fail. You can always run it again with larger values! The execution of such routines are necessarily slow when you consider the number of comparisons that have to be made, so we print out information about the facet being compared, the present value of FREE and the time taken in seconds. You will also find that, used in conjunction with our library of graphics and matrix procedures as well as large data-bases, the program has to be loaded into store with PAGE set to &1100. Even so there will not be enough room if the full MODE 1 screen is used. So

*Listing 12.2*

```
7000 REM hidden surface / general
7010 DEF PROChidden
7020 LOCAL I%,J%,K%,M%
7030 INPUT"Size of HEAP "HSIZ
7040 INPUT"Size of facet list "FLIST
7049 REM setup data structure arrays
7050 DIM G(NOF),LIS(NOF),HEAP%(HSIZ),XF(2,FLIST),YF(2,FLIST)
7060 EPS=0.000001 : FREE=1 : NVIS=0 : TSTO=TIME
7069 REM initialise the HEAP
7070 FOR I%=1 TO HSIZ
7080 HEAP%(I%)=I%+1
7090 NEXT I%
7099 REM orientate projected facet : G(I(%)=-1 clockwise
                                     G(I(%)= 0  anticlockwise
7100 FOR I%=1 TO NOF
7110 I1=FACET(1,I%) : X1=XD(I1) : Y1=YD(I1)
7120 I2=FACET(2,I%) : X2=XD(I2) : Y2=YD(I2)
7130 I3=FACET(3,I%) : X3=XD(I3) : Y3=YD(I3)
7140 DX1=X2-X1 : DY1=Y2-Y1
7150 DX2=X3-X2 : DY2=Y3-Y2
7160 IF DX1*DY2-DX2*DY1 > 0
     THEN G(I%)=0 : NVIS=NVIS+1 : LIS(I%)=0 ELSE G(I%)=-1
7170 NEXT I%
7179 REM compare visible facets G(I%) now holds number of
         facets behind facet I%
7180 FOR I%=1 TO NOF-1
7190 IF G(I%)=-1 THEN 7250
7200 FOR J%=I%+1 TO NOF
7210 IF G(J%)=-1 THEN 7240
7219 REM if facets overlap i.e. facet FRONT in front of facet BACK
          then increment G(FRONT) and add FRONT to linked list for
          BACK. Adjust the HEAP
7220 PROCoverlap(I%,J%)
7230 IF OVER=1 THEN G(FRONT)=G(FRONT)+1 : NFREE=HEAP%(FREE)
     : HEAP%(FREE)=FRONT*10000+LIS(BACK) : LIS(BACK)=FREE : FREE=NFREE
7240 NEXT J%
7250 PRINT"FACET=";I%;" FREE=";FREE;" TIME=";(TIME-TSTO)/100;" SECONDS"
     : NEXT I%
7259 REM draw the background and then topologically sort
     the network of linked lists.
7260 *SPOOL"PICCY"
7270 GCOL0,131 : CLG : PROCbackground : PROCtopsort
7280 *SPOOL
7290 ENDPROC

7800 REM topological sorting procedure
7810 DEF PROCtopsort
7819 REM create STACK. Push on it all facets that lie in
         front of other facets
7820 LOCAL I%,J% : STACK=0
7830 FOR I%=1 TO NOF
7840 IF G(I%)=0 THEN PROCpush(I%)
7850 NEXT I%
7860 FOR I%=1 TO NVIS
7869 REM pop facet(=J%) from STACK
7870 J%=FNpop : IF J%=0 THEN PRINT"facet network has a cycle" : STOP
7879 REM draw the facet
7880 GCOL0,COL(J%) : F1=1 : FS=SIZE(J%)
7890 F=FACET(F1,J%) : MOVE FNX(XD(F)),FNY(YD(F))
7900 F=FACET(FS,J%) : MOVE FNX(XD(F)),FNY(YD(F))
```

```
7910 F1=F1+1 : FS=FS-1
7920 F=FACET(F1,J%) : PLOT85,FNX(XD(F)),FNY(YD(F)) : IF F1=FS THEN 794
7930 F=FACET(FS,J%) : PLOT85,FNX(XD(F)),FNY(YD(F))
     : IF FS-1=F1 THEN 7940 ELSE 7910
7939 REM draw the edges of the facet
7940 F=FACET(SIZE(J%),J%) : MOVE FNX(XD(F)),FNY(YD(F)) : GCOL 0,0
7950 FOR K%=1 TO SIZE(J%) : F=FACET(K%,J%)
     : DRAW FNX(XD(F)),FNY(YD(F)) : NEXT K%
7960 PT=LIS(J%)
7970 REPEAT : F2=HEAP%(PT) DIV 10000 : NEX=HEAP%(PT) MOD 10000
7980 G(F2)=G(F2)-1 : IF G(F2)=0 THEN PROCpush(F2)
7990 PT=NEX : UNTIL PT=0
8000 NEXT I%
8010 ENDPROC

8100 REM push I% onto STACK
8110 DEF PROCpush(I%)
8120 NF=FREE : FREE=HEAP%(FREE)
8130 HEAP%(NF)=I%*10000+STACK : STACK=NF
8140 ENDPROC

8150 REM pop value off STACK
8160 DEF FNpop
8170 NF=STACK : NUMB=HEAP%(NF) DIV 10000 : STACK=HEAP%(NF) MOD 10000
8180 HEAP%(NF)=FREE : FREE=NF
8190 =NUMB
```

what we do is to run the program in MODE 7 and SPOOL the picture on to backing store. When the program is complete we type

NEW

MODE 1

*EXEC PICCY

and it will be drawn on the screen. Note that we also include a call to a 'background' procedure. You can include a complex 'background' like that in listing 12.3, or a trivial procedure that simply clears the screen. We can turn a hidden surface procedure into a hidden line procedure by having a plain background and by drawing each facet in the same (background) colour.

*Example 12.1*
We can now draw a hidden line, perspective view of the scene that we first saw in figure 9.2: one of the two cubes shown in figure 12.1. Note that the background is similar to one of the pictures produced in chapter 1. The scene has HORIZ = 4, VERT = 3 and is viewed from (10, 5, 20) to (0, 0, 0).

The complete program uses 'lib1', 'lib3', 'overlap' (listing 12.1) and 'hidden' etc. (listing 12.2) together with the 'scene3', 'cube' and 'background' procedures given in listing 12.3. This last version of 'cube' means that we have considered all the array methods of constructing an object, that is, stored/not stored and lines/facets. We have deliberately used the cube over and over again in our diagram because it is such a simple object and because it is easy to understand its various constructions; therefore it does not complicate our discussion of the

*Listing 12.3*

```
4ØØØ REM background
4Ø1Ø DEF PROCbackground
4Ø2Ø VDU23,1,Ø;Ø;Ø;Ø; : VDU 19,Ø,4,Ø,Ø,Ø
4Ø3Ø PROCcircle(64Ø,75Ø,1ØØØ,Ø,1) : PROCcircle(64Ø,75Ø,15Ø,2,2)
4Ø4Ø PROCcircle(74Ø,65Ø,7Ø,3,3) : PROCcircle(865,68Ø,1ØØ,3,3)
     : PROCcircle(95Ø,66Ø,8Ø,3,3)
4Ø5Ø MOVE 74Ø,58Ø : MOVE 74Ø,72Ø : PLOT 85,95Ø,58Ø
4Ø6Ø ENDPROC

41ØØ REM circle
411Ø DEF PROCcircle(X,Y,R,C1,C2)
412Ø MOVE X,Y
413Ø F=1 : GCOL Ø,C1
414Ø FOR I=Ø TO 2*PI STEP PI/5Ø : MOVE X,Y : PLOT 81,R*COS(I),R*SIN(I)
415Ø F=1-F : IF F THEN GCOLØ,C1 ELSE GCOLØ,C2
416Ø NEXT I
417Ø ENDPROC

6ØØØ REM scene3 / Figure 12.1
6Ø1Ø DEF PROCscene3
6Ø2Ø LOCAL I%,J%
6Ø3Ø DIM X(16),Y(16),Z(16),XD(16),YD(16),FACET(4,12),COL(12),SIZE(12)
6Ø4Ø DIM A(4,4),B(4,4),R(4,4),Q(4,4)
6Ø5Ø NOV=Ø : NOF=Ø : PPD=3*VERT
6Ø6Ø PROCidR3 : PROClook3 : PROCcube
6Ø7Ø FOR I%=1 TO 4 : FOR J%=1 TO 4
6Ø8Ø Q(I%,J%)=R(I%,J%) : NEXT J% : NEXT I%
6Ø9Ø PROCidR3 : PROCtran3(3,1.5,2)
61ØØ PROCmult3
611Ø FOR I%=1 TO 4 : FOR J%=1 TO 4
612Ø A(I%,J%)=Q(I%,J%) : NEXT J% : NEXT I%
613Ø PROCmult3 : PROCcube
614Ø PROChidden
615Ø ENDPROC

65ØØ REM cube / perspective, stored
651Ø DEF PROCcube
652Ø LOCAL I%
653Ø DATA 1,2,3,4, 5,8,7,6, 1,5,6,2, 2,6,7,3, 3,7,8,4, 4,8,5,1
654Ø DATA 1,1,1,  1,1,-1,  1,-1,-1,  1,-1,1,
          -1,1,1,  -1,1,-1,  -1,-1,-1,  -1,-1,1
655Ø RESTORE 653Ø
656Ø FOR I%=1 TO 6
657Ø READ F1,F2,F3,F4 : NOF=NOF+1
658Ø FACET(1,NOF)=F1+NOV : FACET(2,NOF)=F2+NOV
659Ø FACET(3,NOF)=F3+NOV : FACET(4,NOF)=F4+NOV
66ØØ SIZE(NOF)=4 : COL(NOF)=3
661Ø NEXT I%
662Ø FOR I%=1 TO 8
663Ø READ XX,YY,ZZ : NOV=NOV+1
664Ø X(NOV)=R(1,1)*XX+R(1,2)*YY+R(1,3)*ZZ+R(1,4)
665Ø Y(NOV)=R(2,1)*XX+R(2,2)*YY+R(2,3)*ZZ+R(2,4)
666Ø Z(NOV)=R(3,1)*XX+R(3,2)*YY+R(3,3)*ZZ+R(3,4)
667Ø XD(NOV)=PPD*X(NOV)/Z(NOV)
668Ø YD(NOV)=PPD*Y(NOV)/Z(NOV)
669Ø NEXT I%
67ØØ ENDPROC
```

*Figure 12.1*

general principles of three-dimensional graphics. Now is the time to introduce complexity into our objects: provided that you understand the limitations of the algorithms, you will find that the ideas we have discussed are equally valid.

*Exercise 12.1*
Construct hidden surface scenes that are composed of cubes, tetrahedra, pyramids, octahedra and icosahedra. Introduce new backgrounds and write your own procedures for an octahedron, icosahedron, rhombic dodecahedron etc. (see Coxeter, 1974).

*Example 12.2*
By now you will have realised that hidden surface algorithms are very slow programs – we have to make a large number of comparisons. This means that we are rather limited in the scope of objects we can draw. Nevertheless it is very good practice, and if you have the opportunity to use larger machines you will see that the above algorithm will work on these also, but much faster. We give examples of two three-dimensional star-shaped objects in listing 12.4 (both require a parameter A which changes the elongation of the spikes) as well as a 'scene3' procedure. These two 'star' procedures are based on the tetrahedron and cube. Figure 12.2 was drawn with HORIZ = 4, VERT = 3, and viewed from (35, 20, 25) towards (0, 0, 0).

*Listing 12.4*

```
6000 REM scene3 / two stars
6010 DEF PROCscene3
6020 LOCAL I%,J%
6030 DIM X(22),Y(22),Z(22),XD(22),YD(22),FACET(3,36),SIZE(36),COL(36)
6040 DIM A(4,4),B(4,4),R(4,4),Q(4,4)
6050 NOV=0 : NOF=0 : PPD=3*VERT
6060 PROCidR3 : PROClook3 : A=6 : PROCstar1
6070 FOR I%=1 TO 4 : FOR J%=1 TO 4
6080 Q(I%,J%)=R(I%,J%) : NEXT J% : NEXT I%
6090 PROCidR3 : PROCtran3(5,5,5)
6100 PROCmult3
6110 FOR I%=1 TO 4 : FOR J%=1 TO 4
6120 A(I%,J%)=Q(I%,J%) : NEXT J% : NEXT I%
6130 PROCmult3 : A=4 : PROCstar2
6140 PROChidden
6150 ENDPROC

6500 REM star1 /based on a cube
6510 DEF PROCstar1
6520 LOCAL I%
6530 DATA 1,2,9, 2,3,9, 3,4,9, 4,1,9,  6,5,10, 5,8,10, 8,7,10,
        7,6,10, 2,1,11, 1,5,11, 5,6,11, 6,2,11, 4,3,12, 3,7,12,
        7,8,12, 8,4,12, 1,4,13, 4,8,13, 8,5,13, 5,1,13, 3,2,14,
        2,6,14, 6,7,14, 7,3,14
6540 DATA 1,1,1,  1,1,-1,  1,-1,-1,  1,-1,1,
        -1,1,1,  -1,1,-1,  -1,-1,-1,  -1,-1,1,
        A,0,0,  -A,0,0,  0,A,0,  0,-A,0,  0,0,A,  0,0,-A
6550 RESTORE 6530
6560 FOR I%=1 TO 24
6570 READ F1,F2,F3 : NOF=NOF+1
6580 FACET(1,NOF)=F1+NOV : FACET(2,NOF)=F2+NOV
6590 FACET(3,NOF)=F3+NOV : SIZE(NOF)=3 : COL(NOF)=1
6600 NEXT I%
6610 FOR I%=1 TO 14
6620 READ XX,YY,ZZ : NOV=NOV+1
6630 X(NOV)=R(1,1)*XX+R(1,2)*YY+R(1,3)*ZZ+R(1,4)
6640 Y(NOV)=R(2,1)*XX+R(2,2)*YY+R(2,3)*ZZ+R(2,4)
6650 Z(NOV)=R(3,1)*XX+R(3,2)*YY+R(3,3)*ZZ+R(3,4)
6660 XD(NOV)=PPD*X(NOV)/Z(NOV)
6670 YD(NOV)=PPD*Y(NOV)/Z(NOV)
6680 NEXT I%
6690 ENDPROC

6700 REM star2 /based on a tetrahedron
6710 DEF PROCstar2
6720 LOCAL I%
6730 DATA 2,1,8, 3,2,8, 1,3,8, 1,2,7, 4,1,7, 2,4,7, 2,3,5,
        4,2,5, 3,4,5, 3,1,6, 4,3,6, 1,4,6
6740 DATA 1,1,1,  1,-1,-1,  -1,1,-1,  -1,-1,1,
        -A,-A,-A,  -A,A,A,  A,-A,A,  A,A,-A
6750 RESTORE 6730
6760 FOR I%=1 TO 12
6770 READ F1,F2,F3 : NOF=NOF+1
6780 FACET(1,NOF)=F1+NOV : FACET(2,NOF)=F2+NOV
6790 FACET(3,NOF)=F3+NOV : SIZE(NOF)=3 : COL(NOF)=2
6800 NEXT I%
6810 FOR I%=1 TO 8
6820 READ XX,YY,ZZ : NOV=NOV+1
6830 X(NOV)=R(1,1)*XX+R(1,2)*YY+R(1,3)*ZZ+R(1,4)
```

```
6840 Y(NOV)=R(2,1)*XX+R(2,2)*YY+R(2,3)*ZZ+R(2,4)
6850 Z(NOV)=R(3,1)*XX+R(3,2)*YY+R(3,3)*ZZ+R(3,4)
6860 XD(NOV)=PPD*X(NOV)/Z(NOV)
6870 YD(NOV)=PPD*Y(NOV)/Z(NOV)
6880 NEXT I%
6890 ENDPROC
```

*Figure 12.2*

*Exercise 12.2*

The program in listing 10.1 checks that the order of the vertices of a triangular facet are anticlockwise. The program was devised for use with convex bodies that contain the origin. Extend it so that it can cope with the most general case, that is specify the position of the observer and the coordinates of a point inside the object (not necessarily the origin) so that this point and the observer lie on opposite sides of the infinite plane that contains the facet. Use this program to check the above star-shaped objects (in fact for these figures the origin could act as the inside point).

Then produce your own star-shaped objects that are based on an octahedron, cuboctahedron, icosahedron or dodecahedron. Always check the order of the vertices in your facets. You can produce stars that are based on very simple bodies of revolution, and we need not use only symmetrical objects! It is for these non-symmetrical shapes that you really need the extended version of listing 10.1. Provided that you stay within the restrictions mentioned, then listings 12.1 and 12.2 will draw any shape.

***Example 12.3***
We now give the procedures (listing 12.5) needed to set up and draw a much more complex picture (figure 12.3) which contains 120 facets (about 60 will be visible at any one time). It is viewed from (10, 20, 30) towards (0, 0, 0) and will take about a quarter of an hour to draw. So be patient!

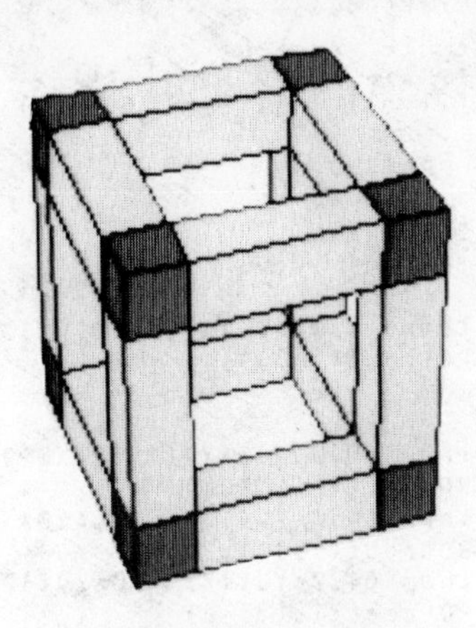

*Figure 12.3*

Now you have read (and understood) chapters 7 to 12 you will have found that we have reached the limits of three-dimensional graphics on the BBC Model B microcomputer. You must get the use of larger computers if you wish to go further in your study of this type of computer graphics. Then you must study the techniques of using data structures and extend the very simple applications given in this chapter. If you use certain structured languages, Pascal for example, you will find that it is not essential to build up your own HEAP, such structures are implicit to the language. This should enable you to use complex data structures for storing useful information about scenes. For example, a complete scene can be regarded as a linked list of pointers, each of which refers to a linked list of information about the facets on a particular type of object. The facets themselves can be stored as lists of vertices! A seemingly complex idea, but one that makes the use of fixed-size arrays obsolete. Certain context relationships between objects may be stored implicitly in the lists. When you have grasped these ideas you can go on to the complicated graphics algorithms which include methods for animating, colouring, patching and shading. You will find the books by Horowitz and Sahni (1976) and Knuth (1973) invaluable for the study of data structures. You should read Newman and Sproull (1979) and Foley and van Dam (1982) for the really complex three-dimensional graphics methods. In the next chapter we take a more advanced look at character graphics and introduce one method of producing animated three-dimensional drawings.

*Listing 12.5*

```
6000 REM scene3 / hollow cube
6010 DEF PROCscene3
6020 LOCAL I%,J%
6030 DIM X(160),Y(160),Z(160),XD(160),YD(160),
     FACET(4,120),SIZE(120),COL(120)
6040 DIM A(4,4),B(4,4),R(4,4),Q(4,4)
6050 DIM XQ(8),YQ(8),ZQ(8)
6060 DATA 1,1,1,  1,1,-1,  1,-1,-1,  1,-1,1,
         -1,1,1,  -1,1,-1,  -1,-1,-1,  -1,-1,1
6070 RESTORE 6060
6080 NOV=0 : NOF=0 : PPD=3*VERT
6090 FOR I%=1 TO 8
6100 READ XQ(I%),YQ(I%),ZQ(I%)
6110 NEXT I%
6120 FOR I%=1 TO 8
6130 PROCidR3 : PROCtran3(4.0*XQ(I%),4.0*YQ(I%),4.0*ZQ(I%))
     : PROCmult3 : PROCrect(1,1,1,1)
6140 NEXT I%
6150 FOR I%=1 TO 4
6160 PROCidR3 : PROCtran3(0.0,4.0*YQ(I%),4.0*ZQ(I%))
     : PROCmult3 : PROCrect(3,1,1,2)
6170 PROCidR3 : PROCtran3(4.0*ZQ(I%),0.0,4.0*YQ(I%))
     : PROCmult3 : PROCrect(1,3,1,2)
6180 PROCidR3 : PROCtran3(4.0*YQ(I%),4.0*ZQ(I%),0.0)
     : PROCmult3 : PROCrect(1,1,3,2)
6190 NEXT I%
6200 PROCidR3 : PROClook3 : A=6 : PROCmult3
6210 FOR I%=1 TO NOV
6220 XX=X(I%) : YY=Y(I%) : ZZ=Z(I%)
6230 X(I%)=R(1,1)*XX+R(1,2)*YY+R(1,3)*ZZ+R(1,4)
6240 Y(I%)=R(2,1)*XX+R(2,2)*YY+R(2,3)*ZZ+R(2,4)
6250 Z(I%)=R(3,1)*XX+R(3,2)*YY+R(3,3)*ZZ+R(3,4)
6260 XD(I%)=PPD*X(I%)/Z(I%)
6270 YD(I%)=PPD*Y(I%)/Z(I%)
6280 NEXT I%
6290 PROChidden
6300 ENDPROC

6500 REM rectangular block
6510 DEF PROCrect(LH,HT,WH,IC)
6520 LOCAL I%
6530 DATA 1,2,3,4, 2,1,5,6, 6,5,8,7, 7,8,4,3, 2,6,7,3, 5,1,4,8
6540 DATA 1,1,1,  1,1,-1,  1,-1,-1,  1,-1,1,
         -1,1,1,  -1,1,-1,  -1,-1,-1,  -1,-1,1
6550 RESTORE 6530
6560 FOR I%=1 TO 6
6570 READ F1,F2,F3,F4 : NOF=NOF+1
6580 FACET(1,NOF)=F1+NOV : FACET(2,NOF)=F2+NOV
6590 FACET(3,NOF)=F3+NOV : FACET(4,NOF)=F4+NOV
6600 SIZE(NOF)=4 : COL(NOF)=IC
6610 NEXT I%
6620 FOR I%=1 TO 8
6630 READ XX,YY,ZZ : NOV=NOV+1
6640 XX=XX*LH : YY=YY*HT : ZZ=ZZ*WH
6650 X(NOV)=R(1,1)*XX+R(1,2)*YY+R(1,3)*ZZ+R(1,4)
6660 Y(NOV)=R(2,1)*XX+R(2,2)*YY+R(2,3)*ZZ+R(2,4)
6670 Z(NOV)=R(3,1)*XX+R(3,2)*YY+R(3,3)*ZZ+R(3,4)
6680 NEXT I%
6690 ENDPROC
```

**Complete Programs**

All these programs should be loaded with PAGE = &1100 and the REMs must be stripped away.

I 'lib1', lib3', listings 12.1 ('overlap'), 12.2 ('hidden', 'topsort', 'push' and 'pop') and 12.3 ('scene3', 'cube', 'background'). Data required: mode, HORIZ, VERT, (EX, EY, EZ), (DX, DY, DZ), size of HEAP and facet list. Try 7, 4, 3, (20, 5, 10), (0, 0, 0), 10 and 10. When the picture has been SPOOLed on to backing store as file PICCY you must then type

```
NEW
MODE 1
*EXEC PICCY
```

II 'lib1', lib3', listings 12.1, 12.2, 12.4 ('scene3', 'star1' etc.) and the 'background' from 12.3. Data required: mode, HORIZ, VERT, (EX, EY, EZ) and (DX, DY, DZ), HEAP and facet counts. Try 7, 4, 3, (40, 30, 20), (0, 0, 0), 50, 20; and EXEC picture on to the screen from PICCY.

III 'lib1', lib3', listings 12.1, 12.2, 12.5 ('scene3', 'box' etc.) and the 'background' from 12.3. Data required: mode, HORIZ, VERT, (EX, EY, EZ) and (DX, DY, DZ), HEAP and facet counts. Try 7, 4, 3, (30, 20, 10), (0, 0, 0), 200, 20; and EXEC picture on to the screen from PICCY.

# 13 Teletext Graphics, Mode 7

Mode 7 on the BBC micro is the only mode in which the shapes of the characters are not explicitly stored in memory. Instead just one byte is used for each of the screen character locations which, in the simplest case, holds the ASCII code of the character to be displayed there. The screen display is then generated by a special micro-chip which contains the data for each character. The chip looks at the screen memory to see which character is to be displayed at that position and then includes the correct data for that character directly into the television signal. This means that the chip has to recalculate the data for the whole screen each time the television display is refreshed, 50 times a second (60 times a second in the U.S.A.).

The memory for the screen is arranged very simply and consists of 1000 locations (40 across by 25 down). Starting at location HIMEM (which is set to &7C00 in mode 7) the data for the screen are stored row by row, with forty locations per row. Hence the location equivalent to the block accessed by PRINT TAB(X, Y) is given by &7C00 + 40 * Y + X. As in chapter 5, we assume that there is no hardware scrolling of the screen.

There are two types of character in this mode: *alphanumeric* and *graphic*. Try the simple program in listing 13.1 which changes one single screen location at a time by storing the ASCII code of an alphanumeric character.

*Listing 13.1*

```
10 MODE 7
20 REPEAT
30 A=&7C00+(RND(25)-1)*40+RND(40)-1
40 ?A=RND(32)+64
50 UNTIL FALSE
```

***Example 13.1***

Invisible control codes may also be placed in these screen locations. These allow control of further display options such as colour, flashing, or distinguishing between alphanumeric and graphic characters. Rerun listing 13.1 (which drew alphanumeric characters by default) with line 40 replaced by ?A = RND(256) – 1. The effect of these codes is to mix up graphics and alphanumerics randomly on the screen.

Table 13.1 shows the ASCII codes that have special effects on the mode 7 teletext screen.

Table 13.1

| | | | |
|---|---|---|---|
| 128 | | 144 | |
| 129 | Alpha red | 145 | Graphic red |
| 130 | Alpha green | 146 | Graphic green |
| 131 | Alpha yellow | 147 | Graphic yellow |
| 132 | Alpha blue | 148 | Graphic blue |
| 133 | Alpha magenta | 149 | Graphic magenta |
| 134 | Alpha cyan | 150 | Graphic cyan |
| 135 | Alpha white | 151 | Graphic white |
| 136 | Start flash | 152 | Conceal |
| 137 | End flash | 153 | Contiguous graphics |
| 138 | | 154 | Separated graphics |
| 139 | | 155 | |
| 140 | Normal height | 156 | Black background |
| 141 | Double height | 157 | New background |
| 142 | | 158 | Hold graphics |
| 143 | | 159 | Release graphics |

Some of these characters are available (from OS 1.0 onwards) directly from the keyboard by using the shift or control keys with the red soft keys. Most useful are the colour codes alpha red to alpha white, which are available with shift on keys f1 to f7 (see table 13.2), and colour codes graphic red to graphic white, which are available with control on the same keys. Other codes can be programmed for the function keys by using the '!' option (see user guide) to produce codes that are numerically greater than or equal to 128. For example, typing *KEY1||!||M would set key f1 to code 141 which corresponds to double height. The control keys H, I, J, K will move the text cursor (left, right, down, up): this will enable you to experiment by placing control codes all over the screen. For example, double-height letters may be placed on the screen by typing f1 (the control code 141) followed by the required text at the text cursor, and then repeating (or copying) the same string (code 141 followed by text) exactly one line above. You can see this in programmed form in the 'brickout' game of listing 13.5.

Each line of the display is treated as an individual unit. Unless told otherwise, the computer assumes that a black background and white alphanumerics are required. For example, to get red text you must type the colour code for alpha red (shift f1), which would appear as a space on the line, followed by any required text. The red code will be effective either for the remainder of the present line or until another colour code is encountered. Naturally all control codes take up one screen block and result in a space being displayed at that position. These codes can be used to highlight REMarks in program listings when viewed in mode 7. The programs on the audio cassettes that accompany this book contain colour codes in the REM statements to make it easier to find individual procedures and to read the explanatory comments.

*Listing 13.2*

```
10 MODE 7
19 REM go through all the codes except the control codes ( <32 )
20 FOR I=32 TO 255 STEP 32
30 VDU 129
40 FOR J=I TO I+31
49 REM don't output character 127 or it will delete previous code.
50 IF J<>127 THEN VDU J
60 NEXT J
70 PRINT '
80 NEXT I
```

***Example 13.2***

Run listing 13.2. The program will display, in red, all the available *alphanumeric characters* (equivalent to ASCII codes 32 to 255). If we change line 30 from VDU 129 (alpha red) to VDU 145 (graphic red) you will see all the available *graphic characters*. The upper case characters are the same in both the graphics and alphanumeric colours, but the remaining characters are different. These other codes will be displayed as the *block graphics characters*, each containing 6 small square blocks (3 vertically by 2 horizontally). The 64 possible characters that are produced from such a combination of 6 blocks may be accessed by typing the normal alphanumeric characters for the ASCII codes 32 to 63 and 96 to 127 after a graphics code. Note that the ASCII codes 65 to 95 still produce their normal symbols. All the codes from 32 to 127 are duplicated on ASCII codes 160 to 255. Therefore should we wish to write a program that PRINTs teletext characters (including teletext codes) it is easier to use the lower ASCII code values which can be typed (into the string inside quotes following PRINT) directly from the keyboard. This, however, has the disadvantage that code 127, which should correspond to a totally filled character, is equivalent to the delete code. The VDU command allows use of the characters with codes 160 onwards. To calculate the appropriate ASCII character for any given pattern of blocks you should use the method detailed in the user guide, which finds the code value for any block character in the higher set (160 to 255) or you can see them in figure 13.1.

***Example 13.3***

It is tedious to access each individual block character, especially if we wish to use them for drawing low-resolution diagrams. A far more sensible approach is to create a library of procedures to do the manipulation for us. For example, the

| | | | |
|---|---|---|---|
| =160 | =161 | =162 | =163 |
| =164 | =165 | =166 | =167 |
| =168 | =169 | =170 | =171 |
| =172 | =173 | =174 | =175 |
| =176 | =177 | =178 | =179 |
| =180 | =181 | =182 | =183 |
| =184 | =185 | =186 | =187 |
| =188 | =189 | =190 | =191 |
| =224 | =225 | =226 | =227 |
| =228 | =229 | =230 | =231 |
| =232 | =233 | =234 | =235 |
| =236 | =237 | =238 | =239 |
| =240 | =241 | =242 | =243 |
| =244 | =245 | =246 | =247 |
| =248 | =249 | =250 | =251 |
| =252 | =253 | =254 | =255 |

*Figure 13.1*

listing 13.3 draws a low-resolution picture of sine and cosine curves. The individual square pixels of this picture are the 1/6th blocks from within the graphics characters. Naturally we must allow for the addition (or deletion) of extra square pixels within a graphics character. We use the locations down the left-hand side of the screen for the graphic white code (or any other graphics colour). This means that the $x$-coordinates for our square pixel-blocks are in the range 2 to 79 (character columns 1 to 39: column 0 holds the colour code) and the $y$-coordinates are in the range 0 to 74 (rows 24 to 0). We introduce a 'plot' procedure which has three parameters, the coordinates of the pixel to be plotted and an integer (1, 2 or 3) that is used to define the type of plot – plot FOREGROUND, plot BACKGROUND or plot EOR respectively. We also give the 'draw' procedure which joins two specified points with an approximation to a straight line.

After running the program, hold down the RETURN key and you will delete all the control codes from the left-hand edge of the screen, and all the equivalent text characters become visible. Now type control Z, which will take the text cursor to the top of the screen. Then continuously press soft key f0 (set by line 180 of the program), which will reset the graphics control codes.

*Listing 13.3*

```
 1Ø MODE 7
 19 REM array D stores values for positioning each 1/6th block
          inside character.
 2Ø DIM D(1,2)
 3Ø FOR I%=Ø TO 1
 4Ø FOR J%=Ø TO 2
 5Ø READ D(I%,J%)
 6Ø NEXT J%
 7Ø NEXT I%
 8Ø DATA 16,4,1,64,8,2
 89 REM place graphics white codes down side of screen
 9Ø FOR L=Ø TO 24
1ØØ A=HIMEM+4Ø*L : ?A=151
11Ø NEXT L
119 REM draw axes
12Ø PROCdraw(1.2,35,79,35)
13Ø PROCdraw(1,4Ø,Ø,4Ø,74)
139 REM plot both curves simultaneously
14Ø FOR I=2 TO 79 STEP 1
15Ø PROCplot(1.I,COS(4-I/1Ø)*3Ø+35)
16Ø PROCplot(1.I,SIN(4-I/1Ø)*3Ø+35)
17Ø NEXT I
18Ø *KEYØ|!|W|J|H
19Ø END

2ØØ REM plot
21Ø DEF PROCplot(M,X,Y)
22Ø LOCAL C,XX,YY
229 REM find address of character block which contains 'pixel'
23Ø A=&7CØØ+(25-(Y DIV 3))*4Ø+X DIV 2
24Ø XX=X MOD2 : YY=Y MOD 3
249 REM make sure we have character in higher set (16Ø to 255)
25Ø C=?A : IF C<128 THEN C=C+128
259 REM modify character
26Ø IF M=1 THEN C=C OR D(XX,YY)
27Ø IF M=2 THEN C=C AND (D(XX,YY) EOR &FF)
28Ø IF M=3 THEN C=C EOR D(XX,YY)
289 REM replace character
29Ø ?A=C
3ØØ ENDPROC

4ØØ REM draw
41Ø DEF PROCdraw(M,X1,Y1,X2,Y2)
42Ø DX=X2-X1 : DY=Y2-Y1 : SX=SGN(DX) : SY=SGN(DY)
43Ø DX=ABS(DX) : DY=ABS(DY)
44Ø IF DX=Ø THEN ST=DY : SX=Ø : GOTO 48Ø
45Ø IF DY=Ø THEN ST=DX : SY=Ø : GOTO 48Ø
46Ø IF DX>DY THEN SY=SY*DY/DX : ST=DX ELSE SX=SX*DX/DY : ST=DY
47Ø IF ST=Ø THEN ENDPROC
479 REM plot each pixel along line
48Ø FOR I=Ø TO ST STEP SGN(ST)
49Ø PROCplot(M,X1,Y1)
5ØØ X1=X1+SX : Y1=Y1+SY
51Ø NEXT
52Ø ENDPROC
```

***Exercise 13.1***

Change the value of NXPIX and NYPIX in the 'start' procedure (listing 2.1) and alter 'moveto' and 'lineto' (listings 2.4 and 2.5) so that they produce calls to the 'plot' and 'draw' procedures. This will allow you to use any of our existing two-dimensional and three-dimensional graphics programs to draw low-resolution teletext pictures. Figure 13.2 is a low-resolution picture of a cube that was drawn by the program from chapter 9 which has been altered in this way.

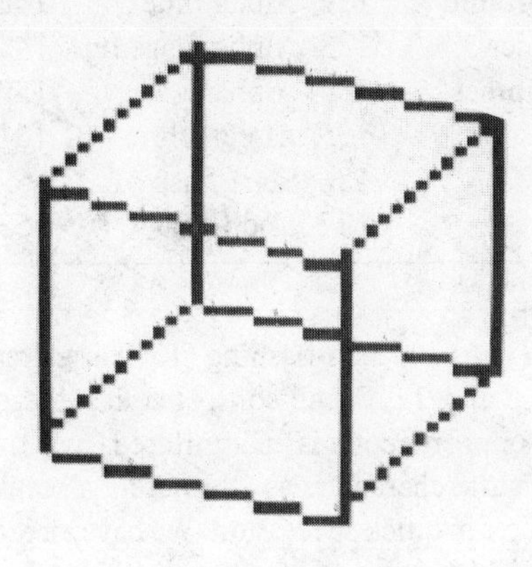

*Figure 13.2*

*Listing 13.4*

```
2ØØØ REM initkeys
2Ø1Ø DEF PROCinitkeys
2Ø2Ø *KEYØ‖!‖L
2Ø3Ø *KEY1‖!‖M
2Ø4Ø *KEY2‖!‖Z
2Ø5Ø *KEY3‖!‖\
2Ø6Ø *KEY4‖!‖]
2Ø7Ø *KEY5‖!‖^
2Ø8Ø *KEY6‖!‖␣
2Ø9Ø ENDPROC
```

We now return to a discussion of the control codes. As we have seen, not all the codes are immediately available from the keyboard so we give a procedure 'initkeys' (listing 13.4) which simplifies the entry of control codes that are not already available on the keyboard by redefining the soft keys. Table 13.2 lists the codes accessible from the keyboard.

Table 13.2 Control codes available on the function keys

| Key | | With shift | With control |
|---|---|---|---|
| f0 | 140 Normal height | 128 | 144 |
| f1 | 141 Double height | 129 Alpha red | 145 Graphic red |
| f2 | 154 Separated graphics | 130 Alpha green | 146 Graphic green |
| f3 | 156 Black background | 131 Alpha yellow | 147 Graphic yellow |
| f4 | 157 New background | 132 Alpha blue | 148 Graphic blue |
| f5 | 158 Hold graphics | 133 Alpha magenta | 149 Graphic magenta |
| f6 | 159 Release graphics | 134 Alpha cyan | 150 Graphic cyan |
| f7 | | 135 Alpha white | 151 Graphic white |
| f8 | | 136 Start flash | 152 Conceal |
| f9 | | 137 End flash | 153 Contiguous graphics |

The codes flashing (136) and non-flashing (137) are already available with shift on function keys 8 and 9. Like all control codes, these affect the remainder of the line (unless the opposite code is encountered) and they each appear as a space. Flashing displays the characters as alternately a blank background and then the normal character in quick succession. We have already seen double-height characters (code 141). This again will affect everything to the end of the line unless the normal height is restored with code 140.

To get different background colours in teletext we must first select a new colour (either graphics or text, it does not matter which) and follow it with the code for a new background (157). Since we are unable to select black as a foreground colour there must also be a special command to set a black background (code 156), and naturally you will have to introduce a new foreground colour. This means that the codes to set a new background will appear as two spaces on the screen. Code 152 enables you to conceal a string with background colour. If you overprint this code with a different code then the string becomes visible.

The last four codes to be considered all relate to the relative position of the graphics characters. Contiguous graphics (code 153) is assumed for all lines and means that 1/6th character blocks all touch. Separated graphics (code 154) slightly separates these square blocks. When pictures are drawn in teletext it is obviously a disadvantage to have a blank space between different colours. The hold graphics code (158) is designed so that subsequent control codes will not be displayed as blanks but will have the previous graphics character repeated and displayed at that location. The release graphics code (159) turns off this effect.

*Example 13.4*

We use some of these commands in the program given in listing 13.5 which plays a 'brickout' game in mode 7. The program first prints out a double-height logo, and requests a skill factor (0 difficult to 10 easy). Five coloured walls are drawn, and on pressing the space bar a bat appears and a ball is served into play. The bat is moved left and right by the corresponding cursor keys, and is used to hit the ball back into play. Whenever the ball hits a wall it knocks a brick out and increments the score. If the ball hits the bottom of the screen then the serve is over. You have three serves per game. If the ball penetrates the five walls and hits the top line then the bat gets smaller.

*Listing 13.5*

```
 10 MODE 7 : HISCORE=0
 20 REPEAT
 30 PROCinit
 40 PROCgame
 50 PROCend
 60 UNTIL FALSE
 70 STOP

100 REM initialise game variables
110 DEF PROCinit
120 SCORE=0 : BALLS=3
130 B$=" ppppp " : LB=5
140 BRICK$="////////////////////////////////"
150 B=2 : *FX15,0
160 REPEAT : CLS
170 PROClogo(3,2)
179 REM print twice for double height letters
180 PRINT TAB(9,12);"SKILL LEVEL (0 TO 10)"
190 PRINT TAB(9,13);"SKILL LEVEL (0 TO 10)"
200 PRINT SPC(40): PRINT TAB(17,14);:INPUT S
210 UNTIL S>=0 AND S<=10
220 SKILL=S*10
230 PROCwall
240 ENDPROC

300 REM game
309 REM repeat all stages of game. Note you have 3 chances to
        move bat each time ball moves
310 DEF PROCgame
320 REPEAT
330 PROCthrow
340 REPEAT
350 PROCkey
360 PROCball
370 PROCkey
379 REM slow down game
380 FOR I=1 TO SKILL : NEXT I
390 PROCkey
400 UNTIL OUT
410 BALLS=BALLS-1
420 UNTIL BALLS=0
430 ENDPROC

500 REM start new ball
510 DEF PROCthrow
520 PRINT TAB(1,17); : VDU 141
530 FOR I%=0 TO 1
540 PRINT TAB(8,16+I%); : VDU 141,136
```

```
 55Ø PRINT"PRESS"; : VDU 13Ø
 56Ø PRINT"""SPACE"""; : VDU 151
 57Ø PRINT"FOR BALL"; : VDU 137
 58Ø NEXT I%
 59Ø REPEAT:UNTIL INKEY(-99)
 6ØØ PRINT TAB(1,17); : VDU 32
 61Ø FOR I%=Ø TO 1
 62Ø PRINT TAB(8,16+I%);"                                   "
 63Ø NEXT I%
 64Ø X=RND(2Ø)+1Ø : Y=22
 65Ø XD=SGN(RND(1)-.5) : YD=-1
 66Ø PRINT TAB(X,Y);"Ø"; : OX=X : OY=Y
 67Ø OUT=FALSE
 68Ø ENDPROC

 7ØØ REM check keyboard
 71Ø DEF PROCkey
 72Ø IF INKEY(-122) AND B<38-LB THEN B=B+1
 73Ø IF INKEY(-26) AND B>2 THEN B=B-1
 74Ø PRINT TAB(B,23);B$;
 75Ø ENDPROC

 8ØØ REM move ball
 81Ø DEF PROCball
 82Ø Y=Y+YD : IF Y>23 THEN OUT=TRUE : GOTO 93Ø
 83Ø IF Y=22 AND YD=-1 AND BRICKOUT THEN PROCwall
 84Ø X=X+XD : IF X<4 THEN X=3 : XD=-XD
 85Ø IF X>37 THEN X=38 : XD=-XD
 86Ø IF Y=2 THEN YD=-YD : IF LB=5 THEN B$=" ppp " : LB=3
     : PRINT TAB(B,23);B$;" ";
 87Ø PRINT TAB(X,Y); : A%=135 : C=USR(&FFF4)
     : C=(C AND &FFØØ)/&1ØØ
 88Ø IF C=47 THEN PROCbrickout : YD=-YD : SOUND Ø,-15,2,1
 89Ø IF C<>112 THEN 91Ø ELSE YD=-YD : SOUND 1,-15,15Ø,1
     : IF X<>(B+1+INT(LB/2)) THEN XD=SGN(XD)*2 ELSE XD=SGN(XD)
 9ØØ IF C=112 THEN 92Ø
 91Ø PRINT TAB(X,Y);"Ø";
 92Ø IF OY=23 THEN 94Ø
 93Ø PRINT TAB(OX,OY);" ";
 94Ø OX=X : OY=Y
 95Ø ENDPROC

1ØØØ REM draw new wall
1Ø1Ø DEF PROCwall
1Ø2Ø CLS : VDU23,1,Ø;Ø;Ø;Ø;
1Ø3Ø VDU 134 : PRINT"   SCORE ";SCORE
1Ø4Ø PRINT TAB(22,Ø);"HISCORE ";HISCORE
1Ø5Ø FOR I%=1 TO 22
1Ø6Ø PRINT TAB(Ø,I%); : VDU 151
1Ø7Ø PRINT" j"
1Ø8Ø PRINT TAB(39,I%); : PRINT"5"
1Ø9Ø NEXT I%
11ØØ FOR I%=5 TO 9
111Ø PRINT TAB(Ø,I%); : VDU 14Ø+I%
112Ø PRINT TAB(3,I%); : PRINT BRICK$
113Ø NEXT I%
114Ø PRINT TAB(3,1);"``````````````````````````````````"
115Ø PRINT TAB(Ø,23);:VDU15Ø
116Ø BRICKOUT=FALSE
117Ø ENDPROC
```

```
1200 REM add score for a brick
1210 DEF PROCbrickout
1220 SCORE=SCORE+10-Y
1230 IF SCORE>HISCORE THEN HISCORE=SCORE
1240 PRINT TAB(10,0);SCORE : PRINT TAB(30,0);HISCORE
1250 IF SCORE MOD 540=0 THEN BRICKOUT=TRUE
1260 ENDPROC

1300 REM end of game
1310 DEF PROCend
1319 REM delete remaining bricks
1320 PRINT TAB(39,9); : I=0
1330 REPEAT
1340 PRINT" "; : VDU 8,8 : I=I+1
1350 A=RND(200)
1360 SOUND1,-10,A,1 : SOUND2,-10,1.5*A,1 : SOUND3,-10,A*1.75,1
1370 UNTIL INKEY(-99) OR I=200
1380 ENDPROC

1400 REM print double height brickout logo on screen
1410 DEF PROClogo(B,F)
1420 PRINT TAB(0,0);
1430 FOR I%=1 TO 25
1440 B=(B+2) MOD 6 : F=(F+2) MOD 6
1450 IF I%<>1 THEN PRINT
1460 VDU 129+B,157,129+F,141
1470 PRINT"*********** BRICKOUT ***********";
1480 NEXT I%
1490 ENDPROC
```

The game was written in a modular fashion similar to that of the worm game in chapter 1. We shall not give a detailed description of the program since the technique of construction should be self-evident from the listing. However, it is instructive to note from the game logo that the background and foreground colours for the two halves of a double-height character need not be the same.

We now consider the construction of the sort of pictures that are familiar to all owners of teletext televisions. It is possible to write a program to generate each individual picture, or painstakingly to create pictures by typing in codes and text from the keyboard. It is far better to use an interactive program for drawing displays like figure 13.3. We give such a program in listing 13.6.

Because the screen is used by the program for displaying messages as well as for drawing the picture, it is essential to store a copy of the picture elsewhere in the memory. We chose the locations between &7800 and &7C00, which we call a *picture buffer*, and set HIMEM to &7800 to protect this area. Any intentional changes made to the diagram on the screen (that is, to the screen memory) are also made to the corresponding buffer locations. Hence even though the screen is overwritten at several stages by the program, the diagram can be restored from the memory buffer when required. The program includes an error-handling routine which ensures that any problems, apart from a deliberate BREAK, will

*Figure 13.3*

*Listing 13.6*

```
 10 ON ERROR GOTO 1510
 20 MODE 7 : HIMEM=&7800
 30 *LOAD EDPIC 7800
 39 REM array giving bit values for blocks in graphics characters
 40 DIM D(1,2)
 50 FOR I%=0 TO 1
 60 FOR J%=0 TO 2
 70 READ D(I%,J%)
 80 NEXT J%
 90 NEXT I%
100 DATA 16,4,1,64,8,2
110 VDU 15 : VDU 23,1,0;0;0;0;
120 *FX4,1
130 PROCinitkeys
139 REM initialise positions of text and graphics cursors
140 TX=20 : TY=10
150 GX=40 : GY=35
160 X1=GX : Y1=GY
169 REM display picture with menu
170 PROCbackon
180 PROCmenu
189 REM printing is done inside one line window at bottom of
        screen to appear flashing
190 REPEAT
200 PRINT'" TELETEXT EDITOR ";
209 REM FNkeys waits for a key press in the same way as INKEY$
        but allows the cursor to move
```

```
210 A$=FNkeys(100)
220 IF A$<>"" THEN PROCcommand
230 PRINT'" INPUT COMMAND ? ";
240 A$=FNkeys(100)
250 IF A$<>"" THEN PROCcommand
260 UNTIL FALSE
270 END
300 REM command
310 DEF PROCcommand
319 REM deal with any keypress
320 PRINT'" INPUT COMMAND ? ";A$;
330 IF A$=CHR$(13) THEN ENDPROC
340 P=INSTR("BGIMT",A$)
350 IF P=0 THEN PRINT" INVALID"; : A$=GET$ : GOTO 320
360 PRINT
370 IF A$="I" THEN PROCinit
380 IF A$="M" THEN PROCmenu
390 IF A$="T" THEN PROCtext
400 IF A$="B" THEN PROCbyte
410 IF A$="G" THEN PROCgraphic
420 ENDPROC

500 REM keys
510 DEF FNkeys(T%)
520 T=TIME
530 REPEAT
540 B$=INKEY$(0)
550 SHIFT=INKEY(-1)
559 REM if shift is pressed remove graphics cursor
560 IF SHIFT THEN PROCplot(1,3,GX,GY)
569 REM alter text/graphics cursor depending on shift
570 IF B$=CHR$(&8B) THEN PROCup : B$=""
580 IF B$=CHR$(&8A) THEN PROCdown : B$=""
590 IF B$=CHR$(&88) THEN PROCleft : B$=""
600 IF B$=CHR$(&89) THEN PROCright : B$=""
609 REM redraw graphics cursor
610 IF SHIFT THEN PROCplot(1,3,GX,GY)
619 REM if non-cursor key pressed or time is up then return
620 UNTIL TIME>T+T% OR B$<>""
630 =B$
700 REM up
710 DEF PROCup
719 REM move graphics cursor position
720 IF SHIFT THEN GY=GY+1 : IF GY=75 THEN GY=0
730 IF SHIFT THEN ENDPROC
739 REM erase text cursor move it and redraw it
740 PROCcursoff : TY=TY-1 : IF TY=-1 THEN TY=24
750 PROCcurson : ENDPROC

800 REM down
809 REM see up
810 DEF PROCdown
820 IF SHIFT THEN GY=GY-1 : IF GY=-1 THEN GY=74
830 IF SHIFT THEN ENDPROC
840 PROCcursoff : TY=TY+1 : IF TY=25 THEN TY=0
850 PROCcurson : ENDPROC

900 REM right
909 REM see up
910 DEF PROCright
920 IF SHIFT THEN GX=GX+1 : IF GX=80 THEN GX=2
```

```
 930 IF SHIFT THEN ENDPROC
 940 PROCcursoff : TX=TX+1 : IF TX=40 THEN TX=0
 950 PROCcurson : ENDPROC

1000 REM left
1009 REM see up
1010 DEF PROCleft
1020 IF SHIFT THEN GX=GX-1 : IF GX=1 THEN GX=79
1030 IF SHIFT THEN ENDPROC
1040 PROCcursoff : TX=TX-1 : IF TX=-1 THEN TX=39
1050 PROCcurson
1060 ENDPROC

1100 REM get
1109 REM return the value stored on the screen at location X,Y
1110 DEF FNget(X,Y)
1120 A%=&7C00+Y*40+X : =?A%
1200 REM put
1210 DEF PROCput(A,X,Y,CHAR)
1219 REM store the CHARacter at X,Y either on the screen (A=1)
         or in the buffer (A=0)
1220 A%=&7800+A*&400+Y*40+X
1230 ?A%=CHAR : ENDPROC

1300 REM curson
1310 DEF PROCcurson
1319 REM remove graphics cursor, store current value at text cursor
         position and replace with a square, replace graphics
1320 PROCplot(1,3,GX,GY) : TST=FNget(TX,TY) : PROCput(1,TX,TY,255)
   : PROCplot(1,3,GX,GY)
1330 ENDPROC

1400 REM cursoff
1410 DEF PROCcursoff
1419 REM remove graphics cursor and replace text cursor by old
         screen value then replace graphics cursor
1420 PROCplot(1,3,GX,GY) : PROCput(1,TX,TY,TST) : PROCplot(1,3,GX,GY)
1430 ENDPROC

1500 REM error section
1509 REM if error occurs in loading EDPIC then carry on
1510 IF ERL=30 THEN 40
1519 REM if any other error occurs save the picture from buffer
         and then...
1520 *SAVE EDPIC 7800 7C00
1529 REM report error in usual way
1530 MODE 7 : REPORT : IF ERL<>0 THEN PRINT" at line ";ERL : VDU 14
1539 REM reset cursor keys and stop
1540 *FX4,0
1550 END

1600 REM backup
1610 DEF PROCbackup
1619 REM copy screen to buffer
1620 LOCAL I% : FOR I%=0 TO 996 STEP 4
1630 I%!&7800=I%!&7C00 : NEXT I%
1640 ENDPROC

1700 REM backon
1710 DEF PROCbackon
1719 REM copy buffer to screen
1720 LOCAL I% : FOR I%=0 TO 996 STEP 4
```

```
1730 I%!&7C00=I%!&7800 : NEXT I%
1739 REM replace cursors
1740 PROCplot(1,3,GX,GY) : PROCcurson
1750 ENDPROC

1800 REM menu
1810 DEF PROCmenu
1819 REM retrieve picture from buffer set window for menu
1820 PROCbackon
1830 VDU 28,2,21,39,4 : CLS
1839 REM put control codes for yellow background outside window
       so they can't scroll away
1840 FOR I%=4 TO 21 : PROCput(1,0,I%,131) : PROCput(1,1,I%,157)
     : NEXT I%
1849 REM print out instructions with pauses making operating system
       scroll window up
1850 PRINT TAB(0,16);" COMMAND M FOR MENU DISPLAY/REMOVAL"
1860 A$=INKEY$(10) : PRINT'" USE CURSOR KEYS TO MOVE TEXT CURSOR "
1870 A$=INKEY$(10) : PRINT'" USE SHIFT/CURSOR KEYS FOR GRAPHICS "
1880 A$=INKEY$(10) : PRINT'" COMMAND T TO PLACE TEXT AT CURSOR"
1890 A$=INKEY$(10) : PRINT'" COMMAND B TO ALTER BYTE AT CURSOR"
1900 A$=INKEY$(10) : PRINT'" COMMAND G FOR GRAPHICS FUNCTION"
1910 A$=INKEY$(10) : PRINT'" COMMAND I TO INIT TEXT/GRAPHICS"
1919 REM back to the top of window print double height header
1920 VDU30 : PRINT'SPC(12);CHR$(141);"COMMANDS"
1930 PRINT SPC(12);CHR$(141);"COMMANDS"
1939 REM alternate colours of two halves of header by colour codes
       while waiting
1940 REPEAT
1950 PROCput(1,10,5,133) : PROCput(1,10,6,130)
1960 C$=INKEY$(50) : IF C$="M" THEN 1990
1970 PROCput(1,10,6,133) : PROCput(1,10,5,130)
1980 C$=INKEY$(50)
1990 UNTIL C$="M"
1999 REM replace picture and remove window
2000 PROCbackon : VDU 28,0,24,39,24
2010 VDU 15,30
2020 ENDPROC

2100 REM plot
2110 DEF PROCplot(A,M,X,Y)
2120 LOCAL C,XX,YY
2129 REM calculate character position containing the point either
       on the screen (A=1) or in the buffer (A=0)
2130 A=A*&400+&7800+(25-(Y DIV 3))*40+X DIV 2
2139 REM find coordinates of point within the character
2140 XX=X MOD 2 : YY=Y MOD 3
2150 C=?A : IF C<128 THEN C=C+128
2160 IF M=1 THEN C=C OR D(XX,YY)
2170 IF M=2 THEN C=C AND(D(XX,YY) EOR &FF)
2180 IF M=3 THEN C=C EOR D(XX,YY)
2190 ?A=C
2200 ENDPROC

2300 REM draw
2310 DEF PROCdraw(A,M,X1,Y1,X2,Y2)
2319 REM draw a line from X1,Y1 to X2,Y2 either on the screen (A=1)
       or in the buffer (A=0)
2320 DX=X2-X1 : DY=Y2-Y1 : SX=SGN(DX) : SY=SGN(DY)
2330 DX=ABS(DX) : DY=ABS(DY)
2339 REM find the amounts by which one coordinate must change assuming
       the other has a larger distance and is moving in steps of one
```

```
2340 IF DX=Ø THEN ST=DY : SX=Ø : GOTO 238Ø
235Ø IF DY=Ø THEN ST=DX : SY=Ø : GOTO 238Ø
236Ø IF DX>DY THEN SY=SY*DY/DX : ST=DX ELSE SX=SX*DX/DY : ST=DY
237Ø IF ST=Ø THEN ENDPROC
2379 REM go along line adding step size to coordinates and plotting
         resulting point
238Ø FOR I=Ø TO ST STEP SGN(ST)
239Ø PROCplot(A,M,X1,Y1)
24ØØ X1=X1+SX : Y1=Y1+SY
241Ø NEXT I
242Ø ENDPROC

25ØØ REM init
251Ø DEF PROCinit
252Ø REPEAT : INPUT" INITIALISE G OR T ? "B$ : UNTIL B$="G" OR B$="T
253Ø REPEAT : INPUT" WHICH COLOUR ( 1 TO 7 ) ? "C : UNTIL C>Ø AND C<
254Ø REPEAT : INPUT" RANGE OF LINES ? "T,B
     : UNTIL T<B AND T>=Ø AND B<=24
255Ø IF B$="G" THEN C=C+144 ELSE C=C+128
2559 REM place a colour code (either text or graphics) at the start
         of each line in range both in buffer and on screen
256Ø FOR I=T TO B : PROCput(1,Ø,I,C) : PROCput(Ø,Ø,I,C) : NEXT I
257Ø ENDPROC

26ØØ REM text
261Ø DEF PROCtext
2619 REM show whole picture and reset cursor so copy can be used
262Ø PROCbackon
263Ø *FX4,Ø
264Ø VDU 23,1,1,Ø;Ø;Ø;Ø; : VDU 28,Ø,24,39,Ø
265Ø PRINT TAB(TX,TY); : INPUT""ANY$ : IF LEN(ANY$)=Ø THEN 267Ø
2659 REM put the string into buffer
266Ø FOR I=1 TO LEN(ANY$) : PROCput(Ø,TX+I-1,TY,ASC(MID$(ANY$,I,1)))
     : NEXT I
2669 REM reset mode 7 in case string was entered on bottom line
         scrolling screen
267Ø VDU 22,7
268Ø VDU 23,1,Ø,Ø;Ø;Ø;Ø; : VDU 28,Ø,24,39,24
2689 REM redisplay picture and reset cursor keys for program use
269Ø PROCbackon
27ØØ *FX4,1
271Ø ENDPROC

28ØØ REM byte
281Ø DEF PROCbyte
282Ø PROCbackon
2829 REM set one line window below byte and scroll to clear
         before printing value
283Ø TT=(TY+1) MOD 25 : TS=(TY-1) MOD 25 : VDU 28,Ø,TT,39,TT
284Ø PRINT'"  CURRENT VALUE IS ";?(&78ØØ+4Ø*TY+TX);
2849 REM set one line window above byte and input new value
         'return'=Ø for no change
285Ø VDU 28,Ø,TS,39,TS
286Ø PRINT
287Ø REPEAT : INPUT" WHAT ASCII CODE ( 32 TO 255 ) ? "C
     : UNTIL C>31 AND C<256 OR C=Ø
288Ø IF C=Ø THEN 291Ø
289Ø PROCput(Ø,TX,TY,C) : PROCput(1,TX,TY,C)
29ØØ IF TY<> 24 THEN TST=C
291Ø PROCbackon : VDU 28,Ø,24,39,24
292Ø ENDPROC
```

```
3000 REM graphic
3010 DEF PROCgraphic
3019 REM plot point at cursor or draw line from last point
     specified to cursor
3020 REPEAT : INPUT" PLOT OR DRAW ( P OR D ) ? "A$
     : UNTIL A$="P" OR A$="D"
3030 REPEAT : INPUT" FOREGROUND,BACKROUND,EOR ( 1,2,3 ) ? "A
     : UNTIL A>0 AND A<4
3040 PROCbackon
3049 REM plot points directly into buffer then restore picture
3050 IF A$="P" THEN PROCplot(0,A,GX,GY)
3060 IF A$="D" THEN PROCdraw(0,A,X1,Y1,GX,GY)
3070 X1=GX : Y1=GY
3080 PROCbackon
3090 ENDPROC

3100 REM initkeys
3110 DEF PROCinitkeys
3119 REM set keys to produce more teletext codes directly
3120 *KEY0|!|L
3130 *KEY1|!|M
3140 *KEY2|!|Z
3150 *KEY3|!|\
3160 *KEY4|!|]
3170 *KEY5|!|^
3180 *KEY6|!|_
3190 ENDPROC
```

save the diagram as file EDPIC on backing store before ending. Before you start any construction you may wish to clear the picture buffer locations by typing

CLS : PROCbackup

Initially the program will try to load the edit picture EDPIC from backing store; however if this is not available the program will continue on to the next line when you press ESCAPE (if you are using tape backing store) or it will continue automatically (if you are using disks) – hence the need to clear the screen at the beginning of a diagram construction. Having loaded this picture (from the backing store or the buffer) the program will display it on the screen and then immediately display a *menu* over the top of it. This menu can be recalled or removed at any time by pressing key M. The other options available with this interactive program are Initialise, Graphics, Text and Byte. These commands are called by typing their initial letter and are described below.

Initialise is used to place a Graphics or Text colour code (of any colour) in the first column of each one of a range of lines (a subset of rows 0 to 24). This will affect the whole line unless countermanded by graphics/text colour codes further along that line.

Text enables the typing of text and control codes on the screen (remember that if you want to start a text string with a space then you must enclose the whole entry in quotes). When text is being typed the copy cursor is enabled, so making it simple to copy parts of the screen to new locations. RETURN enables you to exit from this section of the program so that you can input another command.

Graphics allows you to use point plotting and line-drawing routines which include a choice of 'plot' options (background, foreground or EOR). The 'draw' command will draw from the last point specified either by plot or from the end of the last line drawn. The program creates a graphics cursor, by EORing a single point on the screen, which can be moved by using the shift and cursor keys. When this graphics cursor runs through alphanumeric lines (as opposed to graphics) it will appear as a text character. Sometimes the graphics cursor is invisible, but holding down the shift key makes it flash, thus making it visible. The 'plot' and 'draw' procedures have an extra parameter which allows you to plot either on the screen as with the graphics cursor (which is not stored with the diagram), or directly into the buffer area as with line drawing. The text/graphics cursors must be moved into position prior to entering the Text and Graphics sections.

Byte allows you to read directly the value currently positioned at the text cursor location. This enables you to see exactly which control code or character is at that position, and allows you either to alter it by typing in the replacement value or to RETURN. This is especially helpful if a graphics hold mode is operative, which effectively hides the control codes.

The program will automatically save the picture as file EDPIC on encountering an error, such as typing ESCAPE by accident, so that any alterations are not lost. If you do not wish to save the picture, type BREAK to halt the program. The picture will still be in the buffer in memory.

*Example 13.5: Animation*

We can use the idea of a buffer to hold more than one picture in memory at any one time. This would be convenient for displaying simple teletext diagrams as a slide show in lectures or as advertisements. Since each picture occupies only 1K of store, at least twenty teletext pictures can be fitted into the memory at once. This is impossible for modes 0 to 2 since each screenful takes up 20K of memory in these modes. We simply set HIMEM to protect whatever area we wish to use for picture storage and then transfer each picture to the actual screen memory when required. Listing 13.7 contains an assembler routine to do this. Because user-defined characters are unavailable in mode 7 we can use this part of the memory (locations starting at &C00) to store the machine code produced by this program. It also stores the code as a file DISPLAY on backing store. This routine uses the OSBYTE call with the accumulator A set to 19, which allows the machine to wait for the start of the next refresh of the screen before copying the data to the screen: this helps to eliminate flickering. The program in listing 13.8 allows us to display any one of 20 pictures by typing a number between 0 and 19. Even when called from BASIC programs, this routine is fast enough to display a new picture within the time the machine takes to refresh the screen, and so it enables us to display animated pictures. We simply draw a set of pictures at varying stages of rotation, and arrange that the last frame is the same as the first. The movie section of the program (accessed by typing M) displays all the pictures in rapid succession to get this animation effect. Listing 13.8 draws twenty pictures of a simple curve rotated through a further $\pi/40$ radians with each frame, and stores each picture at the correct location in memory by using a modified version of the 'backup' procedure of the teletext editor (listing 13.6). Then the program allows the slide show and movie procedures to display.

*Listing 13.7*

```
  9 REM display routine transfers a teletext picture to screen
 10 OSBYTE=&FFF4
 20 FOR I=0 TO 3 STEP 3
 30 P%=&C00
 39 REM multiply picture number in A by four and add to start of
        pictures to get hi-byte, use *FX19 to wait, then transfer
 40 [OPT I
 50 ASL A : ASL A
 60 CLC : ADC #&2C
 70 STA &71
 80 LDA #&7C : STA &73
 90 LDY #0 : STY &70 : STY &72
100 LDX #4
110 LDA #19 : JSR OSBYTE
120 .LOOP
130 LDA (&70 ),Y : STA (&72),Y
140 INY : BNE LOOP
150 INC &71 : INC &73
160 DEX : BNE LOOP
170 RTS
180 ]
190 NEXT I
199 REM run address set to an RTS in ROM so that program can be
        loaded from disk by *<fsp>
200 *SAVE DISPLAY C00 +30 FFB8
```

*Listing 13.8*

```
 10 MODE 7
 20 HIMEM=&2C00
 30 DIM D(1,2)
 40 FOR I%=0 TO 1
 50 FOR J%=0 TO 2
 60 READ D(I%,J%)
 70 NEXT J%
 80 NEXT I%
 90 DATA 16,4,1,64,8,2
100 *LOAD DISPLAY
109 REM draw 20 frames of movie with curve rotating through PI/2
110 FOR F=0 TO 19
120 ANG=F*PI/40
129 REM for each frame put graphics white codes down the side
130 CLS
140 FOR I=0 TO 24 : PRINT TAB(0,I); : VDU 151 : NEXT I
149 REM draw clover leaf curve
150 OX=40+30*COS(ANG) : OY=38+30*SIN(ANG)
160 FOR I=0 TO 2*PI STEP PI/100
170 S=SIN(I+ANG) : C=COS(I+ANG)
180 S2=SIN(2*I) : C2=COS(2*I)
```

```
190 R=(C2^3+S2^3)*30
200 X2=40+R*C : Y2=38+R*S
210 PROCdraw(1,OX,OY,X2,Y2)
220 OX=X2 : OY=Y2
230 NEXT I
239 REM store frame F in memory
240 PROCbackup(F)
249 REM until all twenty frames are prepared and stored
250 NEXT F
260 PROCshow
270 END

300 REM plot
310 DEF PROCplot(M,X,Y)
320 LOCAL C,XX,YY
330 A=&7C00+(25-(Y DIV 3))*40+X DIV 2
340 XX=X MOD2 : YY=Y MOD 3
350 C=?A : IF C<128 THEN C=C+128
360 IF M=1 THEN C=C OR D(XX,YY)
370 IF M=2 THEN C=C AND (D(XX,YY) EOR &FF)
380 IF M=3 THEN C=C EOR D(XX,YY)
390 ?A=C
400 ENDPROC

500 REM draw
510 DEF PROCdraw(M,X1,Y1,X2,Y2)
520 LOCAL DX,DY,SX,SY,ST,I
530 DX=X2-X1 : DY=Y2-Y1 : SX=SGN(DX) : SY=SGN(DY)
540 DX=ABS(DX) : DY=ABS(DY)
550 IF DX=0 THEN ST=DY : SX=0 : GOTO 580
560 IF DY=0 THEN ST=DX : SY=0 : GOTO 580
570 IF DX>DY THEN SY=SY*DY/DX : ST=DX ELSE SX=SX*DX/DY : ST=DY
580 IF ST=0 THEN ENDPROC
590 FOR I=0 TO ST STEP SGN(ST)
600 PROCplot(M,X1,Y1)
610 X1=X1+SX : Y1=Y1+SY
620 NEXT I
630 ENDPROC

700 REM show
710 DEF PROCshow
719 REM ensure screen hasn't scrolled and that mode 7 is set
720 VDU 22,7
729 REM if you have a file of twenty frames already stored
730 INPUT" NAME OF SLIDE FILE OR PRESS <RETURN>    ",A$
740 IF A$="" THEN 770
749 REM use CLI to load file
750 $&7D00="LOAD "+A$+" 2C00"
760 X%=0 : Y%=&7D : CALL &FFF7
769 REM alternate between single frame slide show and continuous movi
770 REPEAT
780 REPEAT
790 VDU 26 : INPUT A$
800 A%=VAL(A$)
809 REM put selected frame onto screen
810 CALL &C00
820 UNTIL A$="M"
829 REM if M is pressed start showing frames in quick succession
830 REPEAT
840 FOR A%=0 TO 19
850 CALL&C00
860 NEXT A%
```

```
870 UNTIL INKEY(0)>-1
879 REM never leave until escape
880 UNTIL FALSE
890 ENDPROC

900 REM backup
910 DEF PROCbackup(FRAME)
920 LOCAL I%,A%
929 REM start address from frame
930 A%=&2C00+&400*FRAME
939 REM transfer data from screen
940 FOR I%=0 TO 996 STEP 4
950 I%!A%=I%!&7C00
960 NEXT I%
970 ENDPROC
```

---

**Complete Programs**

I Listing 13.1. No data required.

II Listing 13.2. No data required.

III Listing 13.3. No data required.

IV Listing 13.5. The 'brickout' game. Type in the skill level (try 10), then type a space to start the game and move the bat with the left and right cursors.

V Listing 13.6. The teletext interactive diagram construction package. Try the following sample inputs (those underlined).

Type M, T, move the text cursor into position by using the cursor keys and type hello folks (note lower case characters). Then move the text cursor over the 'e' and type B. This will show the ASCII code for the character that is at present occupying that screen position (namely 'e' = ASCII 101). Type 117 and RETURN. Now move the cursor away and you will see a 'u' replacing the 'e'. Then type I and T and you will be asked for a colour (try 1) and a range of lines (try the whole screen 0, 24). Everything should go red. Now type I, G, a colour (2), and range (again 0, 24), and the lower case red text characters change into green graphics characters.

VI Listings 13.7 and 13.8. First run 13.7 which creates the file DISPLAY. Then run listing 13.8 which reloads DISPLAY and either loads 20 pictures from backing store or on typing RETURN takes about 15 minutes to draw them. Then type an integer between 0 and 19 to get an individual frame, or M to get a movie: any key will stop it.

# 14 Advanced Programming Techniques

To give your programs that really professional quality it is essential to make them *user friendly*. This is one of the few pieces of advertising jargon that actually bears any relation to reality: it is essential to make programs easy to use, not just for yourself but for other people. We have all returned to programs written in a hurry three months previously, only to find that they are so badly structured/commented that we cannot understand them. It is good programming practice to comment all but the most trivial programs, as well as to make their output self-explanatory. Mode 7 listings enable you to introduce colour codes that highlight sections of the program. REMarks do take up a great deal of space in the memory, but you must distinguish between a listing for general distribution and heavily used working programs. If you take a sensible approach at the beginning, and plan your programs, you can save a great deal of time and effort later on. For example, our placing of all BASIC statements on lines ending in 0 and REMs on lines ending in 9 makes the REM stripper (AUTO9, 10) a simple way to turn a readable program into a memory-wise efficient one. Do not take the need to save store to ludicrous extremes; space out statements and never place too many BASIC statements on any one line – this makes programs incomprehensible. Ensure that the *prompts* displayed while you are actually RUNning the program are clear and concise. Another simple way of providing help is to include an introductory instruction routine, as found on many video games.

In programs where a set of routines may be used in any order or combination, the usual method of providing for selection between options is the *menu* (such as the CHARACTER GENERATOR 1 program, listing 5.6). Provided that the prompts are appropriate to the actions that they initiate, then this method is especially useful for people who do not understand the details of the program and are using it only as a drawing tool. Common-sense plays its part in deciding what prompts should be issued. Avoid such classic misprompts as PRESS 1 FOR DUPLICATE DATA OR 2 FOR SINGLE DATA. If possible use cursor keys for movements about the screen (see option 3 of CHARACTER GENERATOR 1); this will seem natural to any regular user of the BBC micro.

As a rule it is best to write programs in modules. In this way each module can be tested individually and errors can be traced more quickly. Placing a coloured REMark before each procedure, routine or function allows us to isolate sections of the program and then read, correct and adapt them with ease.

A common-sense practical approach saves a great deal of time in the long run. It is also very useful to understand exactly how the operating system stores and deals with BASIC programs. This is dealt with later in this chapter but first we introduce a simple disassembler which can be used to look at the storage of such programs. This disassembler is also extremely useful for rescuing programs that have become corrupted, for debugging assembly language programs or for understanding the operating system.

*Listing 14.1*

```
 10 OSBYTE=&FFF4 : OSWORD=&FFF1 : OSASCI=&FFE3
 20 OSRDCH=&FFE0 : CLI=&FFF7
 30 IF ?&8015=49 THEN HEXSP=&856A :HEX=&8570 ELSE HEXSP=&B562 :HEX=&B545
 40 OUT=&70 : PUT=&71 : SP=&72 : BPT=&74
 50 CONBLK=&76 : HI=&81 : LO=&80 : DISP=&82 : DH=&83
 60 UP=&85 : STK=&86 : ACR=&84
 70 OLO=&7B : OHI=&7C
 80 HA=&8D : HB=&8E : HC=&8F
 90 DLINES=&7D : NUMB=&7E : TEMPSTACK=&7F
100 FOR OP=0 TO 3 STEP 3
110 P%=&7000
120 [OPT OP
130 TSX : STX TEMPSTACK
140 \ make sure BASIC rom is paged in since we will use it \
150 LDX #0 : .ROM STX &FE30 : LDA &8009 : INX : CMP #ASC("B") : BNE ROM
160 \ set &600 as address for string for OSWORD with A=0 \
170 LDA #0 : STA CONBLK : LDA #6 : STA CONBLK+1
180 \ set display mode to Dump mode \
190 LDA #ASC("D") : STA DISP
200 \ ST1 is string which sets mode 7 and prints instructions \
210 LDX #(ST1 MOD 256)
220 LDY #(ST1 DIV 256)
230 JSR OUTPUT
240 \ *FX4,1 sets cursor keys to produce ascii codes \
250 LDA #4 : LDX #1 : JSR OSBYTE
260
270
280 \ main loop, update display then deal with commands \
290 .L5 : JSR DISPLAY
300 \ get key, if it's a command then execute else try again \
310 .L7 : JSR KEYIN
320 \ deal with commands common to both modes \
330 CMP #ASC("D") : BNE NOND
340 \ set display mode to either D or L \
350 .STD : STA DISP : JMP L5
360 .NOND : CMP #ASC("L") : BEQ STD
370
380 \ if H command then input hex address \
390 CMP #ASC("H") : BNE NONH
400 \ begin H command, PRINT TAB(15,2); \
410 .HGIN : LDX #15 : LDY #2 : JSR SETAB
420 \ input 4 characters in range 0-F \
430 LDA #4 : LDX #ASC("0") : LDY #ASC("F") : JSR STRIN
440 \ convert first two chars to one byte, if error then reinput \
450 JSR DHEX : BCC HGIN : LDA DH : STA HI
460 \ convert next two chars to one byte \
470 LDA &602 : STA &600 : LDA &603 : STA &601 : JSR DHEX
480 \ if error then reinput \
```

```
 49Ø BCC HGIN : LDA DH : STA LO : JMP L5
 5ØØ
 51Ø \ check display mode if it's L then do L COMmands \
 52Ø .NONH : LDX DISP : CPX #ASC("L") : BNE NONF : JMP LCOM
 53Ø
 54Ø \ commands only available in Dump mode \
 55Ø \ check for cursor keys and alter address accordingly \
 56Ø .NONF : CMP #&88 : BNE NLEFT
 57Ø \ cursor left, take one off \
 58Ø LDA LO : BNE DE1 : DEC HI : .DE1 : DEC LO : JMP L5
 59Ø
 6ØØ .NLEFT  : CMP #&89 : BNE NRT
 61Ø \ cursor right, add one on \
 62Ø INC LO : BNE DE2 : INC HI : .DE2 : JMP L5
 63Ø
 64Ø .NRT : CMP #&8A : BNE NDOWN
 65Ø \ cursor down, add eight on \
 66Ø LDA LO : CLC : ADC #8 : STA LO
 67Ø LDA HI : ADC #Ø : STA HI : JMP L5
 68Ø
 69Ø .NDOWN : CMP #&8B : BNE NMOVE
 7ØØ \ cursor up, take eight off \
 71Ø LDA LO : SEC : SBC #8 : STA LO
 72Ø LDA HI : SBC #Ø : STA HI : JMP L5
 73Ø
 74Ø \ not a cursor movement \
 75Ø .NMOVE : CMP #ASC("A") : BNE NONA
 76Ø \ start of A command to ALTER a byte \
 77Ø .AGIN : LDY #14
 78Ø \ ACR is no of bytes ACRoss cursor is on display \
 79Ø LDA ACR : ASL A : CLC : ADC ACR : CLC : ADC #6
 8ØØ \ set text position TAB(ACR*3+6,14); \
 81Ø TAX : JSR SETAB
 82Ø \ get two characters between Ø and F \
 83Ø LDA #2 : LDX #ASC("Ø") : LDY #ASC("F") : JSR STRIN
 84Ø \ convert chars to byte value, store if valid or reinput \
 85Ø JSR DHEX : BCC AGIN : LDA DH : LDY #Ø : STA (LO),Y
 86Ø JMP L5
 87Ø
 88Ø
 89Ø \ characters to hex conversion routine \
 9ØØ .DHEX : LDA &6ØØ : CMP #ASC("9")+1 : BCS AL1
 91Ø AND #&ØF : BCC TIP
 92Ø .AL1 : CMP #ASC("A") : BCC ERHEX : SBC #ASC("A")-1Ø
 93Ø \ put value of first hex digit in top half of byte \
 94Ø .TIP : ASL A : ASL A : ASL A : ASL A : STA DH
 95Ø LDA &6Ø1 : CMP #ASC("9")+1 : BCS AL2
 96Ø AND #&ØF : BCC BOT
 97Ø .AL2 : CMP #ASC("A") : BCC ERHEX : SBC #ASC("A")-1Ø
 98Ø \ mix value of second digit in as bottom half \
 99Ø .BOT : ORA DH : STA DH : SEC
1ØØØ \ if error detected then carry flag is unset \
1Ø1Ø .ERHEX : RTS
1Ø2Ø
1Ø3Ø
1Ø4Ø \ back to checking commands \
1Ø5Ø .NONA : CMP #ASC("S") : BNE NONS
1Ø6Ø \ start of S command, set text position to ascii dump \
1Ø7Ø .SGIN : LDY #14 : LDA ACR : CLC : ADC #3Ø : TAX : JSR SETAB
1Ø8Ø \ get up to 255 characters between blank and alpha white \
1Ø9Ø LDA #255 : LDX #ASC(" ") : LDY #&87 : JSR STRIN
11ØØ \ copy all characters from buffer to memory \
```

```
1110 LDX #0 : LDY #0
1120 \ stop when we find a carriage return \
1130 .LOP : LDA &600,X : CMP #&0D : BEQ FINLOP
1140 STA (LO),Y : INY : INX : BNE LOP
1150 .FINLOP : JMP L5
1160
1170 \ arrive here if keypress was nonsense \
1180 .NONS
1190 JMP L7
1200
1210
1220 \ deal with commands for listing mode \
1230 .LCOM : CMP #&0D : BNE NONS
1240 \ only return is valid, reset start to one line lower \
1250 LDA OLO : STA LO : LDA OHI : STA HI : JMP L5
1260
1270
1280 \ disassemble routine used in Listing mode \
1290 .DIS : LDX #(ST2 MOD 256)
1300 LDY #(ST2 DIV 256)
1310 \ ST2 removes cursor and sets print position to (0,7) \
1320 JSR OUTPUT
1330 \ set number of lines counter \
1340 LDA #16 : STA DLINES
1350 .LINLOP
1360 \ output address + space \
1370 LDA HI : JSR HEX : LDA LO : JSR HEXSP
1380 \ copy following three bytes to buffer \
1390 \ three bytes in question are now HA,HB,HC \
1400 LDY #0 : LDX #3
1410 .HALOP : LDA (LO),Y : STA HA,Y : INY : DEX : BNE HALOP
1420 \ from opcode type find number of bytes in instruction \
1430 LDX HA : LDA TYPE,X : TAX : LDA NUM,X
1440 \ move address on to next instruction \
1450 STA NUMB : CLC : ADC LO : STA LO : LDA #0 : ADC HI : STA HI
1460 \ output bytes of instruction then... \
1470 LDX NUMB : LDY #3 : LDA HA : JSR HEXSP : DEY : DEX : BEQ PAD
1480 LDA HB : JSR HEXSP : DEY : DEX : BEQ PAD
1490 LDA HC : JSR HEXSP : DEX : BEQ MNEM
1500 \ pad with spaces if necessary \
1510 .PAD : TYA : PHA
1520 LDX #(ST4 MOD 256) : LDY #(ST4 DIV 256) : JSR OUTPUT
1530 PLA : TAY : DEY : BNE PAD
1540 \ add one more space before mnemonic \
1550 .MNEM : LDA #ASC(" ") : JSR OSASCI
1560 \ find which mnemonic starts instruction \
1570 LDX HA : LDA HASH,X : ASL A : ASL A : STA OUT
1580 \ multiply by 4 to find address in string of mnemonics \
1590 LDA #(STRING DIV 256) : STA PUT : LDX #4 : LDY #0
1600 \ output four chars, first one is colour code \
1610 .MNMLOP : LDA (OUT),Y : JSR OSASCI : INY : DEX : BNE MNMLOP
1620 LDA #ASC(" ") : JSR OSASCI
1630 \ form rest of instruction depending on type \
1640 LDX HA : LDA TYPE,X : CMP #1 : BNE NOD1
1650 \ type 1, immediate so format #&HH \
1660 LDA #ASC("#") : JSR OSASCI : LDA #ASC("&") : JSR OSASCI
1670 \ Y is no. of spaces to make format 10 wide \
1680 LDA HB : JSR HEXSP : LDY #5 : JMP NDLINE
1690
1700 .NOD1 : CMP #2 : BNE NOD2
1710 \ type 2, absolute     format &HHHH \
1720 LDA #ASC("&") : JSR OSASCI : LDA HC : JSR HEX
```

```
1730 LDA HB : JSR HEXSP : LDY #4 : JMP NDLINE
1740
1750 .NOD2 : CMP #3 : BNE NOD3
1760 \ type 3, zero page    format &HH \
1770 LDA #ASC("&") : JSR OSASCI : LDA HB : JSR HEXSP
1780 LDY #6 : JMP NDLINE
1790
1800 .NOD3 : CMP #4 : BNE NOD4
1810 \ type 4, accumulator  format A \
1820 LDA #ASC("A") : JSR OSASCI : LDY #9 : JMP NDLINE
1830
1840 .NOD4 : CMP #5 : BNE NOD5
1850 \ type 5, implied      format    \
1860 LDY #10 : JMP NDLINE
1870
1880 .NOD5 : CMP #6 : BNE NOD6
1890 \ type 6, indirect x   format (&HH,X) \
1900 LDA #ASC("(") : JSR OSASCI : LDA #ASC("&") : JSR OSASCI
1910 LDA HB : JSR HEX : LDA #ASC(",") : JSR OSASCI
1920 LDA #ASC("X") : JSR OSASCI : LDA #ASC(")") : JSR OSASCI
1930 LDY #3 : JMP NDLINE
1940
1950 .NOD6 : CMP #7 : BNE NOD7
1960 \ type 7, indirect y   format (&HH),Y \
1970 LDA #ASC("(") : JSR OSASCI : LDA #ASC("&") : JSR OSASCI
1980 LDA HB : JSR HEX : LDA #ASC(")") : JSR OSASCI
1990 LDA #ASC(",") : JSR OSASCI : LDA #ASC("Y") : JSR OSASCI
2000 LDY #3 : JMP NDLINE
2010
2020 .NOD7 : CMP #8 : BNE NOD8
2030 \ type 8, zero page x  format &HH,X \
2040 LDA #ASC("&") : JSR OSASCI : LDA HB : JSR HEX
2050 LDA #ASC(",") : JSR OSASCI : LDA #ASC("X") : JSR OSASCI
2060 LDY #5 : JMP NDLINE
2070
2080 .NOD8 : CMP #9 : BNE NOD9
2090 \ type 9, absolute x   format &HHHH,X \
2100 LDA #ASC("&") : JSR OSASCI : LDA HC : JSR HEX
2110 LDA HB : JSR HEX : LDA #ASC(",") : JSR OSASCI
2120 LDA #ASC("X") : JSR OSASCI
2130 LDY #3 : JMP NDLINE
2140
2150 .NOD9  : CMP #&A : BNE NODA
2160 \ type A, absolute y   format &HHHH,Y \
2170 LDA #ASC("&") : JSR OSASCI : LDA HC : JSR HEX
2180 LDA HB : JSR HEX : LDA #ASC(",") : JSR OSASCI
2190 LDA #ASC("Y") : JSR OSASCI
2200 LDY #3 : JMP NDLINE
2210
2220 .NODA  : CMP #&B : BNE NODB
2230 \ type B, relative     format &HHHH \
2240 LDA #ASC("&") : JSR OSASCI
2250 \ for relative must calculate address from displacement \
2260 LDA HB : CMP #&7F : BCS BACK
2270 \ calculation for forward branch, leave lo-byte on stack \
2280 CLC : ADC LO : PHA : LDA #0 : ADC HI : CLC : BCC REL
2290 \ calculation for backward branch, leave lo-byte on stack \
2300 .BACK : EOR #255 : ADC #0 : STA &70 : LDA LO : SEC : SBC &70
2310 PHA : LDA HI : SBC #0
2320 \ output hi-byte then get lo-byte and print that \
2330 .REL : JSR HEX : PLA : JSR HEXSP
2340 LDY #4 : JMP NDLINE
```

```
2350
2360 .NODB : CMP #&C : BNE NODC
2370 \ type C, indirect     format (&HHHH) \
2380 LDA #ASC("(") : JSR OSASCI : LDA #ASC("&") : JSR OSASCI
2390 LDA HC : JSR HEX : LDA HB : JSR HEX
2400 LDA #ASC(")") : JSR OSASCI : LDY #3 : JMP NDLINE
2410
2420 .NODC : CMP #&D : BNE NODD
2430 \ type D, zero page y  format &HH,Y \
2440 LDA #ASC("&") : JSR OSASCI : LDA HB : JSR HEX
2450 LDA #ASC(",") : JSR OSASCI : LDA #ASC("Y") : JSR OSASCI
2460 LDY #5 : JMP NDLINE
2470
2480 .NODD : LDY #10
2490
2500 .NDLINE : LDA #ASC(" ") : JSR OSASCI : DEY : BNE NDLINE
2510 \ output alpha white control code \
2520 LDA #&87 : JSR OSASCI
2530 \ output ascii equivalents of bytes in instruction \
2540 LDX NUMB : LDY #0
2550 .DISPLOP LDA HA,Y : JSR CHOUT :INY : DEX : BNE DISPLOP
2560 \ if necessary pad with spaces to standard width \
2570 LDA #ASC(" ") : .PAD2 : JSR OSASCI : INY : CPY #4 : BNE PAD2
2580 \ output sufficient spaces to get ready for next line \
2590 LDX #5 : .PAD3 : JSR OSASCI : DEX : BNE PAD3
2600 \ if this was the first line then the address is where we \
2610 \ want to start next time if return is pressed \
2620 LDA DLINES : CMP #16 : BNE OVOLD
2630 \ so store it somewhere \
2640 LDA LO : STA OLO :  LDA HI : STA OHI
2650 \ keep doing lines until 16 done \
2660 .OVOLD : DEC DLINES : BEQ FINLIN : JMP LINLOP
2670 .FINLIN : RTS
2680
2690
2700 \ display routine calls either disassembler or dump \
2710 .DISPLAY : LDY #2 : LDX #15 : JSR SETAB
2720 \ update address display \
2730 LDA HI : JSR HEX : LDA LO : JSR HEXSP
2740 \ check whether Listing mode or not \
2750 LDA DISP : CMP #ASC("L") : BEQ DDISP
2760 \ Dump mode just shows contents of memory \
2770 JSR SHOW : RTS
2780 \ Listing mode produces disassembled display \
2790 .DDISP : JSR DIS : RTS
2800
2810
2820 \ show routine \
2830 .SHOW : LDX #(ST2 MOD 256)
2840 LDY #(ST2 DIV 256)
2850 \ ST2 gets rid of cursor and sets print position to (0,7) \
2860 JSR OUTPUT
2870 \ calculate byte at top so that active byte is central \
2880 LDA LO : AND #&F8 : SEC : SBC #64 : STA UP
2890 LDA HI : SBC #0 : STA STK
2900 \ find how many across to active byte \
2910 LDA LO : AND #7 : STA ACR
2920 \ for X=0 to 15 , address=address+8 \
2930 LDX #0 : .L4 : STX STK+1 : LDA #8 : CLC : ADC UP : STA UP
2940 LDA #0 : ADC STK : STA STK
2950 \ output address plus space \
2960 JSR HEX : LDA UP : JSR HEXSP : LDA #ASC(" ") : JSR OSASCI
```

```
2970 \ for XX=0 to 7 \
2980 LDX #0 : .L2 : STX STK+2 : TXA
2990 TAY
3000 \ output each byte across line \
3010 LDA (UP),Y : JSR HEXSP
3020 \ next XX \
3030 LDX STK+2 : INX : CPX #8 : BNE L2
3040 \ for XX=0 to 7 \
3050 LDX #0 : .L3 :STX STK+2 : TXA
3060 \ output each byte as ascii equivalent \
3070 TAY
3080 LDA (UP),Y : JSR CHOUT
3090 \ next XX \
3100 LDX STK+2 : INX : CPX #8 : BNE L3
3110 \ move on to next line \
3120 LDA #ASC(" ") : JSR OSASCI : JSR OSASCI
3130 \ next X \
3140 LDX STK+1 : INX : CPX #16 : BNE L4
3150 \ calculate position of active byte in display \
3160 LDY #14 : LDA ACR : ASL A : CLC : ADC ACR
3170 ADC #5 : STA STK+1 : TAX : JSR SETAB
3180 \ put an alpha green in front of it \
3190 LDA #&82 : JSR OSASCI
3200 LDA STK+1 : CLC : ADC #3 : TAX : LDY #14 : JSR SETAB
3210 \ put an alpha white after it \
3220 LDA #&87 : JSR OSASCI
3230 RTS
3240
3250
3260 \ chout routine outputs ascii equivalent of byte \
3270 .CHOUT : CMP #ASC(" ") : BCC DUF
3280 \ control codes or codes above &88 are not printed \
3290 CMP #&88 : BCS DUF
3300 \ delete is not printed \
3310 CMP #127 : BNE OK
3320 \ replace unprintables codes with a dot \
3330 .DUF : LDA #ASC(".")
3340 .OK : JSR OSASCI : RTS
3350
3360
3370 \ set tab position by printing ST3 with X,Y in it \
3380 .SETAB : STY ST3+2 : STX ST3+1
3390 LDX #(ST3 MOD 256) : LDY #(ST3 DIV 256)
3400 JSR OUTPUT : RTS
3410
3420
3430 \ keyin clears the buffer and waits for a key \
3440 .KEYIN : LDX #0 : LDA #21 : JSR OSBYTE
3450 JSR OSRDCH : BCS KEYERR : RTS
3460 \ if an error has occurred then reset cursor keys \
3470 .KEYERR : STA STK+1
3480 LDX #(ST6 MOD 256) : LDY #(ST6 DIV 256) : JSR CLI
3490 LDA STK+1 : CMP #&1B : BNE KERR
3500 \ acknowledge escape \
3510 LDA #&7E : JSR OSBYTE
3520 .KERR
3530 \ set the print position, reset the stack \
3540 LDX #0 : LDY #22 : JSR SETAB : LDX TEMPSTACK : TXS : BRK
3550 \ use break to print error message \
3560 ]
3570 $(P%+1)="End of DIS" : P%=P%+11
3580 [OPT OP
```

```
359Ø \ end of error marked by break \
36ØØ BRK
361Ø
362Ø
363Ø \ output a string of codes ending with an &FF \
364Ø .OUTPUT : STX &7Ø : STY &71
365Ø LDY #Ø
366Ø .LOOP : LDA (&7Ø),Y : CMP #&FF : BEQ OUTEND
367Ø JSR OSASCI : INY : BNE LOOP
368Ø .OUTEND : RTS
369Ø
37ØØ
371Ø \ store parameters in control block and use OSWORD \
372Ø \ with A=1 to get a string \
373Ø .STRIN : STA CONBLK+2 : STX CONBLK+3 : STY CONBLK+4
374Ø LDX #(ST5 MOD 256)
375Ø LDY #(ST5 DIV 256) : JSR OUTPUT
376Ø LDA #Ø : LDX #CONBLK : TAY : JSR OSWORD
377Ø BCS ESC1 : RTS
378Ø .ESC1 : LDA #&1B : JMP KEYERR
379Ø ]
38ØØ ST1=P%+1 : !ST1=&ØDØCØ716 : P%=P%+5
381Ø $P%=" BBC Disassembler     D Dump memory        "
382Ø $(P%+4Ø)=" H Hex addr. : ØØØØ  L Listing            "
383Ø $(P%+8Ø)="                     A Alter byte         "
384Ø $(P%+12Ø)="                     S String"
385Ø P%=P%+LEN($P%) : ?P%=&FF
386Ø ST2=P%+1 : !ST2=&ØØØØØ117 : ST2!4=Ø : P%=P%+9
387Ø !P%=&ØØ1FØØØØ : P%=P%+4 : !P%=&FFØ7 : P%=P%+2
388Ø ST3=P% : !P%=&ØØØØØØ1F : P%!4=&FFØØØØØØ : P%=P%+8
389Ø ST4=P% : !P%=&FF2Ø2Ø2Ø : P%=P%+4
39ØØ ST5=P% : !P%=&ØØØ1Ø117 : ST5!4=Ø : P%=P%+8
391Ø !P%=&FFØØØØØØ : P%=P%+4
392Ø ST6=P% : $ST6="FX4,Ø" : P%=P%+6
393Ø RESTORE
394Ø NUM=P% : FOR I=Ø TO 14 : READ N% : P%?I=N% : NEXT I
395Ø P%=P%+15
396Ø P%=(P% DIV 256)+1 : P%=P%*256
397Ø HASH=P% : TYPE=P%+256 : P%=P%+512 : STRING=P%
398Ø NEXT OP
399Ø FOR I%=Ø TO 255 STEP 4 : HASH!I%=Ø : TYPE!I%=Ø
     STRING!I%=Ø : NEXT I%
4ØØØ REPEAT
4Ø1Ø READ A$ : IF A$="*" THEN 4Ø5Ø
4Ø2Ø IF ASC(A$)=ASC("-") THEN I=ABS(VAL(A$)) : GOTO 4Ø1Ø
4Ø3Ø M=EVAL("&"+LEFT$(A$,1)) : MN=EVAL("&"+RIGHT$(A$,2))
4Ø4Ø HASH?MN=I : TYPE?MN=M
4Ø5Ø UNTIL A$="*"
4Ø6Ø A$="    ADC AND ASL BCC BCS BEQ BIT BMI BNE"
4Ø7Ø A$=A$+" BPL BRK BVC BVS CLC CLD CLI CLV CMP CPX"
4Ø8Ø A$=A$+" CPY DEC DEX DEY EOR INC INX INY JMP JSR"
4Ø9Ø A$=A$+" LDA LDX LDY LSR NOP ORA PHA PHP PLA PLP"
41ØØ A$=A$+" ROL ROR RTI RTS SBC SEC SED SEI STA STX"
411Ø A$=A$+" STY TAX TAY TSX TXA TXS TYA"
412Ø $STRING=A$
413Ø END

414Ø DATA1,2,3,2,1,1,2,2,2,3,3,2,3,2,1
415Ø DATA-1,169,26D,365,661,771,875,97D,A79
416Ø DATA-2,129,22D,325,621,731,835,93D,A39
417Ø DATA-3,2ØE,3Ø6,4ØA,816,91E
418Ø DATA-4,B9Ø
```

```
4190 DATA-5,BB0
4200 DATA-6,BF0
4210 DATA-7,22C,324
4220 DATA-8,B30
4230 DATA-9,BD0
4240 DATA-10,B10
4250 DATA-11,500
4260 DATA-12,B50
4270 DATA-13,B70
4280 DATA-14,518
4290 DATA-15,5D8
4300 DATA-16,558
4310 DATA-17,5B8
4320 DATA-18,1C9,2CD,3C5,6C1,7D1,8D5,9DD,AD9
4330 DATA-19,1E0,2EC,3E4
4340 DATA-20,1C0,2CC,3C4
4350 DATA-21,2CE,3C6,7D6,9DE
4360 DATA-22,5CA
4370 DATA-23,588
4380 DATA-24,149,24D,345,641,751,855,95D,A59
4390 DATA-25,2EE,3E6,7F6,9FE
4400 DATA-26,5E8
4410 DATA-27,5C8
4420 DATA-28,24C,C6C
4430 DATA-29,220
4440 DATA-30,1A9,2AD,3A5,6A1,7B1,8B5,9BD,AB9
4450 DATA-31,1A2,2AE,3A6,ABE,DB6
4460 DATA-32,1A0,2AC,3A4,8B4,9BC
4470 DATA-33,24E,346,44A,856,95E
4480 DATA-34,5EA
4490 DATA-35,109,20D,305,601,711,815,91D,A19
4500 DATA-36,548
4510 DATA-37,508
4520 DATA-38,568
4530 DATA-39,528
4540 DATA-40,22E,326,42A,836,93E
4550 DATA-41,26E,366,46A,876,97E
4560 DATA-42,540
4570 DATA-43,560
4580 DATA-44,1E9,2ED,3E5,6E1,7F1,8F5,9FD,AF9
4590 DATA-45,538
4600 DATA-46,5F8
4610 DATA-47,578
4620 DATA-48,28D,385,681,791,895,99D,A99
4630 DATA-49,28E,386,D96
4640 DATA-50,28C,384,894
4650 DATA-51,5AA
4660 DATA-52,5A8
4670 DATA-53,5BA
4680 DATA-54,58A
4690 DATA-55,59A
4700 DATA-56,598,*
```

**The Disassembler**

It is often more reliable to do the job of rescuing programs by hand but it is always useful to have a disassembler that gives a convenient way of examining the memory and altering it. Running listing 14.1 creates a machine-code version of the disassembler program and stores it, starting at the location given by variable P% (line 80), which we set at &7000. It also stores this code in a file called DIS. You can run the code directly by typing CALL &7000 or by typing *DIS which loads the code from backing store and runs it.

The micro immediately switches to teletext mode and displays a simple menu (coloured blue), the hexadecimal address of the *currently active byte* (in green) and a *dump* (in white). This dump is in the standard format generated by the *DUMP command of the disk filing system. It shows the contents of 128 consecutive locations as 16 rows, each row containing (a) an address, (b) the contents of eight consecutive bytes of memory and (c) the characters equivalent to these bytes when treated as ASCII codes (a dot denotes an unprintable code). The address, which is always a multiple of 8, is the location of the first byte in the row. The currently active byte is coloured green and appears in the middle of the dump. We can return to the dump at any time by typing D.

The currently active byte can be changed by typing H, which places a flashing cursor on the screen, thus signifying a request for four hexadecimal digits (it must be exactly four). A new dump centred at this new byte is then displayed. Your can also change the active byte via the cursor keys; the screen scrolls where necessary to keep the active byte in the middle of the screen.

You can alter the value of the currently active byte (and the equivalent ASCII character) by typing A followed by two hexadecimal digits, or by typing S which allows you to replace the ASCII dump with a new string; naturally the machine makes the equivalent alterations to the bytes.

Option L changes the machine code into assembler mnemonics and gives a listing of 16 assembly codes; the code for the currently active byte is at the top of the screen. Immediately the currently active byte is redefined to be the byte that follows the last instruction that was displayed on the screen. Type RETURN and the code that contains this byte scrolls up on to the screen and the currently active byte is changed to one byte after the last code displayed. Typing L again displays the code that contains the currently active byte at the top of the screen and then changes its values in the same way as before so that it is just off the screen. H can be used to alter the currently active byte directly. If the currently active byte is not the first byte of a valid assembler instruction then three light-blue dashes are displayed when it is brought on to the screen. The locations that start at &7800 hold the table of mnemonics that are used by the List option of the disassembler. Each mnemonic is stored as four bytes, one for a colour code and three for the mnemonic characters. JMP has been set to red, JSR to green, branching instructions to yellow, BRK to purple, invalid bytes and NOP to light blue, RTI and RTS to dark blue. This allows us to colour code the mnemonics and makes it easy for us to recognise these codes when Listed. You can change these colour codes if you wish by using the disassembler – you can even add flash.

*Exercise 14.1*
Experiment with this disassembler. LOAD a simple BASIC program at PAGE = &1900 and then type *DIS (having previously RUN listing 14.1). Set the currently active byte to &1900 and read through the BASIC program byte by byte to see how such a program is stored. Also see the sample input at the end of the chapter.

## The Structure of BASIC Programs

The previous exercise will have raised a number of questions about the way the BBC microcomputer stores BASIC programs. You will have noticed that the programs are stored line by line, starting with a cursor-return code (13) at location PAGE. Each line starts with the line number (16 bits) which takes up two locations, the hi-byte followed by the lo-byte; then comes a description of the line as a sequence of characters or TOKENs (see user guide) each of which takes up one byte, and finally a cursor-return (13). Apart from the line number all other numeric values are stored in a standard lo-hi format.

*Example 14.1*
To illustrate this idea we enter the trivial program that consists of a single line 10 REM and use the indirection operator '?'. If we type

```
PRINT ? PAGE, ? (PAGE + 1), ? (PAGE + 2)
```

we shall see that the values 13, 0 and 10 are stored in locations PAGE, PAGE + 1 and PAGE + 2 respectively. If we replace line 10 with another trivial statement, 34 REM, we shall see that the representation of this new number is now stored in the latter two locations.

The third byte for a line gives the length of the present line (the number of bytes including the line number, the third byte itself, the codes for the line and the final cursor-return) and it can be used to find the start of the next program line without traversing the whole of the present line. Whenever a reference is made to another line (for example, in a GOTO or THEN) then this line number is not stored directly but in a devious way. It is given as four bytes: a token &8D to indicate a reference and three 8-bit numbers which are manipulated to give the required line number. The end of a program is indicated by ASCII 255 (&FF) following the ASCII 13 of the final line.

We can get the operating system to print out the equivalent keyword for each token (or a character if not a token) by calling the routine at &B53A in the

ROM which accesses a table stored after location &806D. You should use the disassembler to investigate this table.

## A Search/Replace and Listing Program

We have all written programs to which on completion we would have preferred that different variable names had been given. Also when debugging a program it is difficult to locate the occurrence of specific variables. By using the information about how BASIC programs are stored we can write a program (listing 14.2) that will list any program, including itself. It also searches out text strings in the program and if required replaces them with alternative strings.

*Listing 14.2*

```
 10 MODE 7
 20 INPUT"SEARCH ",A$ : SEARCH=(A$<>"")
 30 IF NOT SEARCH THEN REPLACE=FALSE : GOTO 50
 40 INPUT"REPLACE ",B$ : REPLACE=(B$<>"")
 49 REM use BASIC ROM routine to get keywords from tokens
 50 IF ?&8015=49 THEN DECRUNCH=&B53A ELSE DECRUNCH=&B50E
 60 INPUT"LOCATION OF PROGRAM ",P$
 70 IF LEFT$(P$,1)="&" THEN P%=EVAL(P$) ELSE P%=VAL(P$)
 79 REM assume disk system is used
 80 IF P%=0 THEN P%=&1900
 89 REM find end of program
 90 Q%=P% : REPEAT : Q%=Q%+1 : UNTIL ?Q%=&FF
 99 REM if first byte of line number is 255 then stop
100 P%=P%+1 : I=?P% : IF I=255 THEN END
110 P%=P%+1 : I=I*256+?P%
119 REM pad line number with blanks for printing
120 C$=STR$(I) : IF LEN C$<6 THEN REPEAT C$=" "+C$ : UNTIL LEN C$=6
130 C$=C$+" " : PRINTC$;
140 P%=P%+1
149 REM L% points to byte where lines length is stored
150 L%=P%
159 REM set flag to decide whether characters are inside quotes
160 QUOTE=FALSE
169 REM list each token of line
170 REPEAT
180 P%=P%+1
190 A%=?P% : PROClist
200 UNTIL P%=L%+?L%-3
210 PRINT
220 GOTO100

300 REM list
310 DEF PROClist
319 REM first section deals with line numbers stored in code
320 IF A%<>&8D THEN 390
330 A%=?(P%+1)*4 : B%=?(P%+2) : C%=?(P%+3)
340 S%=A% AND &C0 : B%=B% EOR S%
350 S%=(A%*4) AND &C0 : C%=C% EOR S%
360 PRINT"";B%+C%*256;
370 P%=P%+3
380 ENDPROC
389 REM deal with all other tokens
```

```
390 T$=LEFT$($P%,LEN(A$))
399 REM highlight string if searching
400 IF T$=A$ AND SEARCH AND NOT REPLACE THEN VDU 133 :
    : PROCout(A$) : VDU 135 : P%=P%+LEN(A$)-1 : ENDPROC
409 REM replace string if it isn't inside quotes
410 IF T$=A$ AND REPLACE AND NOT QUOTE THEN PROCreplace : ENDPROC
419 REM if quote symbol encountered reverse quotes flag
420 IF A%=&22 THEN QUOTE=NOT QUOTE
429 REM if character is inside quotes just print it out else
        use decrunch routine
430 IF QUOTE THEN VDU A% ELSE CALL DECRUNCH
440 ENDPROC

500 REM replace
510 DEF PROCreplace
519 REM if the strings are different lengths the rest of the
        program must be moved
520 DIFF=LEN A$-LEN B$
530 IF DIFF>0 THEN PROCdown(DIFF,P%)
540 IF DIFF<0 THEN PROCup(DIFF,P%)
549 REM temporarily save the byte that is overwritten
        by the carriage return
550 T%=?(P%+LEN B$)
559 REM replace string and restore following byte
560 $P%=B$ : ?(P%+LEN B$)=T%
570 A%=0:PROCout(B$):P%=P%+LEN(B$)-1
580 ENDPROC

600 REM down
610 DEF PROCdown(N%,M%)
619 REM move program from M% to end down by N% bytes
620 FOR I%=M% TO Q%
630 ?I%=I%?N%
640 NEXT I%
649 REM change length of current line and whole program
650 ?L%=?L%-N% : Q%=Q%-N%
660 ENDPROC

700 REM up
710 DEF PROCup(N%,M%)
719 REM move program from M% to end up by N% bytes
720 N%=ABS(N%)
730 FOR I%=Q% TO M% STEP -1
740 N%?I%=?I%
750 NEXT I%
759 REM change length of current line and whole program
760 ?L%=?L%+N% : Q%=Q%+N%
770 ENDPROC

800 REM out
810 DEF PROCout(C$)
820 LOCAL I%
829 REM output a string with decrunch
830 FOR I%=1 TO LEN(C$)
840 A%=ASC(MID$(C$,I%,1)) :  CALL DECRUNCH
850 NEXT I%
860 ENDPROC
```

You must load the program that you are investigating into the store at &1900 and then load listing 14.2 into the store somewhat above it (use TOP to find the location of the end of your first program). Now RUN the search program, which will first ask you for a search string. Typing a RETURN means you wish only to list the program. If you do specify a search string it will ask you for a replacement string. You can search/replace BASIC keywords by redefining the soft keys with their corresponding token and then entering them. If you RETURN without a replacement it will place a purple code in front of the search string. The listing then follows, starting at a specified location (RETURN means &1900). You can then SAVE the program in its adjusted form.

***Example 14.2***
Add the line

```
315 IF A% = 58 THEN PRINT'SPC(7);: ENDPROC
```

to the search program and repeat the above procedure. Note that now each individual BASIC statement of your program appears on a new line of a listing that is produced by this program.

**Scrolling**

In chapter 13 we saw the need for machine-code routines for rapid transfer of data (the 'movie'). BASIC is just not fast enough to be of any practical use where such animation is required. In any mode other than mode 7 it takes tens of seconds to reorganise the screen memory. As an example we give both a BASIC and assembly language program (listings 14.3 and 14.4) for scrolling the whole screen in (mode 0) character-size blocks in any of eight directions (up, down, left, right, or diagonally up + left, down + left, up + right, down + right). The direction of movement is passed to the routine via the X-register from the variable X%, and the size of the block to be moved is defined by the four values in locations &70 to &73. In this implementation of software scrolling a line that goes off the top of the screen will reappear on the bottom (and vice versa) and a line that goes off one edge will reappear on the other side, that is we imagine the screen as a torus.

Compare the time taken to run the BASIC procedure with that for the machine-code routine. You will find the machine code is hundreds of times faster. Even so it is often useful to write your routines first in BASIC in order to check that your algorithm works before embarking on the assembly language stage of development.

*Listing 14.3* D.BASCROL

```
 10 REM BASIC version of scroll
 20 MODE 2 : HIMEM=&2D00
 30 HI=&2D00 : TEMP=&2D80
 40 PROCtable
 50 FOR I=1 TO 31 : FOR J=1 TO 20 : VDU ((I+J)MOD 27)+63 : NEXT J,I
 59 REM check cursor keys
 60 REPEAT
 70 IF INKEY(-122) THEN PROCscroll(1)
 80 IF INKEY(-58) THEN PROCscroll(2)
 90 IF INKEY(-26) THEN PROCscroll(3)
100 IF INKEY(-42) THEN PROCscroll(4)
110 UNTIL FALSE
120 END

200 REM scroll
210 DEF PROCscroll(X)
220 IF X=1 THEN PROCright
230 IF X=2 THEN PROCup
240 IF X=3 THEN PROCleft
250 IF X=4 THEN PROCdown
260 ENDPROC

300 REM left
310 DEF PROCleft
319 REM for each row save the first eight bytes
320 FOR I%=0 TO 31
330 ADT=TEMP
340 ADF=(HI?I%)*256+(I% MOD 2)*&80
350 PROCtran(8)
359 REM then move the transfer the rest to the left
360 ADT=ADF : ADF=ADT+8
370 PROCtran(632)
380 ADF=TEMP
389 REM then retrieve the first eight bytes at the end of the row
390 ADT=HI?I%*256+(I% MOD 2)*&80+632
400 PROCtran(8)
410 NEXT I%
420 ENDPROC

500 REM up
510 DEF PROCup
519 REM store the whole top row
520 ADT=TEMP
530 ADF=(HI?0)*256
540 PROCtran(640)
549 REM set the address-to pointer to the current row
        and the address-from pointer to the next row
550 FOR I%=0 TO 30
560 ADT=(HI?I%)*256+(I% MOD 2)*&80
570 N%=I%+1
580 ADF=(HI?N%)*256+(N% MOD 2)*&80
589 REM transfer a whole row
590 PROCtran(640)
600 NEXT I%
609 REM retrieve the top row from temporary store to the bottom
610 ADF=TEMP
620 ADT=(HI?31)*256+&80
630 PROCtran(640)
640 ENDPROC
```

```
 700 REM down
 710 DEF PROCdown
 719 REM save bottom row
 720 ADT=TEMP
 730 ADF=(HI?31)*256+&80
 740 PROCtran(640)
 749 REM transfer current row to the row below
 750 FOR I%=30 TO 0 STEP -1
 760 ADF=(HI?I%)*256+(I% MOD 2)*&80
 770 N%=I%+1
 780 ADT=(HI?N%)*256+(N% MOD 2)*&80
 790 PROCtran(640)
 800 NEXT I%
 809 REM retrieve row for top
 810 ADF=TEMP
 820 ADT=(HI?0)*256
 830 PROCtran(640)
 840 ENDPROC

 900 REM right
 910 DEF PROCright
 920 FOR I%=0 TO 31
 929 REM for each row save the final eight bytes
 930 ADT=TEMP
 940 ADF=(HI?I%)*256+(I% MOD 2)*&80+632
 950 PROCtran(8)
 959 REM set a pointer to the start of the row
 960 TT=(HI?I%)*256+(I% MOD 2)*&80
 969 REM for each block of eight bytes from right to left
         move the block to the right
 970 FOR K%=78 TO 0 STEP -1
 980 ADF=TT+8*K%
 990 ADT=ADF+8
1000 PROCtran(8)
1010 NEXT K%
1019 REM retrieve the bytes for the start of the line
1020 ADT=TT
1030 ADF=TEMP
1040 PROCtran(8)
1050 NEXT I%
1060 ENDPROC

1100 REM tran
1110 DEF PROCtran(A)
1119 REM move A bytes from pointer ADF to pointer ADT
1120 FOR J%=0 TO A-1
1130 ADT?J%=ADF?J%
1140 NEXT J%
1150 ENDPROC

1200 REM table
1210 DEF PROCtable
1219 REM construct table of hibytes of addresses for screen
1220 M%=&3000
1230 FOR I%=0 TO 31
1240 M=M%+640*I%
1250 HI?I%=M DIV 256
1260 NEXT I%
1270 ENDPROC
```

*Listing 14.4* D.MCSCROL

```
 1Ø REM M/C code version of scroll
 2Ø MODE 2 : HIMEM=&2AØØ
 3Ø HI=&2DØØ : TEMP=&2D8Ø
 4Ø PROCtable : PROCassemble
 5Ø FOR I=1 TO 31 : FOR J=1 TO 2Ø : VDU ((I+J)MOD 27)+63
    : NEXT J : NEXT I
 59 REM check cursor keys
 6Ø REPEAT
 7Ø IF INKEY(-122) THEN A%=1 : CALL scroll
 8Ø IF INKEY(-58) THEN A%=2 : CALL scroll
 9Ø IF INKEY(-26) THEN A%=3 : CALL scroll
1ØØ IF INKEY(-42) THEN A%=4 : CALL scroll
11Ø UNTIL FALSE
12Ø END

2ØØ REM assemble
21Ø DEF PROCassemble
22Ø VDU 22,7,14
23Ø ADFL=&7Ø : ADFH=&71
24Ø ADTL=&72 : ADTH=&73
25Ø TTL=&74 : TTH=&75
26Ø TAL=&76 : TAH=&77
27Ø FOR I%=Ø TO 3 STEP 3
28Ø P%=&2AØØ
29Ø [ OPT I%
3ØØ \ scroll routine \
31Ø
32Ø .scroll
33Ø CMP #1 : BNE NO1 : JSR right : RTS
34Ø .NO1
35Ø CMP #2 : BNE NO2 : JSR up : RTS
36Ø .NO2
37Ø CMP #3 : BNE NO3 : JSR left : RTS
38Ø .NO3
39Ø CMP #4 : BNE NO4 : JSR down
4ØØ .NO4
41Ø RTS
42Ø
43Ø
44Ø \ left routine \
45Ø
46Ø .left
47Ø LDA #Ø
48Ø .LOOP1 : PHA
49Ø LDA #(TEMP MOD 256) : STA ADTL : LDA #(TEMP DIV 256) : STA ADTH
5ØØ PLA : PHA : JSR calc
51Ø LDA TAL : STA ADFL : LDA TAH : STA ADFH
52Ø LDA #Ø : LDX #8 : JSR tran
53Ø LDA ADFL : STA ADTL : LDA ADFH : STA ADTH
54Ø LDA ADTL : CLC : ADC #8 : STA ADFL
55Ø LDA #2 : LDX #12Ø : JSR tran
56Ø LDA #(TEMP MOD 256) : STA ADFL : LDA #(TEMP DIV 256) : STA ADFH
57Ø PLA : PHA : JSR calc
58Ø LDA TAL : CLC : ADC #12Ø : STA ADTL : LDA TAH : ADC #2 : STA ADTH
59Ø LDA #Ø : LDX #8 : JSR tran
6ØØ PLA : CLC : ADC #1 : CMP #32 : BNE LOOP1
61Ø RTS
62Ø
```

```
630
640 \ up routine \
650
660 .up
670 LDA #(TEMP MOD 256) : STA ADTL : LDA #(TEMP DIV 256) : STA ADTH
680 LDA HI : STA ADFH : LDA#0 : STA ADFL
690 LDA #2 : LDX #128 : JSR tran
700 LDA #0
710 .LOOPU1 : PHA
720 JSR calc : LDA TAL : STA ADTL : LDA TAH : STA ADTH
730 PLA : PHA : CLC : ADC #1
740 JSR calc : LDA TAL : STA ADFL : LDA TAH : STA ADFH
750 LDA #2: LDX #128 : JSR tran
760 PLA : CLC : ADC#1 : CMP #31 : BNE LOOPU1
770 LDA #(TEMP MOD 256) : STA ADFL : LDA #(TEMP DIV 256) : STA ADFH
780 LDX #31 : LDA HI,X : STA ADTH : LDA #&80 : STA ADTL
790 LDA #2: LDX #128 : JSR tran
800 RTS
810
820
830 \ down routine \
840
850 .down
860 LDA #(TEMP MOD 256) : STA ADTL : LDA #(TEMP DIV 256) : STA ADTH
870 LDX #31 : LDA HI,X : STA ADFH : LDA #&80 : STA ADFL
880 LDA #2: LDX #128 : JSR tran
890 LDA #30
900 .LOOPD1 : PHA
910 JSR calc : LDA TAL : STA ADFL : LDA TAH : STA ADFH
920 PLA : PHA : CLC : ADC #1 : JSR calc
930 LDA TAL : STA ADTL : LDA TAH : STA ADTH
940 LDA #2: LDX #128 : JSR tran
950 PLA : SEC : SBC #1 : BPL LOOPD1
960 LDA #(TEMP MOD 256) : STA ADFL : LDA #(TEMP DIV 256) : STA ADFH
970 LDA HI : STA ADTH : LDA #0 : STA ADTL
980 LDA #2 : LDX #128 : JSR tran
990 RTS
1000
1010
1020 \ right routine \
1030
1040 .right
1050 LDA #0
1060 .LOOPR1 : PHA
1070 LDA #(TEMP MOD 256) : STA ADTL : LDA #(TEMP DIV 256) : STA ADTH
1080 PLA : PHA : JSR calc
1090 LDA TAL : CLC : ADC #120 : STA ADFL : LDA TAH : ADC #2 : STA ADFH
1100 LDA #0 : LDX #8 : JSR tran
1110 LDA #0
1120 .LOOPR2 : PHA
1130 LDA ADFL: STA ADTL : SEC : SBC #8 : STA ADFL : LDA ADFH
     : STA ADTH : SBC #0 : STA ADFH
1140 LDA #0 : LDX #8 : JSR tran
1150 PLA : CLC : ADC #1 : CMP #79: BNE LOOPR2
1160 LDA TAL : STA ADTL : LDA TAH : STA ADTH
1170 LDA #(TEMP MOD 256) : STA ADFL : LDA #(TEMP DIV 256) : STA ADFH
1180 LDA #0 : LDX #8 : JSR tran
1190 PLA : CLC : ADC #1 : CMP #32 : BNE LOOPR1
1200 RTS
1210
```

```
1220
1230 \ tran routine \
1240
1250 .tran
1260 TAY : TXA : PHA : TYA : BEQ NOHI
1270 .LOOPT1
1280 PHA : LDY #0
1290 .LOOPT2
1300 LDA (ADFL),Y
1310 STA (ADTL),Y
1320 INY : BNE LOOPT2
1330 INC ADTH : INC ADFH
1340 PLA : SEC : SBC #1 : BNE LOOPT1
1350 .NOHI : PLA : TAX
1360 .LOOPT3
1370 LDA (ADFL),Y
1380 STA (ADTL),Y
1390 INY : DEX : BNE LOOPT3
1400 RTS
1410
1420
1430 \ calc routine performs \
1440 \ TA=(HI?A%)*256+(A% MOD 2)*&80 \
1450
1460 .calc
1470 TAX : LDA HI,X : STA TAH
1480 TXA : AND #1 : CLC : ROR A : ROR A : STA TAL
1490 RTS
1500 ]
1510 NEXT I%
1520 VDU 22,2
1530 ENDPROC

1600 REM table
1610 DEF PROCtable
1619 REM construct table of hibytes of addresses for screen
1620 M%=&3000
1630 FOR I%=0 TO 31
1640 M=M%+640*I%
1650 HI?I%=M DIV 256
1660 NEXT I%
1670 ENDPROC
```

*Exercise 14.2*
Write a BASIC program that specifies a fixed window on the screen and then software scrolls the contents of that window as above, while the outside of the window stays fixed.

*Animation: hardware scrolling*
Software scrolling can only achieve fast animation on relatively small areas. To move large areas of screen about we need to use hardware scrolling. The simplest way to get this without learning the complexities of programming the 6845 CRT display controller is to force the operating system to scroll the screen for you. This is done by moving the text cursor to either the top or bottom of the screen and by printing the appropriate control code (control K or control J) to force

the cursor off the screen and thus to initiate a scroll. We use this method in a simple game (listing 14.5). The object of the game is to catch randomly appearing apples in an ever-increasing shower of bricks. If a brick hits your hand then the game is over.

To get the speed of animation we hardware scroll the whole screen and then PRINT (or perhaps software scroll) stationary text and characters back in position. Machine code is needed for more complicated tasks and this requires a great deal more thought and study. A good book on the subject and preferably specifically written for the BBC Micro should be consulted; see, for example, Birnbaum (1982) and Zaks (1978).

*Listing 14.5*

```
 10 ENVELOPE 1,2,5,10,15,5,3,1,64,4,0,-126,100,126
 20 MODE 5
 29 REM get rid of cursor and define characters for game
 30 VDU 23,1,0;0;0;0;0;
 40 VDU 23,128,&FF,&BD,&C3,&DB,&DB,&C3,&BD,&FF
 50 VDU 23,129,&18,&10,&7C,&FE,&FE,&FE,&7C,&38
 60 VDU 23,130,&10,&54,&55,&D5,&FF,&FE,&7C,&3C
 70 VDU 19,3,6,0,0,0 : VDU 19,2,2,0,0,0
 79 REM reset keyboard to give better response
 80 *FX4,1
 90 *FX11,15
100 *FX12,13
110 X=10
120 COLOUR 3 : PRINT TAB(X,20);: VDU 130
130 DEAD=FALSE : C=0 : SCORE=0
140 REPEAT
150 HARD=(SCORE DIV 20)
160 COLOUR1
169 REM put some bricks on top row
170 FOR I%=1 TO RND(HARD)
180 PRINT TAB(RND(20)-1,0);: VDU 128
190 NEXT I%
200 COLOUR 2
209 REM add an apple
210 PRINT TAB(RND(20)-1,0);: VDU 129
220 NX=X
229 REM check for left or right cursor
230 A$=INKEY$(0)
240 IF ASC(A$)=&88 AND X>0 THEN NX=X-1
250 IF ASC(A$)=&89 AND X<19 THEN NX=X+1
259 REM erase hand before scrolling
260 PRINT TAB(X,20);" ";
269 REM force scroll down with home and cursor up
270 VDU 26,11
279 REM prepare to reprint hand
280 X=NX : PRINT TAB(X,20);
289 REM read character at hands new position
290 A%=135 : C=(USR(&FFF4) DIV &FF) AND &FF
299 REM was it a brick
300 IF C=55 THEN DEAD=TRUE
309 REM score one for an apple
310 IF C=56 THEN SCORE=SCORE+1 : SOUND 1,1,60,4
320 COLOUR 3 : IF NOT DEAD THEN VDU 130
330 PRINT TAB(0,31);"SCORE ";SCORE;
340 T=TIME : REPEAT UNTIL TIME>T+4
```

```
350 UNTIL DEAD
359 REM crunching noise
360 FOR I%=1 TO 6 : SOUND 0,-15+I%*2,4,3 : NEXT I%
369 REM use text window to display game over message
370 VDU 28,4,10,16,6
380 COLOUR 129 : CLS : COLOUR 3
390 PRINT''"  GAME OVER"
399 REM return keyboard to normal
400 *FX4,0
410 *FX12,0
420 *FX15,1
430 COLOUR 128 : COLOUR 2
440 VDU 26 : END
```

## Unusual Displays

The BBC micro is a very sophisticated machine that allows you to perform complicated manipulations on the screen. It would be impossible to give all the techniques, so to give you a flavour we introduce two such methods: (a) changing the print vector, and (b) synchronous display.

*(a) Changing the print vector*

The print vector (locations &20E and &20F) contains the address of that section of the PRINT routine that places characters on the screen. We can write our own routine and let the print vector refer to it instead. Subsequent calls to PRINT inside a BASIC program will use the revised output routine. Take the simple example that is given in listing 14.6. If you run this program it will place a machine-code routine which prints a character and two backspace codes at location &C00. Soft key 1 is defined to change the print vector to this location, soft key 0 returns it to normal. If you now load another program and LIST it, having pressed f1, you will see that the listing appears backwards. Press f0 and LIST and a normal listing appears.

### *Exercise 14.3*

You can adjust the 'prynt' routine of chapter 5 and make it available to PRINT by changing the print vector. Note that 'prynt' could draw only simple strings. By using this adjusted method quite complex strings of multi-coloured characters can be printed, with all the complex evaluation being done by the BASIC PRINT statement before it calls your new output routine.

*(b) Synchronous display*

The television display is completely redrawn every 1/50th of a second (1/60th in the U.S.A.). *FX19 is used to wait until the start of the next frame, and thus gives us a method of starting instructions at a fixed time relative to each refresh of the display. If we change the logical-actual colour relationship partway through the drawing of the display, then for that frame only the top part of the screen

*Listing 14.6*

```
 1Ø FOR I=Ø TO 3 STEP 3
 2Ø OUTPUT=!&2ØE AND &FFFF
 3Ø P%=&CØØ
 4Ø [OPT I
 5Ø CMP #1Ø : BNE OD : JSR OUTPUT
 6Ø .OD
 7Ø CMP #32 : BCC OF
 8Ø JSR OUTPUT
 9Ø LDA #8 : JSR OUTPUT
1ØØ LDA #8
11Ø .OF
12Ø JSR OUTPUT
13Ø RTS
14Ø ]
15Ø NEXT I
159 REM f1 changes vector to routine
16Ø *KEY1?&2ØE=Ø : ?&2ØF=&C|M
169 REM fØ changes vector back
17Ø O%=OUTPUT DIV 256 : P%=OUTPUT MOD 256
18Ø *KEYØ?&2ØE=P% : ?&2ØF=O%|M
```

will show one actual colour while the remainder of the screen shows another. Obviously we could use *FX19 to wait for the start of the next frame and repeat the process. Provided that we keep repeating the same actions, this will result in the display of a multi-colour steady(ish!) picture, even in mode 0! Listing 14.7 draws a simple picture in mode 0 and then redefines the background colour continuously. There is a little flickering at the junctions of the colours so we cover this up by placing blocks of foreground colour across the screen. Type any key and the coloured bands move because we have interrupted the time balance.

*Listing 14.7*

```
 1Ø MODE Ø
 2Ø A%=19 : Z%=Ø
 3Ø GOSUB 13Ø
 4Ø GCOLØ,1
 5Ø FOR Y=75 TO 1Ø25 STEP 165
 6Ø MOVE Ø,Y : MOVE Ø,4Ø+Y
 7Ø PLOT 85,128Ø,Y : PLOT 85,128Ø,4Ø+Y
 8Ø NEXT Y
 9Ø REPEAT
1ØØ FOR I%=1 TO 6 : VDU A%,Z%,I%,Z%,Z%,Z% : NEXT I%
11Ø *FX19
12Ø UNTIL FALSE
129 REM draw lace curtains
13Ø FOR I=Ø TO 128Ø STEP 16
14Ø MOVE Ø,I : DRAW 128Ø-I,Ø
15Ø MOVE 128Ø,I : DRAW 128Ø-I,1Ø24
16Ø MOVE Ø,1Ø24-I : DRAW 128Ø-I,1Ø24
17Ø MOVE 128Ø,1Ø24-I : DRAW 128Ø-I,Ø
18Ø NEXT I
19Ø RETURN
```

**Complete Programs**

Sample input will be underlined.

I Listing 14.1. RUN the program and then CALL &7000. Then type H and 8000 which will bring you to the start of the BASIC ROM. Now H and 7000 will bring you to the start of the disassembler. H and 7C00 is the start of the mode 7 screen. Type S and What's up Doc?. Type H, 78DC, which will get you into the table that holds mnemonics, specifically code TXS. A and 81 will change the value of the currently active byte from 87 to 81. Now type H and 7000 and List through the program to locate TXS code which will be in red.

II Listing 14.2. First load any program (such as listing 13.2) at PAGE = &1900. Then load listing 14.2 at PAGE = &3000 and RUN. Try the following sample data.

Search?RETURN, , location?RETURN

Search?J , replace?RETURN, location?&1900

Search?J , replace?K , location?&1900

III Listing 14.3 or 14.4. RUN and use the cursor keys to scroll the screen.

IV Listing 14.5. The apple-catching game. RUN to start, move the 'hand' left or right by means of the cursor keys.

V Listing 14.6. RUN, press f1 and LIST, then f0 and LIST.

VI Listing 14.7. Type any key.

# 15 A Worked Example of a Video Game

In this chapter we examine the use of both BASIC and Assembler programming for animated video games. In general games are expensive, and the players interest can be short-lived. If players can achieve a reasonable result themselves then most would prefer to write their own simple video games, and spend their money only on good-quality sophisticated games. Tape cassette 2 contains an extensive example of the sort of game that most competent programmers can reasonably expect to write, without going to the extreme of putting the whole game into machine code. The game itself, *RON the ROBOT in the WASTE of TYME*, is a typical 'shoot-em up' game; however the techniques we discuss here could just as easily be applied to 'bat and ball' (such as TENNIS) or 'tactical' games (such as PAC-MAN). For you to make the most of the explanations in this chapter we advise you to get the companion cassette tapes, and LOAD and RUN these program listings.

The most important part of writing any game is the planning. It is helpful to draw a plan of the intended screen on graph-paper: sketch in the proposed size and positions of fixed objects (the background) and the areas to be traversed by moving objects (the foreground). Both background and foreground are usually composed of user-defined characters. This should fix a scale for the objects and will give a general impression of the final game. It is worth spending some time at this stage to ensure that the proposed action can actually fit into the graphics area. Once you have decided on a screen layout you must create the multi-coloured objects for the foreground and the background by using the CHARACTER GENERATOR 2 of chapter 5. Before writing any complex code for moving these characters about you must first place them on the screen, both singly and in groups, in order to see what impression they make. We saw that the fastest way of putting a large number of characters on the screen is to 'prynt' them (see chapter 5). In our program we shall adjust 'prynt' so that it draws strings of characters down the screen.

*Exercise 15.1*
Alter the CHARACTER GENERATOR 2 program to allow characters to be defined in neighbouring blocks of two or four, which will allow compound shapes to be constructed with ease. This option will need the INPUT of two

or four ASCII codes to tell the program where to store the multiple character data.

Always conceive and write your game programs as modules. Such subtasks can be programmed separately either in BASIC or directly in assembly code, and tested individually before they are combined into larger modules or the final program. Speed is the essence, so that most of the BASIC procedures should be translated into machine code for the final version of the game. There are, however, some sections of the game that do not need speed, such as any explanatory text before the game starts and some initialisation processes. These can be left in BASIC.

Since we are aiming at speed of execution we must make all routines as explicit as possible. We calculate every possible value at the programming stage or by a previously run initialising program. The barest minimum of computation should be done while the game is being played.

One important technique for minimising the calculation, which we use in the example program, is the *cascade* or *multiple entry point* method. We write cascade routines which are called by a pointer, each cascade being made up of separate sections. Only one section is entered per execution of the routine. Inside the routine the pointer may be changed so that with the next entry a different section is obeyed. This continues with the pointer usually moving down through the sections of the cascade until it reaches the bottom, where it will usually be reset to the top. Such cascades are normally implemented by GOSUB with variable labels in BASIC, or as indirect jumps or conditional branching statements in assembly language. Normally this technique is used on several cascades which are called from within a loop. This loop describes the major tasks needed in playing the game. It gives us the ability to carry on different processes in an interwoven yet independent manner. Apparent parallelism of this sort is essential for games, where independent events may be following complicated courses. Effectively the program operates on two or more routines simultaneously, with one section only from each cascade being executed each time through the loop.

Consider the following two simple programs run in mode 7, which perform independent functions. Listing 15.1 waits until a key is pressed and then shoots a point across the screen. Listing 15.2 continuously moves a cross up the screen in a zig-zag pattern. Both programs use the fast animation techniques that are found in the game that follows, so it is necessary to slow them down with the *FX,19 command (except on OS 0.1) and REPEAT loops. Excess speed is sometimes a problem in assembler programs, but only when programs are very simple. We combine these two programs into a simple loop of cascades. We set pointers ('cross' and 'point') to the top of the cascades and control entry to the corresponding cascades by changing their values inside the routines (listing 15.3). In this simple game you type any key and the point moves across the screen: when the point and cross coincide – SPLAT.

*Listing 15.1*

```
200 REM dot
209 REM fire dot across screen when a key is press"
210 MODE 7 : VDU23,1,0;0;0;0;
220 PRINT TAB(0,11);"."
230 A$=GET$
240 D=0
250 PRINT TAB(D,11);" " : D=D+1
260 IF D=40 THEN 220
270 PRINT TAB(D,11);"."
279 REM wait for start of frame to slow movement down
280 *FX19
290 GOTO 250
```

*Listing 15.2*

```
300 REM cross
309 REM continually move cross up the screen
310 MODE 7 : VDU 23,1,0;0;0;0;
320 X=8 : Y=23
330 PRINT TAB(X,Y);"+"
340 PRINT TAB(X,Y);" " : Y=Y-1
350 IF Y<0 THEN 320
359 REM make cross move in zig-zag
360 IF Y>12 THEN X=X+1 ELSE X=X-1
370 PRINT TAB(X,Y);"+"
379 REM slow down movement of cross
380 T=TIME : REPEAT UNTIL TIME>T+2
390 GOTO 340
```

*Listing 15.3*

```
100 REM main loop
110 dot=200 : cross=300 : D=0
120 MODE 7 : VDU 23,1,0;0;0;0;
129 REM run modified dot and cross programs at same time
130 REPEAT
140 GOSUB dot : GOSUB cross
150 UNTIL FALSE

200 REM dot cascade
210 PRINT TAB(0,11);"." : dot=220 : RETURN
219 REM now use INKEY$ to check for keypress so cross can move
220 IF INKEY$(0)="" THEN RETURN
230 D=0 : dot=240 : RETURN
240 PRINT TAB(D,11);" " : D=D+1
250 IF D=40 THEN dot=210 : RETURN
260 PRINT TAB(D,11);"."
270 RETURN

300 REM cross cascade
310 X=8 : Y=23
320 PRINT TAB(X,Y);"+" : cross=330 : RETURN
330 PRINT TAB(X,Y);" " : Y=Y-1
340 X=X+1 : PRINT TAB(X,Y);"+"
```

```
350 IF Y<=11 THEN cross=380
360 T=TIME : REPEAT UNTIL TIME>T+2
370 RETURN
379 REM as cross changes direction check for dot hitting
380 IF Y=11 AND X=D THEN PRINT TAB(X,Y);"SPLAT!" : END
390 PRINT TAB(X,Y);" " : Y=Y-1
400 IF Y<0 THEN cross=310 : RETURN
410 X=X-1
420 PRINT TAB(X,Y);"+"
430 T=TIME : REPEAT UNTIL TIME>T+2
440 RETURN
```

*Exercise 15.2*

Add a line to the calling loop to reset the pointers to the top of the cascades and continue the game after a SPLAT, perhaps printing the score (number of hits). Write a 'duck-shoot' game with a hunter who moves left and right under keyboard control while shooting with a shotgun at ducks that are flying across the screen.

**How to Write a Game**

For a simple game as outlined in the above example (and the worm game of chapter 1) the saving in time and programming effort from using the cascade technique is significant. We shall now describe a good approach for writing a non-trivial game by using the aforementioned ideas, with RON as an illustration. First define and plan your game carefully.

*The definition*

In our game you are RON, the last robot remaining after a nuclear disaster and you are trying to rescue the few surviving microcomputers, the BEEBS. While doing this you must avoid the Mutant Typists (MUTTS) who are trying to stop you. RON is equipped with a ray gun which he can fire in any of four directions (up, down, left, right), although this will not save him if the MUTTS get their MITTS on him. RON is currently rescuing BEEBS in the WASTE of TYME where there are many pools of radioactive materials that are fatal to MUTTS and RON alike, although RON can vapourise these with his ray gun.

The gun has four firing directions that are specified by pressing 's' for left, 'd' for down, 'f' for right and 'e' for up. If a blast from the gun hits either the MUTTS or the pools they will disappear; however if the MUTTS touch RON he dies. The movement of RON is similarly controlled by 'j', 'k', 'l' and 'i'. A great deal of time at the planning stage of a game should be given to making the controls usable, and the keys you chose must be easy to reach. (If you have joysticks then things are much simpler.)

Just to make things tricky there are occasional appearances of antinuclear demonstrators (DEMONs) wearing 'I told you so' tee-shirts. They are intent on shooting RON, since it was very probably all his fault anyway!

*The characters*

You need to create single or multiple multi-colour characters for each participant in a game. This game will be run in mode 2 so we use CHARACTER GENERATOR 2 to draw the pools, RON, the MUTTs, the BEEBs and the DEMONs which will all be two characters high. Because we do not want to be limited to mode 2 character blocks, each object will be stored as the equivalent of 5 characters. (All the characters are stored between ASCII codes 65 and 89.) The screen is considered as a coordinate system with *x*-values from 0 to 79 and *y*-values from 0 to 63 (not 0 to 31). We move in half-characters up the screen, hence the need for 5 characters per object: two are used to draw the object in normal character block position, but three are needed if it moves up half a block since it will range over three blocks. The 'prynt' routine has to be changed to move them about in this fashion. The characters will be stored as file RONCHAR.

*The initialisation*

The characters can go anywhere on the screen, but to start with we would like them to be fairly randomly spread, but without overlapping. So we start with a BASIC program (stored in file XYDATA P) that finds suitable positions for 128 objects: 32 BEEBs, 32 pools and 64 MUTTs. It draws coloured squares on the screen to show you where they go, yellow for BEEBs, green for pools and magenta for MUTTs. If you do not like these positions run the program again. These are the *x*/*y* coordinates of the objects and are placed in store between locations &1100 and &1400. RON has 16 waves of MUTTs to contend with, each wave containing more than the one before. The positions within a wave are a subset of the total calculated above. The table of data that specifies the number of occurrences of each object in a round is also stored by this program in the same area of store. Finally the program calculates a table of the addresses of the beginning of each screen line and stores this as well. Once all the data have been prepared it is saved as the file XYDATA.

*The logo*

This section (file BJPRSNT) would probably be written last of all and simply draws a logo for the game on the screen and follows it with a brief description of the rules of the game. There is no need to use machine code, BASIC is more than adequate for this section. When interrupted by pressing 'S' it will load the main game program (a previously constructed machine-code program) and execute it.

*The main game program*

We finally come to the main game program (file GAME) which consists of a loop of calls to cascade routines:

MBEEB moves one BEEB each time through the loop.
CHKEYS checks the keyboard to find any change in direction of RON's movement or when the ray gun has been fired.

FIRE moves the photon blasts from the gun around the screen.
MMUT moves some of the mutants each time through the loop. Some of them will change direction to chase RON.
Then the flag KILLED checks whether RON has been killed by a MUTT.
MRON moves RON.
Then the flag DEAD checks to see if RON has hit a pool; if so a new RON appears or the game is over. (You have three RONs to start with.)
DEMO tells if a demonstrator is on the screen, in which case we enter the cascade for its movement. It will use the same FIRE routine as RON.
We then move back to the top of the loop and repeat. Naturally there are a few other checks, such as to see if RON has blasted all the MUTTs or if your score is high enough to gain another RON.

In the game we have tried to show an elementary modular way of approaching the programming of video games in a mixture of BASIC and machine code, where large amounts of data are stored in a variety of tables. The positions for everything on the screen are stored in large tables of $x$-coordinates and $y$-coordinates and collisions are detected simply by assuming that the background is all black (zero). Objects are moved by printing them in their new positions and then by obliterating any leftover parts from their previous positions with blanks. The missiles are drawn by calculating the appropriate byte(s), and then by over-printing the data into the byte and out of that byte after the shot has passed. Reprinting often takes less time when removal of the old position can be combined with the printing at the new (see the sections where RON is moving vertically). Remember that discretion is the better part of valour and it is far better to check for problems and to cover them up, rather than to rewrite your program and find that another fault has appeared. When trying to remove faults also remember that a brute-force cover-up will probably be quicker than a fancy fault-avoidance routine.

There is no background in this game for the simple reason that it would necessitate the removal of data from the screen prior to printing. This would be essential in order to allow the background to be restored after the object in the foreground had moved on.

By combining these techniques for moving objects and allowing objects to pass each other, displays of very high quality can be made. Of course for the really fast and complex games efficient machine-code routines with even greater numbers of look-up tables must be used. However many of the initialisation and instruction routines can still be in BASIC so do not bother trying to produce completely machine-code programs unless you wish to sell your games.

Finally, as your games' programs become more and more interwoven and cross-connected you must try to keep a simple overview of the game. Use sensible variable names, put in plenty of comments during development, and above all, Don't Panic!

**Complete Programs**

I Listing 15.1. Type any key.
II Listing 15.2. No data required.
III Listing 15.3. Press any key.
IV See description of tape 2 in the appendix for the video game RON.

# 16 Projects

I Use your BBC micro to draw a digital clock. Produce the special large characters for the digits and use a colon to separate them. Your clock can be made to keep correct time by using the internal clock of the Model B (see the user guide).

II Make a program that tests the Morse Code proficiency of the user. The data for the program will be a paragraph of text, which the Model B should translate into Morse and then print out by means of dots and dashes using the teletext block graphic characters. It can also use SOUND to simulate the sound of Morse. Your program should have a variable rate of production of the code so that the speed of the test increases as the user gets more proficient.

III Draw a set of International Road Signs. Your program should draw the background of the figures, such as red triangles, and then use your own special routines or the programs of chapters 5 and 6 to finish off the foreground.

IV Construct crossword puzzles on your television set. Each square of the puzzle should be 2 by 2 character blocks. The four blocks will either be black (in which case nothing goes in the square), or white with the bottom left-hand corner holding the letter of a solution, and either the top two characters holding the clue numbers (if any) or the top left character holding two 'thin' digits. This allows space for a 16 by 16 puzzle.

You also have to place the clues on the screen, and these can be printed on request on the remaining area of the screen. Solutions to the puzzle can be added by a 'cursor' method or by having a special input code, such as letter 'A' (across) or 'D' (down) followed by the number of the clue, followed by your solution.

V Write programs or use the character generator and the diagram routines (chapters 5 and 6) to produce the flags of all nations. You can draw company logos, or even design new ones. Use the techniques in chapter 14 for accessing screen memory locations to add an extra option to the diagram routines. This option should allow you to make a copy of a set of character blocks (already on the screen and specified by 'cursor') to another set of blocks of the same size elsewhere on the screen (also specified by 'cursor'). You could even rotate or reflect them!

VI The user manual shows you how to use SOUND to create music(?). While SOUND is making the noises you can draw the musical notation on the screen. You can construct the staves and then use special characters to place quavers, minims etc. on the screen. The old Music Hall method of the 'bouncing ball' could be used to beat the time of the tune.

VII Use the character block method to draw mazes. Naturally your program must generate mazes with real solutions. You can give yourself time limits for getting through the maze. You can make them dynamic by changing them as the game progresses. Add extra problems: man-eating monsters that roam the maze; holes that suddenly appear and can swallow you up; 'space warps' that can transfer you anywhere in the maze if you do not move fast enough.

VIII Extend the ideas of chapter 6. Draw your own special histograms, pie-charts and graphs. Make them dynamic (either by the 'movie' method of chapter 13, or by drawing a new graph on the old axes). Generate whole sets of special characters. Draw solid data graphs by joining each point on the graph to the $x$-axis. Extend the mathematical surface program (listing 10.6) to draw three-dimensional histograms. For every rectangle on the $x/z$ grid there must now be one $y$-value. So for each such grid rectangle, starting at the back and working forward, you simply need to draw the rectangular block from the grid base up to this $y$-value.

IX Create patterns. Use EOR with large numbers of random lines or triangles about the screen. Or draw lines in a dense but regular way to get Moiré patterns. For example, draw lines that join the points (0, I) to (1279, 1023 – I) for $0 \leqslant I \leqslant 1023$, and points (I, 0) to (1279 – I, 1023) for $0 \leqslant I \leqslant 1279$ in varying step sizes. Extend the ideas of the pattern program of chapter 5 to produce complex symmetrical patterns – any introductory book on crystallography (such as Phillips, 1956) will give you lots of ideas. Draw two spirals in mode 0, one slightly off centre, and see what patterns emerge.

X Crystallography books (such as Phillips, 1956) will give you many ideas for three-dimensional objects. Extend into four dimensions – each vertex is simply a vector of four numbers and so requires 5 x 5 matrices for transformations. The simplest orthographic projection of a four-dimensional point is where we ignore two of the coordinates (as opposed to one, $z$, in three dimensions). There are many more complex projections. What are translation, scale and rotation in four dimensions?

XI We have already presented one board game – Chess. There are many more possibilities: draughts (or checkers), Scrabble, Hangman, ludo, Master Mind. You can create a compendium of games. The BBC micro can simply act as the board, or it can also act as a referee. If you feel really adventurous it can even act as an opponent.

XII Use special characters to construct a deck of playing cards. These can be incorporated into a program to play blackjack (or pontoon) with the Model B acting as the bank and opponent.

XIII You can draw certain types of brain-teasers on your television screen. For example, suppose you have nine squares and each is divided into quarters down the diagonals. Each quarter has a colour (red '1', green '2', yellow '3' and blue '4') and a sign (+ or –). Denote each square as a sequence of four numbers that represent the areas taken clockwise around the centre. For example we could have (–1, –2, 1, 4), (–1, 3, 4, –2), (1, –4, –2, 3), (1, 2, –3, –4), (1, 3, –2, –4), (1, 4, –3, –2), (2, –3, –4, 3) and two occurrences of (–1, –4, 3, 2). The problem is to place the nine squares in a four by four arrangement, so that if two quarters on neighbouring squares touch, then they must be of the same colour but of opposite sign. You can use the BBC microcomputer to draw the squares initially on the left side of the screen and a three by three grid of the same sizes on the right. Then you take squares from the left and place them in the grid, or replace them back to the left. Write a program to find the two independent solutions of the above problem.

XIV Use the low-resolution graphics package of chapter 13 to manipulate the teletext screen so that it produces an approximation to a photograph. Take any photograph of yourself and superimpose a grid of 80 by 75 on it that corresponds to the graphic blocks of 2 by 3 small squares that will be placed on the screen in a matrix of 40 by 25. For each small square, decide whether it is mainly light or dark, and colour the corresponding 1/6th block accordingly. This seems like a lot of work. But note that most of the picture will be a light background, so if we use white background and blue foreground then most of the squares need not be considered. You could draw two heads side by side on the screen.

XV Write a Pac-Man type of video game in BASIC. This involves drawing five moving objects on the screen at a time. In order to make the game move faster allow only two of the ghosts to move with each move of

Pac-Man. The ghosts should find the shortest path towards the player when they are in hunting mode, and the best escape route in running mode. Because of the complex layout of the screen you will have to compromise. Simply move towards (or away from) the player if there is no wall in the way. Find a quick way of coding their movements as this will be the most time-consuming parts of the game. Speed is the essence of a good video game. Perhaps a simple machine-code routine could be used to print all five figures on the screen after altering their PRINT TAB positions.

XVI Write a program that first prints a graphics menu of special symbols on some part of the screen in mode 4. For example, use the stylised components for electronic circuits (resistors, capacitors etc.). These symbols should consist of combinations of lines. Keep a copy of the area under the menu in the same way that the whole screen is buffered in the teletext editor (listing 13.6). Use a cursor to point at any menu-symbol and then (using EOR (GCOL 3, COL)) drag a copy of it to a required position on the screen. Also add a facility for drawing connecting lines and labelling them with 'thin' numeric and special characters (such as Ω for ohms). You should also allow the deletion of symbols that are inadvertently placed in the wrong position. Extra options could include saving and loading.

XVII In all our perspective diagrams it is assumed that the objects lie totally in front of the eye. Change our programs so that they deal with the general case where vertices may lie anywhere in space, including behind the eye. See Newman and Sproull (1979) and Foley and van Dam (1982) for details about this concept of three-dimensional clipping.

Change the three-dimensional procedures so that they form an interactive program. Set up a complex scene (such as a group of houses) and use the menu technique to specify and change the observation point. You can change the observation point or a point on the straight-ahead ray by moving it a specified distance in the $x$-direction, $y$-direction or $z$-direction – see listing 9.12.

XVIII Produce stereoscopic hidden line views of three-dimensional objects. Now the facets must be coloured in background white and the edges in red or cyan. Remember that when you are drawing the facets for the second eye that they must not obliterate the lines drawn for the first eye.

XIX Draw a Rubik's cube or Rubik's Revenge. Enter the rotation details from the keyboard and redraw the cube in each new position.

# *References and Further Reading*

## References

Birnbaum, I. (1982). *Assembly Language Programming for the BBC Microcomputer.* Macmillan, London
Cohn, P. M. (1961). *Solid Geometry*. Routledge and Kegan Paul, London
Coxeter, H. S. M. (1974). *Regular Polytopes.* Dover Publications, New York
Davenport, H. (1952). *The Higher Arithmetic.* Hutchinson, London
Finkbeiner, D. T. (1978). *Introduction to Matrices and Linear Transformations*, 3rd edition. W. H. Freeman, San Francisco
Foley, J. D. and van Dam, A. (1982). *Fundamentals of Interactive Computer Graphics.* Addison-Wesley, Reading, Massachusetts
Horowitz, E. and Sahni, S. (1976). *Fundamentals of Data Structures*. Pitman, London
Knuth, D. (1973). *The Art of Computer Programming. Volume 1: Fundamental Algorithms*, 2nd edition, 1973. *Volume 2: Semi-numerical Algorithms*, 2nd edition, 1981. *Volume 3: Sorting and Searching*, 1972. Addison-Wesley, London
Liffick, B. W. (1979). *The BYTE Book of Pascal.* Byte Publications, New Hampshire
Mandelbrot, B. B. (1977). *Fractals.* W. H. Freeman, San Francisco
McCrae, W. H. (1953). *Analytical Geometry of Three Dimensions.* Oliver and Boyd, London
Newman, W. M. and Sproull, R. F. (1979). *Principles of Interactive Computer Graphics.* McGraw-Hill, London
Phillips, F. C. (1956). *An Introduction to Crystallography*, 2nd edition. Longmans, London
Stroud, K. A. (1982). *Engineering Mathematics*, 2nd edition. Macmillan, London
Tolansky, S. (1964). *Optical Illusions.* Pergamon, New York
Zaks, R. (1978). *Programming the 6502.* Sybex, Berkeley, California

### *Further Reading*

Read any periodical, magazine or journal that is relevant to computer graphics such as *SIGGRAPH, CADCAM, CAD journal* (and there are many, many more), and the more advanced graphics textbooks (such as Newman and Sproull, 1979; Foley and van Dam, 1982), as well as the general computer newspapers and monthly magazines (such as *Byte, Personal Computer World, Practical Computing, Interface, BEEBUG* etc.). It does not matter if you do not immediately understand the more advanced articles: it is important to appreciate the flavour, excitement and achievement of the subject. Obtain the promotional and advertising literature of the major graphics companies (Tektronix, Imlac, A.E.D., Sigma, Hewlett-Packard, D.E.C. etc.), and get as much information as possible about graphics software packages. Keep an eye on the television usage of computer graphics, whether it be in science programs, science-fiction melodramas or advertisements. Study video games and try to understand from the display how the characters are drawn and manipulated.

# *Appendix: Contents and Availability of the Two Related Software Cassettes*

There are two companion audio-cassette tapes for this book. TAPE 1 contains complete listings of the larger programs relating to high-resolution graphics (that is, two-dimensional and three-dimensional graphics), while the listings on TAPE 2 relate to low-resolution graphics (that is, characters, data diagrams, video games, the disassembler etc.). Each tape contains two CATALOG(ue) programs (one at the start of each side of the tape) that give concise details of each listing on the tape and explains the PAGE setting for LOADing, MODE of execution etc. A brief description of the two tapes is given below.

TAPE 1

| *File Name* | *Contents* |
|---|---|
| PTOPT | Program to join points on a regular polygon (listing 2.8 etc.) |
| ROSE | Program to draw rose pattern (listing 2.9 etc.) |
| ILLUSION | Draws rotating spirals by varying logical/actual colours and the illusion of the expanding square (listing 2.11 etc.) |
| ENVELOPE | Draws a simple envelope (listing 2.12 etc.) |
| SPIROGRAPH | Emulation of Spirograph (listing 2.13 etc.) |
| SQINSQS | Draws 21 squares, one inside another (listing 3.1 etc.) |
| INTER2L2D | Intersection of two lines in two-dimensional space (listing 3.2) |
| FLAGS2D | Draws four flags in two-dimensional space (Listings 4.11, 4.12 etc.) |
| INTERLP3D | Intersection of a line and a plane in three-dimensional space (listing 7.1) |
| INTER2L3D | Intersection of two lines in three-dimensional space (listing 7.2) |
| DOTVEC | Example program of dot and vector product (listing 7.3) |
| INTER3P3D | Intersection of three planes in three-dimensional space (listings 7.4, 7.5) |
| INTER2P3D | Intersection of two planes in three-dimensional space (listings 7.4, 7.6) |
| ORIENT2 | Orientation of a triangle in two-dimensional space (listing 7.7) |
| GENROT | Rotation of point about a general axis in three-dimensional space (listing 8.5 etc.) |

| | |
|---|---|
| ORTHOCUBES | Orthographic projection of two 'wire' cubes (listings 9.4, 9.5 etc.) |
| MOVIE | Movie program of a rotating 'wire' cube (listing 9.12 etc.) |
| ORIENT3 | Orientation of a triangle in three-dimensional space (listing 10.1 etc.) |
| JET | Orthographic view of a 'wire' jet (listing 9.9 etc.) |
| REVBOD | Orthographic view of a 'wire' body of revolution (a sphere) (listing 9.10 etc.) |
| SPHERE | Orthographic hidden surface view of a sphere (listings 9.10, 10.5 etc.) |
| FLAGCUBE | Orthographic hidden surface drawing of a cube with flags on faces (listing 10.3 etc.) |
| MATHSURF | Orthographic hidden surface view of a mathematical surface (listing 10.6 etc.) |
| PERSPCUBES | Perspective view of two 'wire' cubes (listings 9.6, 11.1 etc.) |
| CUBESTACK | Perspective hidden surface view of a stack of 27 cubes (listing 11.2 etc.) |
| STEREO | Stereoscopic view of two 'wire' cubes (listing 11.3 etc.) |
| HIDSURFACE | Hidden surface view of two cubes on a coloured background (listings 12.1, 12.2, 12.3 etc.) |
| EXSTARS | EXEC file to overwrite SETUP procedure in previous program. It draws two stars on the same background (listing 12.4) |
| EXBOX | EXEC file to overwrite SETUP procedure in program HIDSURFACE. It draws a hollow cube on the same background (listing 12.5) |
| lib1 | EXEC library file of real-to-pixel procedures |
| lib2 | EXEC library file of two-dimensional procedures |
| lib3 | EXEC library file of three-dimensional procedures |

TAPE 2

| | |
|---|---|
| LOGACT | Program to show relationship between logical and actual colours (listing 1.9) |
| TRIANGPAT | Spiral pattern formed from triangles. Example of animation: rotation caused by redefinition of logical colours (listing 1.12) |
| WORMGAME | The worm game (listing 1.13) |
| PIC1.16 | Listing 1.16 |
| FONT | Character font calculations |
| COLFONT | Coloured-character font calculations (listing 5.2) |
| CHARG0 | Simple two-colour character generator (listing 5.3) |
| THIN | Construction of 'thin' characters (listing 5.4) |
| CHARG1 | CHARACTER GENERATOR1 (listing 5.6) |
| CHESS | Chess board program (listing 5.7) |

| | |
|---|---|
| CHESSP1 | Characters for CHESS program |
| CHESSP2 | More characters for CHESS program |
| PREPRYNT | Assembly code construction of the PRYNT routine (listing 5.8) |
| CHARG2 | CHARACTER GENERATOR2 (listing 5.9) |
| CHARG3 | Program that enables keyboard to print out multi-coloured characters (listing 5.10) |
| COLCHAR | Sample character set for use with CHARG3 |
| HISTO1 | First histogram (listings 6.1, 6.2) |
| HISTO2 | Second histogram (listings 6.1, 6.3) |
| PIE | Pie-chart (listings 6.1, 6.3) |
| GRAPHS | Scientific graphs (listings 6.1, 6.4) |
| LABELS | Labelling program (listings 6.1, 6.5) |
| TRIG7 | Low-resolution trigonometric curves with TELETEXT (listing 13.3) |
| BRICKOUT | TELETEXT game 'Brickout' (listing 13.5) |
| TELTEXTED | TELETEXT editor (listing 13.6) |
| DCODE | Assembly code for generation of DISPLAY (listing 13.7) |
| CLOVER | Animation of a 'clover leaf' using rapid transfer of screen data (listing 13.8) |
| DISASSEM | The disassembler (listing 14.1) |
| SANDR | Search and replace program (listing 14.2) |
| BASCROLL | Screen scrolling using BASIC (listing 14.3) |
| MCSCROLL | Screen scrolling using machine code (listing 14.4) |
| APPLES | Apples and bricks game (listing 14.5) |
| SPLAT | Simple cascade program (listing 15.3) |

The following files are needed for the large-scale video game RON:

| | |
|---|---|
| XYDATAP | Should be RUN to produce a file like XYDATA below |
| START | Sets up SOUND envelopes, resets PAGE boundaries and CHAINs in BJPRSNT |
| BJPRSNT | Logo at the beginning of the game |
| XYDATA | Tables of random data needed for game and produced by XYDATAP above |
| GAME | Machine-code routine to play game produced by ACGAME below |
| RONCHAR | Character set for game |
| ACGAME | Assembly code for game |

**Availability**

These cassettes are available through all major bookshops, but in case of difficulty order direct from

Globe Book Services
Canada Road
Byfleet
Surrey KT14 7JL

| | | |
|---|---|---|
| Cassette 1 | **ISBN 0 333 35053 7** | £9.00 (including VAT) |
| Cassette 2 | **ISBN 0 333 36141 5** | £9.00 (including VAT) |

If bought together as a set, the cost is £16.00 (including VAT) for the two cassettes. The prices quoted apply to the United Kingdom.

# *Index*

# *Where to Find Procedures referred to in Text*